WAR, MEDICINE AND MODERNITY

EDITED BY

ROGER COOTER, MARK HARRISON AND STEVE STURDY

SUTTON PUBLISHING

First published in 1998 by
Sutton Publishing Limited · Phoenix Mill
Thrupp · Stroud · Gloucestershire · GL5 2BU

British Library Cataloguing in Publication Data
A catalogue record for this book is available from the British Library

ISBN 0-7509-1801-2 (*hardback*)

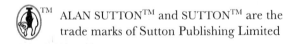 ALAN SUTTON™ and SUTTON™ are the
trade marks of Sutton Publishing Limited

Typeset in 10/12pt Baskerville.
Typesetting and origination by
Sutton Publishing Limited.
Printed in Great Britain by
Bookcraft, Midsomer Norton, Somerset.

CONTENTS

LIST OF CONTRIBUTORS   v

1. Roger Cooter and Steve Sturdy
OF WAR, MEDICINE AND MODERNITY: INTRODUCTION   1

2. Bertrand Taithe
THE RED CROSS FLAG IN THE FRANCO-PRUSSIAN WAR: CIVILIANS,
HUMANITARIANS AND WAR IN THE 'MODERN AGE'   22

3. Molly Sutphen
STRIVING TO BE SEPARATE? CIVILIAN AND MILITARY DOCTORS IN
CAPE TOWN DURING THE ANGLO-BOER WAR   48

4. Steve Sturdy
WAR AS EXPERIMENT. PHYSIOLOGY, INNOVATION AND ADMINI-
STRATION IN BRITAIN, 1914–1918: THE CASE OF CHEMICAL WARFARE   65

5. Joel D. Howell
'SOLDIER'S HEART': THE REDEFINITION OF HEART DISEASE AND
SPECIALITY FORMATION IN EARLY TWENTIETH-CENTURY GREAT
BRITAIN   85

6. Kimberly Jensen
PHYSICIANS AND CITIZENS: US MEDICAL WOMEN AND MILITARY
SERVICE IN THE FIRST WORLD WAR   106

7. Roger Cooter
MALINGERING IN MODERNITY: PSYCHOLOGICAL SCRIPTS AND
ADVERSARIAL ENCOUNTERS DURING THE FIRST WORLD WAR   125

8. Mathew Thomson
STATUS, MANPOWER AND MENTAL FITNESS: MENTAL DEFICIENCY
IN THE FIRST WORLD WAR   149

9. Lutz D.H. Sauerteig
SEX, MEDICINE AND MORALITY DURING THE FIRST WORLD WAR   167

10. Penny Starns
FIGHTING MILITARISM? BRITISH NURSING DURING THE SECOND
WORLD WAR   189

11. Peter Neushul
FIGHTING RESEARCH: ARMY PARTICIPATION IN THE CLINICAL
TESTING AND MASS PRODUCTION OF PENICILLIN DURING THE
SECOND WORLD WAR   203

12. Joanna Bourke
DISCIPLINING THE EMOTIONS: FEAR, PSYCHIATRY AND THE
SECOND WORLD WAR   225

BIBLIOGRAPHY   239

INDEX   253

LIST OF CONTRIBUTORS

Joanna Bourke is reader at Birkbeck College, University of London. In addition to books on the history of women in Ireland, and on British working-class culture, she is the author of *Dismembering the Male: Men's Bodies, Britain and the Great War* (1996) and *An Intimate History of Killing: Face-to-Face Killing in Twentieth-Century Warfare* (1999). She is currently writing a history of fear in the nineteenth and twentieth centuries.

Roger Cooter is Professor of Social History and Director of the Wellcome Unit for the History of Medicine, University of East Anglia, Norwich. The author of *The Cultural Meaning of Popular Science* (1984) and *Surgery and Society in Peace and War* (1993), he has also edited volumes on the history of child health, alternative medicine, and accidents in history. He is currently writing a social history of medicine, and co-editing and contributing to *The Twentieth Century History of Medicine* and *Socialism in Anglo-American Medicine, 1850–1950*.

Mark Harrison is a lecturer in the History Department at Sheffield Hallam University. The author of *Public Health in British India, 1859–1914* (1994), he has also published widely in the areas of military and imperial medicine. His *Medicine in the British Military* is shortly to appear.

Joel D. Howell is a professor in the Department of Internal Medicine and History at the University of Michigan. The author of *Technology in the Hospital* (1995), his research focuses on medical technology in Britain and the USA in the nineteenth and twentieth centuries.

Kimberly Jensen is Associate Professor of History and Coordinator of the Gender Studies Program at Western Oregon University. She received her Ph.D. from the University of Iowa in Women's History in 1992. Her research focuses on women, citizenship and military service in the First World War.

Peter Neushul is a visiting researcher at the California Institute of Technology and at the University of California, Santa Barbara. The author of articles on the history of antibiotics, birth control technology and ocean farming, he is currently completing *Arsenal of Democracy: Science and Technology on the Home Front*.

Lutz D.H. Sauerteig received his doctorate from the Humboldt University, Berlin. Formerly a research fellow at the Institute for Modern History, University of Munich, he is now at the Institute for the History of Medicine, University of Freiburg. The author of *Krankheit, Sexualität, Gesellschaft: Geschlechtskrankheiten und Gesundheitspolitik in Deutschland im 19. und frühen 20. Jahrhundert* (forthcoming), he has also published on the history of venereal disease in Germany and England. He is currently researching the medical market place in twentieth-century Germany.

Penny Starns practised for many years as a nurse before completing her Ph.D. in social history at the University of Bristol in 1997. Formerly a researcher for the BBC, she is now researching the impact of Second World War evacuation on teaching methods for a project in the School of Education, University of Cambridge.

Steve Sturdy is Wellcome Lecturer in the History of Medicine at the Science Studies Unit, University of Edinburgh. He has written widely on the relations between medical science, practice and policy in the nineteenth and twentieth century. He is currently completing *Medicine, Science and Statecraft in Britain 1900–1920*, and is engaged with Michael Barfoot and Christopher Lawrence on a study of clinical science in interwar Edinburgh.

Molly Sutphen received her Ph.D. from Yale University and is currently an adjunct assistant professor at the University of California, San Francisco. She is at present completing *British Imperial Hygiene: Medicine, Public Health and Colonial Society, 1880–1930*.

Bertrand Taithe read history at the Sorbonne and Manchester University and is a senior lecturer in the History Department of the University of Huddersfield. He has published articles on the Franco-Prussian War, is the author of a forthcoming monograph, *Meanings of War: Sense of Defeat and the Making of Modern France*, and has co-edited *Prophecy* (1997), *War* (1998) and *Propaganda* for the Sutton Publishing series 'Themes in History'.

Mathew Thomson is a lecturer in the Department of History, University of Warwick. He is the author of *The Problem of Mental Deficiency: Eugenics, Democracy, and Social Policy in Britain, 1870–1959* (1998). He is currently working on the popular and cultural impact of psychology in early twentieth-century Britain and on the comparative history of mental hygiene.

1

OF WAR, MEDICINE AND MODERNITY: INTRODUCTION

Roger Cooter and Steve Sturdy

Historians have paid remarkably little attention to the relationship between war, medicine and modernity. This is surprising in view of the efforts that have been devoted to exploring two of the three sides of the triangle – the connections between war and modernity and between medicine and war. Thus we have a wealth of studies which argue that war is a crucible of modernity, or at the very least that it epitomizes the social forms and forces that are seen to constitute modern society. Likewise, the relationship between war and the development of medicine has been subject to increasingly detailed, though often less critical, historical analysis. By contrast, few studies have sought to examine the place of medicine in the constitution of modernity. This volume aims to advance all three areas of scholarship by looking explicitly at the relationship between war, medicine and modernity.

To begin with, however, it is necessary to define what we mean by 'modernity'. The word has been variously interpreted, but our usage follows that originally set out by Max Weber. Writing in the years around the First World War, Weber identified a constellation of social processes and forms that he saw crystallizing about him. These included the growth, differentiation and integration of bureaucracy and other organizational and managerial systems; the standardization and routinization of administrative action; and the employment of experts to define and order such systems. Unification and uniformity, Weber perceived, were fundamental aspects of 'rational' as opposed to 'traditional' society. Whereas 'traditional' social systems operated through diverse forms of social interaction and bonding, 'rational' ones aspired to conformity through the imposition of bureaucratic planning and administration. Underlying this, as indicated by Weber's designation of such a society as 'rational', was a form of calculative and evaluative thought that both legitimized and advanced the extension of bureaucratic structures into ever more intimate areas of social life.[1] Weber also appreciated that an important expression of this rationality was the development and application of scientific and technical productions which further transformed older social legitimations and ways of knowing.[2] Many subsequent writers have taken this constellation of social and intellectual forms and processes as characteristic of 'modernity'.[3]

Weber did not approve of this modernity. Technical means of calculation of every sort contributed to the 'disenchantment' of his world.[4] He loathed the stranglehold of bureaucracy that he saw all around him before his death in Germany in 1920: 'This passion for bureaucracy', he wrote, 'is enough to drive one to despair. It is as if in politics . . . we were deliberately to become men who need "order" and nothing but order.'[5] Yet he also appreciated that this 'passion' was not all-pervasive. Whatever the tendencies towards the imposition of bureaucratic and rational order on human life, such ordering remained imperfect and partial, confounded by the local contingencies of social existence. For Weber, 'rational' society was only one of a number of *ideal* types of social organization – the others being 'traditional' and 'charismatic' – that could be seen by the sociological eye to be operating in the world of his time. 'Rational' society – comprising the social forms that we take to be distinctive of modernity – is thus an analytic and heuristic category. It provides a way of talking in generalized terms about certain kinds of social structures and tendencies that might be seen to characterize a particular historical age or a particular society; but it should not be supposed that such structures or tendencies have ever defined a society in its entirety. It is in this spirit that this volume draws on Weber's insights to talk about the relationship between war, medicine and modernity.

WAR AND MODERNITY

Modern war is often regarded as central to the Weberian notion of modernity. Indeed Weber himself recognized that the characteristics of bureaucracy were epitomized in the army: concentration of administration in the hands of masters; tight hierarchy and strict subordination; the pursuit of technical mastery, speed, precision, unambiguity, discretion, secrecy; and above all, 'discharge of business according to *calculable rules* and "without regard of persons"'.[6] Modern wars are 'total wars', involving the mobilization of all the resources of a society for war-like purposes, including those of science, medicine and technology. To accomplish their ends, they necessarily entail massive bureaucratization and teams of expert managers. They thus exemplify administrative ways of knowing and acting. As such, while the slaughter of war has ever been rationalized, it might be said of modern wars that they epitomize the rationalization of slaughter.[7]

The material and intellectual origins of this linkage between war and modernity can be traced at least as far back as the late seventeenth century when England began her emergence as the first modern fiscal-military state – a state wherein war and increased taxation demanded a highly developed government bureaucracy.[8] More commonly, however, such origins are sought in France in the Revolutionary and Napoleonic Wars (1792–1815) with their integration of military and civilian enterprise through the mobilization of 'citizen armies'.

Although recent studies have called into question the extent of this popular support and participation, there is no doubt that even before Napoleon's takeover, the French state underwent a process of bureaucratic militarization.[9] New levels of control and compulsion were introduced into everyday life, and local customs and practices were replaced by centralization and uniformity in the pursuit of primarily military goals. New forms of industrial production were also pursued, most notably in the arsenals of Paris. As early as 1785 Thomas Jefferson marvelled at the production of standardized interchangeable gun parts in the workshop of Honoré Blanc, while in 1792 Goethe witnessed the triumph of such methods when the artillery of the Revolutionary army routed the advancing Prussians. It was, Goethe declared, 'the beginning of a new epoch'.[10]

Most historians tend to trace the links between modernity and war to the American Civil War of 1861–5, however, and more especially the Franco-Prussian War of 1870–1 – though in these instances modernity is often equated simply with industrialization. The American Civil War was remarkable not only for its use of railways, steamships, early machine-guns and so on, but also for its mass mobilization of 'citizen soldiers' and its routinization and standardization of managerial procedures and technologies. The latter included techniques for gathering and abstracting information about populations in general, and about the bodies of soldiers in particular – techniques of surveillance and regulation which aimed at greater control and efficiency of military manpower. The Franco-Prussian War carried these developments further, rendering the organization of war comparable to that of the 'scientifically managed' factory, or, as Daniel Pick has provocatively suggested, to the systematization of slaughter and butchery that took place in the new Parisian abattoirs of the 1860s.[11] As in the rationalized slaughterhouse, geared as it was to maximum production and profit, so in warfare: specialized divisions of labour, uniformity, centralized inspection and work discipline became the hallmarks of a new and more systematic organization of concerted human endeavour. The waging of war and the killing of enemy soldiers had become an efficiency driven mechanized industrial process, perhaps best symbolized in and realized through the new technology of the machine-gun.[12]

At the same time, the differences between civil and military spheres were becoming increasingly blurred, both in practice and in ideology. Like the late Victorian city with its expanding system of integrated public utilities, the field of battle was now networked by railways, telegraphic lines of communication and specialized and coordinated emergency services. The same kinds of rationalization deemed necessary for the conduct of large-scale business, philanthropy and industry were seen to be essential for the efficient operation of mass armies. Both the military and the civilian spheres were reorganized and disciplined in accordance with the same notions of socio-economic efficiency.[13] Weber was inclined to see such processes as originating in the military itself, declaring that 'The discipline of the army gives birth to all discipline.'[14] Others, like the French poet and philosopher Paul Valéry, regarded the military command structure as the epitome and 'ideal' of modern socio-economic organization.[15] Karl Marx saw modern warfare as the perfect confirmation of his theory of capital: 'Is there anywhere', he asked Engels during the American Civil War, 'where our theory that the *organization of labour is determined by the means of production* is more brilliantly confirmed than in the manslaughter industry?'[16]

The First and Second World Wars vastly extended the forms and processes of modernity: the size of bureaucracies, the numbers of managers, the extent of the integration of civilian and military spheres, as well as the scale and sophistication of the mass manufacture of armaments and the routinized treatment of their effects on human bodies. The waging of war was thoroughly industrialized, as human life and labour were increasingly subordinated to the imperatives of mechanical and other technologies. During the First World War, the troops – widely beheld as 'poor cogs in the pitiless, devastating machine of war',[17] or like automata as in Wyndham Lewis's 1918 painting of *Officers and Signallers* – went to the front in shifts, engulfed as they themselves perceived in 'the industrialism of war'.[18] Their war was not one of 'politics by other means', as Clausewitz would have it, but of industry under a different name. At the same time, industrial production itself came to be seen as a way of pursuing international competition – a form of war by other means. Industrialization and militarization were both shaped to the same ends of conflict between nations.

It is therefore hardly surprising that the blurring of boundaries between civil and military concerns can be seen particularly clearly in the political impetus towards the organization of welfare states. By the dawn of the twentieth century, virtually all industrialized nations were expanding the scope of public (though not necessarily statutory) welfare activity in the simultaneous pursuit of both economic and military advantage. In the modern world, the welfare and the warfare state increasingly become indistinguishable from one another.[19]

Before leaving our survey of the relationship between war and modernity, it is worth mentioning one other body of scholarly writings besides that inspired by Weber. A number of authors have documented the influence of war on the emergence of 'modernist' aesthetics, discerning in the music of Stravinsky, the paintings of Munch and the Dadaists, and the poetry of Sassoon, Brook and Eliot, the intellectual impulses behind the 'birth of the modern'. In the literary and cultural histories of Modris Eksteins, Samuel Hynes and Paul Fussell, for example, 'modernism' – understood to be 'the principal urge of our time'[20] – is born as the First World War severs the cord between present and past 'beliefs, values and imagination',[21] and finds its voice in the articulation of a uniquely 'modern memory' that has no knowledge of events before the carnage of Flanders.[22]

Although some authors within this tradition, for instance Daniel Pick, challenge the decisiveness of the First World War in the making of the modern,[23] there is a marked tendency among the analysts of modernism to hypostasize and concretize cultural and intellectual idealizations. In Eksteins's work, for example, the First World War is portrayed as a clash of cultures symbolized by the principal opponents – Britain standing for old and stable forms of common culture, while Germany becomes the bearer of a modern sensibility characterized by a preoccupation with speed, newness, transience and psychological interiority. Such work also tends to dwell upon tensions and contradictions supposedly inherent within the intellectual and affective framework of modernism; a case in point is the literary critic Elaine Showalter, who shows how the contradictory polarities of gender were problematized by the unprecedented experiences of the First World War.[24] More problematically, this genre of cultural history is pervasively haunted by an awareness of what is commonly taken to be the ultimate expression of the contradictions of modern 'rational' society, namely the Holocaust. But while such writing frequently draws directly on sociological studies of the Holocaust – now routinely represented as 'industrial killing'[25] – it is generally far more inclined to deal with the psychological than the sociological, and with the representational than the political.

At its best, this literature locates new psychologies of remembering and identity within the shared social experience of war, and within the new forms of communal life and culture that came out of it.[26] But at its worst, the critical analysis of modernist mentalities operates in a sphere quite unconnected with the historical and sociological examination of modernity itself. Most writing on the culture of modernism signally fails to engage with Weber. Few contributors to this genre have noticed Weber's disdain for the 'rage of order' and the expansion of military and civil discipline,[27] let alone asked what all this might mean for the discipline of sociology that Weber inspired.[28] 'Modernity' itself is rarely questioned; often it is assumed to be historically and sociologically unproblematic – a culturally and politically undifferentiated phase of cultural evolution, or even a material force equivalent to 'industrialization' or to war itself. As Ulrich Beck has remarked, even contemporary sociologists are often content to use the word 'modernity' unthinkingly, in a spirit of 'haplessness' born of academic exhaustion, disciplinary collapse, or loss of political appetite for the old frameworks of social analysis.[29] Seen from this perspective, modernity – and modernism – becomes little more than a prelude to the invention of post-modernity, while sociological and historical investigation is reduced to the distinctly subordinate role of providing 'ammunition for Theory'.[30]

On the whole, then, the literature on modernism and war tells us rather more about the concerns of some late twentieth-century scholars than about the social and political history of the relations between war and modernity. Above all, this literature should not be mistaken for an account of war and modernity; at best, it may provide insights that sociologists and historians can pursue through more concrete and contextually located studies. Modernity does not reside solely in the literary expressions of a few gifted individuals, nor in the tensions and contradictions between different sets of social assumptions and experiences. While contradiction and ambiguity are often the stuff of literature, individuals habitually move between different and often inconsistent social institutions with unthinking ease. Rather, what distinguishes modernity in the Weberian sense – including modern warfare – is the tendency for ever larger spheres of social life and institutions to be brought under a unified and coherent system of rationalization and administration. It is in the concrete realities of social life that we must look for any satisfactory account of war and modernity.

WAR AND MEDICINE

If the relationship between war and modernity has been subjected to at least a measure of thoughtful and theoretically sophisticated sociological and historical analysis, the same cannot be said of the interactions between war and medicine. Though there exists an abundant literature on medicine in wartime, such writing pays little attention to the wider context in which war was waged, or to the role of war in the making of modern society. Indeed, until very recently, this literature has been overwhelmingly dominated by practitioner-centred accounts of how medicine has benefited from and been advanced by war. Such triumphalist reckonings are as implicitly militarist as they are naively positivist and partial.[31]

Of course, some medical practitioners, specialisms, research programmes and commercial concerns have done rather well from war. So too have certain patient populations, notably those whose military, industrial or reproductive fitness has been seen as crucial for the conduct of warfare, and whose health has accordingly attracted the intervention of the state and other national bodies.[32] But it is equally the case that many aspects of medical welfare have suffered as a result of wartime reallocations of material and human resources. Weak, vulnerable and unproductive groups such as the aged and the mentally and physically handicapped have usually seen a deterioration in medical and other welfare provision. While it is widely recognized that research into preventive and therapeutic medicine has often intensified during wartime, little has been written on how the direction of such research was determined by the particular agendas of warfighting, or how other potentially valuable lines of investigation were marginalized and neglected. On the whole, pressing questions about the impact of war on the aims, concerns and social configurations of medicine have been ignored in favour of simple and self-serving narratives of technical and organizational advancement.

Moreover, work in the 'war-is-good-for-medicine' tradition has generally overlooked the experiences of the vast majority of practitioners during wartime – experiences that ranged from boredom and frustration with administrative red tape, to horror at the attitudes of brutality and barbarity that many medical men donned with their uniforms and officers' stripes.[33] Although only a minority of practitioners and biomedical researchers have ever pursued human experimentation with the same enthusiasm as some Nazi and Japanese doctors during the Second World War,[34] few ambitious and enterprising physicians and surgeons have been able to resist the research opportunities afforded by the mobilization of large numbers of medical 'subjects' under the authoritarian conditions of war. This temptation is hardly new; as early as 1587, Barnaby Rich's *Pathway to Military Practice* advised surgeons to 'worke according to arte, not practisinge newe experiments upon a poore souldier'.[35] What *is* new about modern warfare is the sheer scale of such mobilization, and the extent and scope of the machinery for ensuring subjection to military and medical controls. Again, little has been done to ask how the experiences of war may have contributed to a dehumanization of medicine, not just among the demonized losers, but also among the victorious, whose wartime activities have largely been obscured behind a veil of moral rectitude.

If there is a need for a more critical history of war and medicine, we should not be content simply to aim at a more balanced account of the relative benefits and hindrances that might have accrued to medical practice and provision during wartime. Rather, we need to be aware of, and to work around, a pervasive assumption that limits the conclusions drawn by most writers in this field, namely the supposition that war is no more than an 'aberrant disaster' that disrupts but does not substantially influence the normal course of social and cultural life.[36] Invariably, existing accounts fail to perceive both war and medicine in terms of wider sociocultural, economic and medico-professional contexts that transcend the social boundaries of military life and the temporal boundaries of wartime itself. As suggested above, it is one of the defining characteristics of modern war that it helps to break down the distinctions between civilian and military spheres. With the emergence of the modern nation state, it has become increasingly difficult to distinguish between the pursuit of national interests by peaceful and by warlike means. As Richard Titmuss observed in the aftermath of the Second World War, we must consciously abandon the assumption that 'war is an abnormal situation, [and] that peace is – or ought to be – the normal lot of mankind'.[37] War, in other words, is not separate or distinct from the constitution and processes of the society in which it is practised,[38] any more than is medicine.[39]

Consequently, it is not enough to ask simply whether war is good or bad for medicine. What is needed is an account of the relationship between war and medicine that is sensitive to the role of both in society more generally. For one thing, we need to understand the reciprocal processes of the civilianization of medicine in war and its militarization during peacetime.[40] But this can hardly be enough. If the story of war and medicine is to be recounted in any satisfactory way, it must be in the light of a proper analysis of the relationship between medicine and modernity, which will complement the accounts we already have of the relationship between modernity and war.

MEDICINE AND MODERNITY

In surveying past work on the history of medicine, one is immediately struck by the absence of a historical literature that focuses on medicine and modernity. Curiously, while historians have written about many aspects of modern medicine – its therapeutic shifts, politics, culture, economics, ethical problems, and so on – none have attempted to set it in the framework of any generalized understanding of modernity, Weberian or otherwise. Typically, a recent volume of historical essays with 'medicine and modernity' in the title nevertheless fails to make any explicit mention of the concept.[41] The nearest we get to any such analysis is a handful of studies which incorporate specific aspects of medicine into broadly sociocultural and intellectual histories of modernity. A fine example is Anson Rabinbach's history of the transformation of medical and managerial perceptions of labour in Europe between the mid-nineteenth and mid-twentieth centuries. Subtitled 'The Origins of Modernity', Rabinbach's study examines the work of psychologists and physiologists who redefined the human body as a 'human motor' capable of generating measurable and regulable amounts of physical and mental work.[42]

Another example of this type of partial engagement with medicine is Wolfgang Schivelbusch's history of the coming of the railway – one of the most vivid symbols of modernity, and a powerful stimulus to medical debate over the effects of modern life on the human organism.[43] Railway accidents, or simply the unprecedented speed and physical jarring of train travel, were commonly identified as the precipitating causes of a condition known as 'railway spine'. This condition in turn figures prominently in one of the few literatures to engage explicitly with medicine and modernity, that on the history of psychology and psychiatry.[44] This psychological literature is also the only one that seeks to address the relationship between medicine and war in the larger context of the development of modernity, chiefly through its analysis of shell-shock.[45] A word of caution is in order, however: with its concentration on psychology and on subjective sensibilities, historical writing about shell-shock often has more in common with literary analysis of modern*ism* as opposed to any properly historical or sociological investigation of modern*ity*.

Admittedly, some sociologists of medicine bring aspects of modernity into their purview. This is especially the case among those who follow Foucault in showing how medical views of the body serve the aims of social surveillance and administrative regulation and self-regulation.[46] In so doing, these writers assimilate medicine to narratives of modernity linked to 'the establishment of disciplines, knowledge, and technologies that serve to proffer advice on how individuals should conduct themselves'.[47] Their work stresses the importance of medical knowledge and the 'normalization' of health regimes that discipline individuals to the larger aims of modern society. But though they comment lucidly on the regimentation of the body, as well as on the medical activities that contribute to the setting and policing of administrative norms and standards, they offer no detailed accounts of how, if at all, such conditions came to prevail. These sociologists offer only grand assumptions which, at best, are parasitic on medical history. By and large, historians have not taken up these themes for themselves.

WAR, MEDICINE AND MODERNITY

There is thus a crying need for a sustained analysis of the place of medicine in the larger history of the relationship between war and modernity. The chapters collected in this volume sketch in some of the starting points for such an analysis. Taken together, they demonstrate and provide insight into medicine's increasing involvement in the processes of modernity between the Franco-Prussian War and the Second World War. The chapters are presented in chronological order, but the coverage is inevitably episodic, and no effort is made to cover all the wars that might be regarded as relevant to the theme of medicine and modernity. America's war against Spain in 1898, for instance, like the war between Russia and Japan in 1904–5 and the Spanish Civil War of 1936–9, are all omitted, even though each of these was important for introducing new methods of organizing and treating military and civilian casualties, and for precipitating realignments in the relations between military and medical personnel and between civilian and military forms of medical aid.[48] Other less familiar wars, too, might well be relevant to an analysis of war, medicine and modernity. Thus a fuller narrative might have to consider some of the innumerable civil struggles, rebellions, nationalist uprisings, revolutions, guerrilla wars and massacres that occurred in China, Africa, India, Turkey, South America and elsewhere over the period.[49] After all, many of these conflicts were conducted against or provoked by imperialist rule, one of whose principle agents from the late nineteenth century was medicine.[50]

Indeed, in the work of public health agencies, including those funded around the world by the Rockefeller Foundation, medicine served as a way of imposing the rationalizations of capital and philanthropy on native populations.[51] In some cases, such medical agencies can clearly be seen as pursuing war by other means. In the Philippines, for instance, the guerrilla war of resistance against American control officially ended in May 1902. But it was followed by a further two years of sustained assault on a cholera epidemic that transformed the war from a struggle for territory into one for dominance over the indigenous people's bodies, beliefs and social practices. American military surgeons supplemented the combat troops of the initial period of imperial conquest, prosecuting the 'war on cholera' along military lines, armed with experimental 'magic bullets' for 'shooting down' the germs of disease and resistance.[52] In such cases, the attack on, containment and elimination of the 'enemy agents' extended well beyond any metaphoric war on disease. A fuller narrative would also have to include the continuing role of military medical organizations during peacetime, and also the ways that changes in medical organization achieved during wartime were developed and adapted to suit the needs of nation states and international relations in the periods between wars. The role of doctors in the League of Nations and in the Red Cross deserves further consideration in this respect.[53]

Nevertheless, the wars focused on here, and the chronological approach adopted, provide a valuable first step towards a unified narrative of war, medicine and modernity. On the one hand, the chapters collected in this volume demonstrate that medical modernization during wartime took place, not according to some overarching and timeless logic, but rather through a multiplicity of local and contingent negotiations over power relations between doctors, military and civil authorities, and other interested medical actors and organizations. These case studies make clear the multiplicity of actors involved, and the local and specific nature of many of the medical problems addressed and the solutions adopted. Any fuller survey of the relations between war and modern medicine must inevitably pay attention to such diverse local developments. But on the other hand, it also becomes clear in reading these chapters that a number of themes do recur at different times and in different local contexts. Consequently, it also becomes possible to point to at least some of the features that may come to be regarded as characteristic of medicine in the age of modern warfare, and of medicine's role in bringing that age into being.

Taithe's chapter begins the analysis by looking at the part that medicine has played in blurring the boundaries between the spheres of military and civilian activity during wartime. He takes up the story during the Franco-Prussian War of 1870–1, as French military leaders appealed to the spirit of the revolution and the *levée en masse* to recruit civilians as well as soldiers to the war effort. As Taithe makes clear, the mobilization of medical resources through new 'humanitarian' agencies – notably the Red Cross – was officially sanctioned as a civilian operation free from any taint of nationalist military interest, and intended to mitigate the brutalizing effect of modern mechanized warfare. But such activities quickly became linked to the national war effort; Red Cross organizations came to serve as conduits for channelling civilian energies into the conduct of the war, and as a means of linking the pursuit of war to the pursuit of national identity more generally. Under the cover of this ambiguous humanitarianism, medical men were able to create for themselves a leading role in the management of modern warfare. In this instance, wartime medicine contributed to the consolidation of the nation state precisely because it was seen to fulfil a caring and curing role that could ostensibly be distanced from the particularistic national interests that it in fact served.

Sutphen's study of medical initiatives during the Anglo-Boer War of 1899–1902 makes clear that such processes were nevertheless heavily dependent upon particular local circumstances. This conflict is often seen as another in which the boundaries between civilian and military spheres became obscured, particularly with the British forces' decision to intern large sections of the enemy civilian population during the closing stages of the conflict. This blurring did not extend to the medical management of health, however. During 1901, civilians and soldiers alike were threatened by the outbreak of plague in and around Cape Town. But as Sutphen shows, while the civil authorities were keen to draw the military into an expansion of their own public health measures by establishing a unified system of plague administration, the military saw little advantage in such collaboration. They feared that civilian measures, far from assisting in the maintenance of the health of the Army, would rather interfere in their efforts to manage their fighting forces. In the context of a colonial war, in which the Army relied primarily on manpower and supplies shipped in from overseas, the military had little need to mobilize the resources of colonial civilians. In this setting, military medicine remained just that; it was defined by the immediate needs of the military alone, and was conducted largely without reference to civilian expertise or advice.

No such separation between military and civilian medicine would be maintained during the First World War, the first of the 'total wars' of the twentieth century. In this conflict, the combination of mass mobilization with the growth of increasingly interventionist state machinery in many of the combatant nations provided unprecedented opportunities to create systems of medical practice and administration that effectively spanned the military-civilian divide. The point is explored in the six chapters in this volume that examine the development of medicine during the crucial years from 1914 to 1918.

Sturdy and Howell investigate how British physiologists managed to secure a role for themselves in the conduct of war-related research, and ultimately came to enjoy a position of some authority in managing and organizing that research and its application in the field. Their recruitment was part of a larger administrative experiment in which experts from various areas of civilian endeavour, including industry and business as well as academic science, were brought into the government to assist in organizing the nation's resources for the purposes of fighting the war.

Sturdy argues that the success with which physiologists established themselves as expert advisers to the government and the military at this time – particularly in relation to chemical warfare – cannot be attributed solely to their skill in generating innovations in military *matériel* and technique. It also owed much to their ability to liaise between and help coordinate the work of different sections of the government machine, including both military and civilian branches of the state. Sturdy goes on to suggest that this combination of technical and organizational skills was not accidental; rather, the rational analysis and management of natural phenomena, and the forms of social organization needed to sustain such procedures, were already well established in the discipline of experimental physiology. Consequently, physiologists were well suited, by the very nature of their scientific training, to respond to and exploit the peculiar technical and social demands of modern warfare.

Howell's chapter likewise examines the recruitment of physiologists to address the novel problem of heart disease that arose in the course of the First World War. 'Soldier's heart' had long been known as one of the occupational hazards of soldiering, but in the context of the mass mobilization of 1914–18 disability due to this condition became a major manpower problem for the first time. As Howell shows, laboratory based clinical scientists were able to address these problems by formulating new functional definitions of heart disease rooted in physiological accounts of cardiac processes rather than in older ideas about anatomical lesions. This functional account of the processes taking place in living bodies, including the bodies of disabled soldiers, lent itself to the development of effective methods of managing those bodies, leading to significant improvements in the recovery and rehabilitation of heart disease cases. As a result, a new medical specialism – cardiology – began to coalesce, both during and after the war, around the deployment of these new technical knowledges and practices, and particularly around their application to the administrative problems of dealing with pensions claims from disabled soldiers.

The First World War is thus shown to provide a crucial site for the development of new kinds of medical organization and division of labour. Medicine was no longer simply an ancillary discipline to warfare, concerned merely with patching up the bodies of the injured. By the war's end it had become a key site for pursuing the kinds of technical and administrative innovations that were now increasingly seen as crucial for the prosecution of modern warfare. In particular, medical experts came to be valued for the contributions they were able to make to the mobilization of manpower and other resources – be they military or civilian, public or private – for the purposes of total war, and ultimately also for the pursuit of international competition by peaceable industrial and cultural means. As a result of the war, certain kinds of scientific medicine became central to the efforts of the modern state to maintain the health and productivity of the working population.

It is important to bear in mind that both Sturdy's and Howell's chapters are concerned chiefly with the high culture of government science and administration, and with the formulation and legitimation of policy rather than the details of its implementation. From this perspective, at least, it may be possible to begin to sketch a narrative of modernization based around the growth of an increasingly inclusive medical gaze and system of medical administration. But as other chapters in this volume make clear, at the level of implementation such policies commonly met with resistance and negotiation, or were hedged around with qualifications and restrictions on the limits of their applicability. Nothing was inevitable.

Thus Jensen's chapter examines the efforts of American women physicians to secure a place in military medicine after the United States entered the war in 1917. Their demands to be considered for service alongside their male colleagues were backed up by a language of citizenship drawn from recent successful campaigns for women's suffrage. In the context of mobilization for total war, one might expect that this universalizing and integrationist language would have served to make a compelling case for including women doctors among the nation's warfighting resources. In the event, however, while women physicians were offered work in the lowly capacity of contract surgeons, they were denied the commissions and officer status granted to their male counterparts. Whatever the war may have done to blur the boundaries between military and civilian life, pre-war assumptions about the demarcation of masculine from feminine gender roles still posed a serious barrier to the recruitment of women into military medicine.

Cooter's chapter on military and medical concerns about malingering among soldiers identifies a rather different source of resistance to the totalizing and universalizing trends of modernity. On the one hand, official efforts to detect and discipline malingerers did indeed give rise to medical theorizations and policy recommendations that cast doctors as agents of a supervisory and regulatory warfare state, charged with managing military manpower by means of new psychological and clinical techniques. But on the other hand, the impact of such theories and policies on the actual practices of military doctors appears to have been strictly limited. As Cooter shows, grass-roots practitioners resisted the disciplinary role they were expected to play in relation to the soldiers under their charge. Moreover, they did so as part of a more general antipathy to the imposition of disciplinary controls upon their own practice – an antipathy that extended, not just to the terms of their military service during the war, but also to the threat of state control of the profession during peacetime. Ironically, in this respect, doctors were well aware of the extent to which the military and civilian arms of the modern state tended to operate in concert within a common and increasingly integrated system of government administration. As a result, they resisted subjection to the disciplinary power of the state in both areas simultaneously.

In the following chapter, Thomson looks at how the identification and treatment of 'mental defectives' was affected by the events of the First World War in Britain and the United States. In Britain, where military manpower issues revolved chiefly around the need to pour ever larger numbers of men into the trenches with little regard for their levels of training or skill, questions of mental fitness commanded little attention. Consequently, many who might otherwise have been identified as mentally defective were simply absorbed into the anonymous mass of fighting men. In the United States, by contrast, recruitment from a much larger population, combined with the expense of maintaining a fighting force a long way from home, meant that far more attention was paid to weeding out the mentally unfit and defective by means of various psychometric and educational tests. In the US, then, systems of medical surveillance and manpower management – quintessential elements of medical modernity – were strengthened as a result of the war, whereas in Britain no such system was deemed necessary; in this instance modern warfare, and its medical corollary, was instantiated differently in different national contexts. Any attempt to identify universal patterns of medical modernization must therefore take account of the contingent local circumstances that influenced the way in which manpower problems, among other things, were construed.

One area of moral activity in which medical surveillance and control was unequivocally expanded in all major combatant nations during the First World War was sexuality. Sauerteig's paper charts this expansion by looking at the management of venereal disease in the theatre of war and on the home front, particularly in Germany and Britain. Like heart disease, venereal disease quickly came to be seen as a serious threat to fighting power. Medical men responded with unprecedentedly public debates over the nature and regulation of sexuality, and with recommendations for the rational management of sexual behaviour. The difficulties of keeping large armies of men away from home quickly led to the temporary suspension of normal sexual restraints and to acceptance of extramarital sexual activity – tacitly, through provision of prophylactics and the means of post-coital disinfection, and expressly, through licensing and policing of brothels. In such measures, and in their legitimizing rhetoric of sexuality as a normal biological urge whose fulfilment is a natural part of a healthy life, we might discern the beginnings of a shift away from an older world of respectable sexual restraint and illicit sexual activity, and towards a more modern epoch of free sexual expression.

As Sauerteig makes clear, however, this liberalization of sexual norms was chiefly restricted to men, and especially fighting men. He thus follows Jensen in demonstrating that, whatever medicine may have contributed to the development of more rational forms of social integration and mobilization between 1914 and 1918, these processes were limited by the persistence of older gender roles and identities. The First World War is commonly depicted as a time of political and occupational emancipation for women. It is clear, however, that women were generally recruited into wartime industry on terms much less favourable than those of adult male workers.[54] Likewise, the liberalization of sexual norms was far less marked for women than for men. Indeed, formal and informal methods of policing the sexual activity of women in civilian life generally became more extensive and more repressive than ever before, at the same time as women were recruited into army brothels to provide sexual amenities for soldiers.

If anything stands out about the processes of medical modernization during the First World War, it is the growing dominance of modes of thought and practice informed by dynamic and functionalized understandings of the body. Such thinking was central to many of the innovations in preventive and therapeutic practice and in medical surveillance and regulation that were developed in the course of the war. But physiological and psychological models also contributed to the emergence of new ways of thinking about *social* functions, and about how best to harness diverse social resources, in particular manpower, to the national effort. War itself now came to be seen as a process of technical, strategic and social innovation that tested the vigour and adaptability, not just of the military, but of the social organism as a whole. In this context, medicine in both its military and civilian aspects was increasingly seen to fulfil a vital function in the organization, mobilization and management of entire societies.

Nevertheless, it cannot be stressed too strongly that the advancement of such ways of thinking – rational, processual, calculative and integrative – did not simply follow some preordained and disembodied logic of modernization. On the contrary, they were adapted to take account of the particular circumstances under which different nations went to war and the different military and industrial manpower problems they faced, as well as older traditional suppositions about men's and women's roles in war and peace. The story of medicine in the First World War is thus one of piecemeal and partial realization of the social processes deemed characteristic of modernity. Moreover, it is simply not clear just how far these elements of medical modernity persisted into the interwar years, though there are suggestions in the chapters by Cooter, Thomson and Sauerteig that many of the medical developments of the war were quickly abandoned or forgotten thereafter.

With the descent into renewed global conflict in 1939, however, the relations between medicine, war and modernity were once again thrown into stark relief. The chapter by Starns on British nursing during the Second World War suggests that gender roles, and especially the inferior status of women workers, again tended to be reinforced rather than alleviated by the recruitment of women to the war effort. Though military nurses enjoyed a modest rise in status during the war, their civilian counterparts suffered a contrary fate. Large numbers of barely trained women were recruited to care for the anticipated casualties of enemy bombing, and the profession suffered dilution, deskilling and a general loss of status and respect as a result. Subsequently, some nursing reformers sought to reverse this process by remodelling the profession along expressly militarist lines. They did so, however, by looking back to an older military culture of unquestioning obedience, discipline

and 'character' rather than training, skill and functional efficiency. The adoption of
this image tended to confirm older popular notions of nursing as an extension of
women's domestic work, and thus contributed to its continued low status. In the
postwar world, civilian women were unwilling to submit to such discipline without
the compensation of travel and adventure, and recruitment fell rather than rose.
For the nursing profession then, the Second World War was an unmitigated
disaster; far from becoming part of modern technical medicine, nursing tended to
retreat into a more traditional world of gendered subordination.

This contrasts dramatically with the modernization that took place in certain
spheres of war-related industrial production. Neushul's chapter looks at a key
medical contribution to the war effort, namely the development of penicillin.
Despite some encouraging clinical results from Britain, and considerable interest
from the military, American pharmaceutical companies were reluctant to
undertake production using existing fermentation methods. They preferred to
hold out in the hope of developing a commercially advantageous synthetic
process. They only adopted fermentation following a number of crucial
interventions by government organizations, most importantly the development of
a pilot plant which demonstrated that the drug could be produced in commercial
quantities by fermentation, and the organization of clinical trials which made
clear the medical, strategic and commercial value of the new drug. As Neushul
stresses, the war greatly accelerated the transfer of medical technology across a
number of important boundaries: from Britain to the US, from the civilian to the
military sphere and back, from state science laboratories to private companies
and mass production, and from clinical testing to the bedside. Importantly, these
lines of transfer and communication remained open after the war had ended.
The pharmaceutical industry underwent a lasting modernization as increased
integration of private companies with the state, and of scientific research with
industrial production, led to further developments in the mass production and
administration of new and standardized medical treatments.

Other boundaries to be broken down in the course of the Second World War
included those that demarcated the limits of the individual self. Bourke's paper
examines the medical literature on psychological management – particularly the
management of fear – that burgeoned during the war, to show how the emotions
were brought under the purview of scientific accounts of human behaviour.
Privileged in these accounts was a dual understanding: of internal processes of
development and learned control; and of the social connections to the group that
enforced and reinforced these internal mechanisms. Psychologists posited
deterministic theories and recommended mechanisms for the regulation of both
these dimensions of mental discipline. The inward self at once became visible to
the scientific gaze and was located within a social nexus that rendered it capable
of direct supervision and manipulation. Bourke argues that this discourse of total
psychological control developed as a response to what was seen to be the

emotional impact of modern mechanized warfare with its awesome and dehumanizing power to kill. Within this discourse, modernity itself was conceptualized as a threat to psychological well-being, as over-refined emotional sensibilities were confronted by the speed and technological sophistication of modern life, of which war was only an extreme manifestation.

Weber would not have been surprised at this diagnosis; here was an echo of his own views, not only on modernity, but on war in relation to it. What he would not have shared was the solution favoured by psychologists and military commanders alike: the advancement of ever more refined scientific techniques for studying the soul of modern humanity and for managing the emotions and behaviour of mass armies and the populations from which they were drawn. In the twenty-five years since his death, the world had moved on. And while modernity certainly brought with it its own tensions and contradictions, stresses and anxieties, it was also increasingly seen to offer the solutions to these problems. Medicine was one of the foremost among the institutions offering such solutions, be it through the elucidation of individual and crowd psychology, or through the astonishing new drugs issuing from the laboratories and plant of the pharmaceutical industry.

The essays in this volume document in precise historical detail some of the ways that medicine participated in the making of that modernity. It was central to the creation of a calculus of rational society, to the elaboration of an administrative way of knowing, and to the development of bureaucratic technologies for managing the human body and mind. Medicine did not simply minister to modernity; it was one of the key means of bringing that modernity into being. And medicine's involvement in war, in particular, provided a crucial moment for the emergence of many of the material and social technologies that we now see as quintessentially modern. Weber himself realised that this was the case. Involved in the administration of army hospitals in Baden during the First World War, he had observed the way that military bureaucracy enhanced medical efficiency and patient discipline.[55] The chapters collected here expand on this observation. By examining the role of medicine in war, we can begin to understand the processes by which some of the most pervasive institutions of modernity, from the vast machinery of medical industry and administration to the most intimate of bodily and mental experiences, were shaped by the imperative to regiment and regulate human life for the purpose of conflict between nations.

ACKNOWLEDGEMENT

Thanks to Lutz Sauerteig for his comments on an earlier draft of this introduction.

Notes

1 Max Weber, 'Bureaucracy' in H.H. Gerth and C. Wright Mills (trs and eds), *From Max Weber: Essays in Sociology* (London, Routledge & Kegan Paul, 1948), pp. 196–244.

2 Jurgen Habermas, 'Technology and Science as "Ideology"' in his *Toward a Rational Society*, tr. Jeremy Shapiro (London, Heinemann, 1971), p. 81.

3 See Scott Lash and Sam Whimster (eds), *Max Weber, Rationality and Modernity* (London, Allen & Unwin, 1987); Detlev J.K. Peukert, *Max Webers Diagnose der Moderne* (Göttingen, Vandenhoeck and Rupprecht, 1989); Peter Wagner, *A Sociology of Modernity: Liberty and Discipline* (London, Routledge, 1994).

4 Weber, 'Science as a Vocation' in *From Max Weber*, pp. 129–56.

5 Quoted in J.P. Mayer, *Max Weber and German Politics* (London, Faber & Faber, 1943), pp. 127–8.

6 Weber, 'Bureaucracy', p. 215.

7 See Daniel Pick, *War Machine: The Rationalization of Slaughter in the Modern Age* (New Haven, Yale University Press, 1993).

8 John Brewer, *The Sinews of Power: War, Money and the English State, 1688–1783* (New York, Knopf, 1988).

9 Alan Forrest, *Conscripts and Deserters: The Army and French Society During the Revolution and Empire* (Oxford University Press, 1989); Forrest, *Soldiers of the French Revolution* (Durham, NC, Duke University Press, 1990). See also Geoffrey Best, *War and Society in Revolutionary Europe, 1770–1870* (Leicester University Press, 1982).

10 Ken Alder, *Engineering the Revolution: Arms and Enlightenment in France, 1763–1815* (Princeton University Press, 1997). Thanks to Donald MacKenzie for this reference.

11 Pick, *War Machine*, ch. 12: 'The Rationalization of Slaughter'.

12 John Ellis, *The Social History of the Machine Gun* (London, Cresset Library, 1975), esp. ch. 2: 'Industrialised War'.

13 See Michael Mann, *States, War and Capitalism: Studies in Political Sociology* (Oxford, Blackwell, 1988), p. 124; Alfred Vagts, *A History of Militarism: Civilian and Military* (London, Hollis & Carter, 1959), p. 453; Michael Geyer, 'Militarization of Europe, 1914–1945' in John R. Gillis (ed.), *The Militarization of the Western World* (New Brunswick, NJ, Rutgers University Press, 1989), pp. 78–9.

14 Weber, 'The Meaning of Discipline' in *From Max Weber*, p. 261.

15 Cited in Pick, *War Machine*, p. 101.

16 Marx to Engels, 7 July 1866, in Karl Marx and Friedrich Engels, *Selected Correspondence* (3rd edn, Moscow, Progress Publishers, 1975), p. 169, original emphasis. Engels was to generalize on this point a decade later in *Anti-Dühring*.

17 Guy Emerson Bowerman, Jr, *The Compensations of War: The Diary of an Ambulance Driver During the Great War*, ed. M.C. Carnes (Austin, University of Texas Press, 1983), p. 32.

18 Guy Chapman, *A Passionate Prodigality: Fragments of an Autobiography* (Leatherhead, Ashford, Buchan & Enright, 1985, 1st edn 1933), p. 80.

19 The literature linking the welfare to the warfare state is surprisingly thin. While theories of state formation up to the early twentieth century pay due regard to the importance of militarist interests, work on the welfare state is overwhelmingly concerned with the influence of socio-economic development and the politicization of the working class. Only recently have historians begun to explore the militarist dimensions of welfare. See Young-Sun Hong, *Welfare, Modernity and the Weimar State, 1919–1933* (Princeton University Press, 1998). Theda Skocpol, *Protecting Soldiers and Mothers: The Political Origins of Social Policy in the United States* (Cambridge, MA, Belknap Press, 1992), attributes the

limited extent and strongly maternalist orientation of American welfare in the early to mid-twentieth century to the relative weakness of the warfare state at that time.

20 Modris Eksteins, *Rites of Spring: The Great War and the Birth of the Modern Age* (New York, Doubleday, 1989), p. xvi.

21 Samuel Hynes, *A War Imagined: The First World War and English Culture* (New York, Atheneum, 1991).

22 Paul Fussell, *The Great War and Modern Memory* (Oxford University Press, 1975).

23 Pick, *War Machine*, esp. p. 260. See also Cecil D. Eby, *The Road to Armageddon: The Martial Spirit in English Popular Literature, 1870–1914* (Durham, NC, Duke University Press, 1987). Jay Winter, not in this tradition, challenges 'modernist' interpretations, arguing that communities made sense of the First World War within traditional frames of reference: *Sites of Memory, Sites of Mourning: The Great War in European Cultural History* (Cambridge University Press, 1995).

24 Elaine Showalter, 'Rivers and Sassoon: The Inscription of Male Gender Anxieties' in Margaret R. Higonnet, J. Jensen, S. Michael and M.C. Weitz (eds), *Behind the Lines: Gender and the Two World Wars* (New Haven, Yale University Press, 1987), pp. 61–9; Showalter, *The Female Malady: Women, Madness, and English Culture, 1830–1980* (New York, Pantheon Books, 1985).

25 Omer Bartove, *Murder in Our Midst: The Holocaust, Industrial Killing, and Representation* (New York, Oxford University Press, 1996); Zygmunt Bauman, *Modernity and the Holocaust* (Cambridge, Polity Press, 1989). See also Anthony Giddens, *The Nation-State and Violence* (Cambridge, Polity Press, 1985). Correcting the historically slipshod nature of much of this work is Paul Weindling, *Delousing Eastern Europe: German Bacteriology between Disinfection and Genocide, 1890–1940s* (Oxford University Press, forthcoming). For debate on structure and agency in the Holocaust, see Michael Burleigh, *Death and Deliverance: 'Euthanasia' in Germany, c. 1900–1945* (Cambridge University Press, 1994); Henry Friedlander, *The Origins of Nazi Genocide: From Euthanasia to the Final Solution* (Chapel Hill, University of North Carolina Press, 1995); Daniel J. Goldhagen, *Hitler's Willing Executioners: Ordinary Germans and the Holocaust* (New York, Alfred A. Knopf, 1996). Goldhagen's book has excited furious controversy; see for instance Norman G. Finkelstein and Ruth Bettina Birn, *A Nation on Trial: The Goldhagen Thesis and Historical Truth* (New York, Holt, 1998).

26 See also Eric Leed, *No Man's Land: Combat and Identity in World War I* (Cambridge University Press, 1979); George Mosse, *Fallen Soldiers: Reshaping the Memory of the World Wars* (Oxford University Press, 1990).

27 Weber, 'The Meaning of Discipline', p. 261.

28 Cf. Scott Lash, 'Modernity or Modernism? Weber and Contemporary Social Theory', in Lash and Whimster (eds), *Max Weber*, pp. 355–77.

29 Ulrich Beck, 'How Modern is Modern Society', *Theory, Culture & Society*, 9 (1992), p. 163. Beck's own concern with risk calculation and labour indicate his Weberian lineage. Interestingly, he even takes Giddens to task for his preoccupation with knowledge to the exclusion of other more concrete aspects of social life.

30 Mick Imlah, *Independent on Sunday*, 30 October 1994, p. 40 in his review of Geoff Dyer, *The Missing of the Somme* (London, Hamish Hamilton, 1994). See also Craig Calhoun, 'Postmodernism and Pseudohistory', *Theory, Culture & Society*, 10 (1993), 75–96; David Harvey, *The Condition of Postmodernity* (Oxford, Blackwell, 1990).

31 For a fuller account and critique, see Roger Cooter, 'War and Modern Medicine' in W.F. Bynum and Roy Porter (eds), *Companion Encyclopedia of the History of Medicine* (London, Routledge, 1993), pp. 1536–73.

32 See Deborah Dwork, *War is Good for Babies and Other Young Children: A History of the Infant and Child Welfare Movement in England, 1898–1918* (London, Tavistock, 1987); J.M. Winter, *The Great War and the British People* (London, Macmillan, 1985); Richard Titmuss, 'War and Social Policy' in his *Essays on 'The Welfare State'* (2nd edn, London, Allen & Unwin, 1963), pp. 75–87.

33 There are good examples in Erich Maria Remarque's *All Quiet on the Western Front* (Boston, Little, Brown & Co., 1993, orig. pub. 1928); for many other examples (including those of boredom and bureaucracy), see the diaries cited in Joanne Bourke, *Dismembering the Male: Men's Bodies, Britain, and the Great War* (University of Chicago Press, 1996).

34 Michael Kater, *Doctors Under Hitler* (Chapel Hill, University of North Carolina Press, 1989); Sheldon H. Harris, *Factories of Death: Japanese Biological Warfare 1932–45* (London and New York, Routledge, 1994). See also David Rothman, *Strangers at the Bedside: A History of How Law and Bioethics Transformed Medical Decision Making* (New York, Basic Books, 1991), ch. 2: 'Research at War'.

35 C.H. Firth, *Cromwell's Army* (London, Methuen, 1902), quoted in 'The Army Surgeon in Cromwell's Time', *Medical Record* (6 September 1902), 379.

36 The term is Wilfred R. Bion's who criticized such 'othering' of war in his *The Long Week-End, 1897–1919, Part of a Life*, ed. Francesca Bion (London, Free Association Books, 1986).

37 Titmuss, 'War and Social Policy', p. 77.

38 Geoffrey Best, '[Series] Editor's Preface' in his *War and Society*; Arthur Marwick (ed.), *Total War and Social Change* (London, Macmillan, 1988).

39 For historical essays on this theme, see Peter Wright and Andrew Treacher (eds), *The Problem of Medical Knowledge: Examining the Social Construction of Medicine* (University of Edinburgh Press, 1982).

40 See Mark Harrison, 'The Medicalization of War – The Militarization of Medicine', *Social History of Medicine*, 9 (1996), 267–76.

41 Manfred Berg and Geoffrey Cocks (eds), *Medicine and Modernity: Public Health and Medical Care in Nineteenth- and Twentieth-Century Germany* (Cambridge University Press, 1997).

42 *The Human Motor: Energy, Fatigue, and the Origins of Modernity* (Berkeley, University of California Press, 1992).

43 *The Railway Journey: The Industrialization of Time and Space in the 19th Century* (Leamington Spa, Berg, 1977).

44 For an excellent overview and bibliography, see Paul Lerner and Mark S. Micale, 'Trauma, Psychiatry and History: An Introduction' in Lerner and Micale (eds), *Traumatic Pasts: Studies in History, Psychiatry and Trauma in the Modern Age* (Cambridge University Press, forthcoming).

45 For example, Martin Stone, 'The Military and Industrial Roots of Clinical Psychology in Britain, 1900–1945' (unpub. Ph.D. thesis, University of London, 1985); Paul Lerner, 'Hysterical Men: War, Neurosis and German Mental Medicine, 1914–1921' (unpub. Ph.D. thesis, Columbia University, 1996); Marc Oliver Roudebush, 'A Battle of Nerves: Hysteria and its Treatment in France During World War I' (unpub. Ph.D. thesis, University of California, Berkeley, 1995).

46 See, for example, David Armstrong, *Political Anatomy of the Body: Medical Knowledge in Britain in the Twentieth Century* (Cambridge University Press, 1983); Armstrong, 'Public Health Spaces and the

Fabrication of Identity', *Sociology*, 27 (1993), 393–410; Armstrong, 'The Temporal Body' in Roger Cooter and J.V. Pickstone (eds), *The History of Medicine in the Twentieth Century* (Reading, Harwood International, forthcoming); Bryan Turner, *Regulating Bodies: Essays in Medical Sociology* (London, Routledge, 1992); *idem, The Body and Society: Explorations in Social Theory* (Oxford, Blackwell, 1984). See also Nikolas Rose on the history of psychology: *Governing the Soul: The Shaping of the Private Self* (London, Routledge, 1990).

47 Deborah Lupton, *The Imperative of Health: Public Health and the Regulated Body* (London, Sage, 1995), p. 9.

48 Little has been written on medicine in either the Spanish-American War or the Russo-Japanese War, but see Jim Connor, '"Before the World in Concealed Disgrace": Physicians, Professionalization and the Cuban Campaign of the Spanish-American War', and Claire Herrick, 'The Russo-Japanese War of 1904–5 and British Military Medicine', both in Roger Cooter, Mark Harrison and Steve Sturdy (eds), *Medicine and the Management of Modern Warfare* (Amsterdam, Rodopi, forthcoming). On medicine and the Spanish Civil War, see Jim Fyrth, *The Signal was Spain: The Aid Spain Movement in Britain, 1936–39* (London, Lawrence and Wishart, 1986).

49 See George C. Kohn, *Dictionary of Wars* (New York, Anchor, 1986), for an alphabetical listing of such events.

50 See David Arnold (ed.), *Imperial Medicine and Indigenous Societies* (Manchester University Press, 1988); Roy MacLeod and Milton Lewis (eds), *Disease, Medicine and Empire* (London, Routledge, 1988); Donald Denoon, *Public Health in Papua New Guinea: Medical Possibility and Social Constraint, 1884–1984* (Cambridge University Press, 1989); Megan Vaughan, *Curing Their Ills: Colonial Power and African Illness* (Cambridge, Polity, 1991).

51 See John Ettling, *The Germ of Laziness: Rockefeller Philanthropy and Public Health in the New South* (Cambridge, MA, Harvard University Press, 1981); A. Solarzano, 'Sowing the Seeds of Neo-imperialism: The Rockefeller Foundation's Yellow Fever Campaign in Mexico', *International Journal of Health Services*, 22 (1992), 529–54; Soma Hewa, 'The Hookworm Epidemic on the Plantations in Colonial Sri Lanka', *Medical History*, 38 (1994), 73–90; Paul Weindling, 'Public Health and Political Stabilization: The Rockefeller Foundation in Central and Eastern Europe Between the Two World Wars', *Minerva*, 31 (1993), 253–67.

52 Reynaldo C. Ileto, 'Cholera and the Origins of the American Sanitary Order in the Philippines' in Arnold (ed.), *Imperial Medicine*, pp. 125–48, at pp. 131–3.

53 See, however, Paul Weindling (ed.), *International Health Organizations and Movements* (Cambridge University Press, 1995); John Hutchinson, *Champions of Charity: War and the Rise of the Red Cross* (Boulder, Colorado, Westview Press, 1996).

54 Higonnet et al. (eds), *Behind the Lines*. And on the use of medical experts to regulate the activity of women in wartime industry, see Antonia Ineson and Deborah Thom, 'T.N.T. Poisoning and the Employment of Women Workers in the First World War' in Paul Weindling (ed.), *The Social History of Occupational Health* (London, Croom Helm, 1985), pp. 89–107.

55 Max Weber, *Zur Politik in Weltkrieg. Schriften un Reden, 1914–1918*, ed. Wolfgang J. Mommsen (Tübingen, J.C.B. Mohr), pp. 1–16.

2

THE RED CROSS FLAG IN THE FRANCO-PRUSSIAN WAR: CIVILIANS, HUMANITARIANS AND WAR IN THE 'MODERN AGE'

Bertrand Taithe

Everyone has a position in the city [Paris] and a place to fight. The walls are perpetually guarded by the national guard, which, from dawn to dusk, trains and exercises for war with the greatest patriotic attention. One feels these soldiers are gaining every day in experience and solidity. . . . Behind this guarded wall is a third line of defense, built by the barricade commission; behind these artfully piled cobblestones, the children of Paris have rediscovered, for the defence of Republican institutions, the genius of street fighting. . . .

*This situation imposes great duties on you. The first is not to let anything distract you from war, the struggle to the last [*guerre à outrance*]; the second, is to accept like brothers the republican command issued out of necessity and legality.*

Léon Gambetta, Tours, 9 October 1870[1]

Gambetta's famous first telegram to the French people during the German invasion of 1870 outlined the military doctrine of war to the last – *guerre à outrance* – and called on men, women and children to fight the invaders by any available means. This all-inclusiveness of *guerre à outrance* has allowed some historians to see the Franco-Prussian War as one the first instances of a style of 'modern, total war' that originated in practice and theory in the crucial wars of the 1860s, the other exemplars being the German wars of 1864 and 1866 and the American Civil War.[2] This view of the Franco-Prussian War stresses its 'modernity' and its seminal importance for later conflicts.

Modernity is commonly conflated with literary modernism of the twentieth century which either prefigured the First World War or was produced during or immediately afterwards. It always related modern sensibility to the horror and alienation of technology-led mass conflicts of attrition. Consequently, the notion of modernity in warfare is commonly seen as a peculiarly twentieth-century phenomenon. Moreover, modern warfare is often identified with the concept of 'total war'. The concept of total war as applied to the First World War is often traced back to the work of Baron Carl von Clausewitz.[3] Writing in the 1820s,

Clausewitz was reflecting on his experience of the French Revolutionary Wars to outline a conceptual 'absolute war' that remained more a Kantian ideal type than a practicable political option. Many observers have since put more emphasis on the limits of this idealistic genealogy. Notably, the philosopher Raymond Aron has argued that Clausewitz's notion of 'absolute war' is commonly misrepresented as 'total war', in the sense of 'the total mobilisation of all resources in order to achieve a radical victory'.[4] Aron went on to observe that Clausewitz could simply not have anticipated the scale of mobilization achieved in the twentieth-century world wars. Seen in this light, the Franco-Prussian War was perhaps closer in scale to Clausewitz's understanding of mobilization than to the battles of the Somme or Verdun. Moreover, the fact that Gambetta's rhetoric used many 1790s tropes might be seen as connecting it more directly with Clausewitz's first-hand experience than with anything written afterwards.[5]

That said, however, the fact that Clausewitz's reflections on the French wars of the Revolutionary and imperial eras were eventually echoed in the slaughter of 1914 has led some writers to consider the long nineteenth century from 1789 to 1914 as a Clausewitzian century.[6] Daniel Pick, in particular, argues that the nineteenth century saw the rise of autonomous 'war-machines', 'mass societies' unified for the purposes of an almost autonomous and leaderless war effort. Seen in this light, the Clausewitzian model of 'total war' – as exemplified, for instance, by the military dictatorship of Ludendorff in the second half of the First World War – becomes one of mass militarization replacing the social hierarchies of peace. Pick specifically identifies the Franco-Prussian War as crystallizing these concepts in preparation for 1914.[7] Moreover, the contested concept of militarization presumes a reorientation of both military and governmental control and initiative in order to mobilize national manpower for the purposes of fighting the war and for industrial war production.[8] As a result, civilian activities become redirected to military aims, such that any distinction between civilian and military spheres becomes meaningless.

Seen from this perspective, while Gambetta's call to arms might have seemed to his contemporaries to be an almost nostalgic look backwards to the French Revolutionary Wars, it might also be announcing the complete involvement of societies in total wars. Thus in 1870 the French fought a 'people's war', organized around Gambetta's call for universal conscription and for *guerre à outrance* or war to the last. These two aspects are recognizable features of total warfare; mass mobilization would have united the whole nation in the war effort, while *guerre à outrance* stated uncompromising war aims of unconditional victory. To an extent, this interpretation has been challenged by historians who argue, firstly, that war to the last ceased to be an option in January 1871, and secondly, that mass mobilization failed to be enthusiastically endorsed in much of France.[9] I will suggest, however, that those who argue this latter point have taken too narrow a view of the war effort, have focused too much on volunteering and other obvious signs of patriotism and have failed to take account of other forms of mobilization. Specifically, I will argue that ostensibly 'humanitarian' efforts were also an important form of mobilization for the war.

This vision of entire societies engaged in total war had direct implications for how war must be fought to achieve the new aim of unconditional victory. Shelling civilian targets and installations, starving populations and taking hostages now became legitimate forms of total warfare. In parallel to this narrative of increased brutalization and barbarization, as Omer Bartow and George Mosse have put it,[10] there is also another narrative of humanitarianism described by such authors as Michael Howard and Geoffrey Best.[11] These historians argue that the 'long nineteenth century' witnessed not only the making of tools of mass destruction but also a growing awareness of human sufferings. This 'humanitarian' sensibility, they argue, led to international legislation and jurisdiction on 'restraints' on war. Twentieth-century instances spring to mind, from Nuremberg to the current trials in the Hague, which chart the rise of 'civilian legal values' challenging the horrors implicit in total warfare. In this grand narrative the Franco-Prussian War was a key moment during which humanitarian sensibilities and ideals were organized and subverted. In final analysis, the war made clear some of the contradictions and tensions inherent in the idea of humanitarianism and in its realization.

During the second phase of the war, and especially between September 1870 and January 1871, the French Red Cross became a potent symbol of the civilian war effort and of French 'civilising ideals'. Humanitarianism in the war context represented a way of reinforcing peacetime social structures as well as a way of channelling civilian energy towards common war goals. As John Hutchinson has recently argued,[12] the 1870 war saw the first application of a Utopian project for which national organizations worked within established 'transnational solidarities' – solidarities which endured even after the crisis ended.[13] This relief work built on nearly two hundred years of religious work like that carried out by organizations such as the Society of Friends in Ireland.[14] The Red Cross differed from earlier relief work in considering controversially political crises as the equivalent of natural disasters, a point of view which implied that the principle of war was not to be questioned.[15] Moreover, though humanitarian efforts of the 1870 war grew out of earlier forms of relief work, they were crucially important for determining how the Red Cross would subsequently develop. Most significantly, they led to the long-term militarization of civilian relief agencies analysed by John Hutchinson, and arguably contributed to the emergence of the complex war machine described in Daniel Pick's work.[16]

Thus the Franco-Prussian War plays a crucial part in several narratives of the emergence of modern warfare, and of modernity more generally. Firstly, the French concept of *guerre à outrance* can be seen as a step on the way to 'total war' both in theory and in practice, while German war aims of unconditional surrender also seem to fit Clausewitz's model. Secondly, the war witnessed a peculiarly modern blurring of the categories of civilian and military activity. Thirdly, the war witnessed the 'rise' across Europe of the most emblematic international symbol of humanitarianism at war: the Red Cross. It is this organization – specifically the French Red Cross – that provides the focus for this chapter and that I take as the starting point from which to investigate in more detail the various themes just raised.

In particular, I aim to demonstrate that the practices of total war and of humanitarianism at war were closely related to one another, and indeed that each in effect reinforced the other. In so doing, however, I will also raise some questions concerning just how we think about total war.

Firstly, by looking in particular at the example of the French Red Cross, I will argue that a 'pyramidal' model of total war, controlled from the top down, is not valid, at least in 1870, and that the possibility of other forms of social organization and mobilization for total war needs also to be recognized. In this respect, it should be noted that, during the Franco-Prussian War, the French state was at its weakest in three hundred years.[17] The Ollivier government which started the war lasted but a few weeks, while its successor and the regime itself collapsed after the military disaster of Sedan in September 1870. The republic proclaimed to fill this vacuum had to fight the German invasion with limited resources, and with minimal administrative structures.

Secondly, I will also show that, while the boundary between the military and the civilian sphere – in effect, between the social orders of war and of peace – became more blurred and porous than ever before, at the same time it also became more central to thinking about the nature of civilization.

DEFINITIONS: 'HUMANITARIANISM', 'CIVILIANS' AND 'NEUTRALS'

The *Oxford English Dictionary* indicates that, in the nineteenth century, the adjective 'humanitarian' had mostly negative connotations, something like present-day notions of 'bleeding-heart liberal'. This use of the term can be found, for instance in the writings of the most violent critics of the French Red Cross.[18] To avoid confusion I intend to use 'humanitarian' in its modern meaning of 'humanitarian help', to imply a modernist sensibility of respect for basic human rights in warfare, as discussed in the work of Geoffrey Best or Thomas Laqueur.[19] This new sensibility was expressed in 1870 in a shift from an unwritten common law of war to internationally recognized written legal codes, reflecting a growing belief in both international jurisdiction and, more implicitly, in legal arbitration. By 1870, however, the Red Cross provided the most concrete embodiment of this new humanitarianism, and especially of new laws of war and ethics of medical relief.

The establishment of the Red Cross was also built upon the legal foundations of the Geneva Convention, which guaranteed neutrality to medical staff and wounded soldiers. The concept of neutrality in war originated from a strict understanding of the unwritten right of the people – *droit des gens* – including the right to property and life for the civilians.[20] This concept was not new in 1870.[21] In spite of significant historical precedents, however, the idea of neutrality as a contractual obligation between two enemies was first extended to include civilians during the Franco-Prussian War. This apparently simple axiom of the new laws of war led to much confusion, both real and disingenuous. Early in the conflict, the Prussian government declared that it intended to wage 'war on the French Imperial government and not on the French people'.[22] However, this statement was confounded by the revival, after 4 September 1870, of such French Revolutionary ideals as the *levée en masse* and *guerre à outrance*.[23] The supposedly total involvement of a 'people's war' challenged conventional war cabinet views of warfare. As the Germans saw it, this universal call to arms also demonstrated that the French did not fully comprehend or even rejected the implications of Genevan neutrality.[24] Likewise, while sick and wounded combatants were protected by the Geneva Convention, it was not clear whether their status was really neutral or when they stopped enjoying that status.[25]

In the war of 1870, any rigid division of society into separate civilian and military spheres was impossible to sustain for any length of time. Civilian society meshed with the military. Uniforms superficially covered a civilian identity, while armed civilians seemed out of place. Moreover, the military tradition of the Second Empire itself was based on nation-making wars, particularly in Italy.[26] The concept of neutrality, based as it was on a view of war as an extension of diplomacy, and moderated as it was by the new humanitarianism, was therefore at odds with the whole way the French thought about war.[27] In 1870 the boundaries between civilian and military thus faded and became circumstantial. Each occupying soldier had to decide for himself whether a French peasant should be regarded as a neutral civilian or as a guerrilla.[28]

These ambiguities in effect created a situation in which claims and counter-claims of atrocities could be mobilized. Prussian and other German troops consistently denied military status to guerrillas and armed civilians, who were conventionally regarded as spies, to be executed sometimes along with their families or their neighbours.[29] Thus when Prussian, Bavarian or Saxon troops (the French only gradually came to consider them as one German collective entity) shot down villagers for breaking the presumed rules of war, they were applying a strictly defined understanding of legitimate enemies. This slaughter mirrored the events of Prussian *Nationalverein* of 1813, when Prussian volunteers resisted French occupation. During that episode the French occupying forces had hanged a number of the volunteers. To undermine the relevance of this sad precedent the French press of 1870 – echoed by subsequent generations of French historians – were quick to argue that the earlier events had occurred before the Geneva Convention, and that in the new context of modern ethical warfare the adoption of similar methods by the Germans revealed the brutality and hypocrisy of the invading armies.[30]

A similar situation was created by the fact that the Geneva Convention also encoded the neutrality of ambulance (i.e., field hospital) staff on the battlefield. Many of the outrages in the early stages of the war resulted from the French using buildings near the front line as ambulances. As the French forces retreated, the ambulance frequently became a stronghold which an advancing enemy needed to destroy,[31] while the presence of Red Cross flags in convenient proximity to troops often provided useful sights on which the German gunners could train their guns.[32] This pattern occurred several times during the war, when the whole staff of the ambulance either died in the action or was executed soon afterwards.[33] The identification of medical personnel was further hindered by the fact that French medical staff ignored the Genevan rules and did not wear suitably stamped Red Cross armbands during the first few months of the war.[34] The killing or shelling of supposedly neutral personnel provided another source of outrage for the French press. This sense of outrage was only increased by the fact that many of those serving in the town ambulances were women, be they professional nurses on the English model or French nuns, bourgeoisie or actresses.[35]

The shelling of civilian targets likewise created new opportunities for accusations of brutality. The Prussian press had first deployed such accusations during the shelling of Saarbrücken in July 1870, to stir public indignation against the invading French army. The arguments were simply reversed when, in turn, the Germans invaded France.[36] The shelling of Paris in January 1871 was thus a double-edged weapon which, as the Prussian crown prince feared, undermined the German cause and provoked a negative reaction in Europe.[37] The fears of the crown prince were political and humanitarian. He accurately perceived the emotional impact of bombing civilians, but this attitude was reinforced by a new humanitarian sensitivity to civilian suffering which was echoed and amplified through the media of Europe. Shelling civilians did not kill in large numbers, especially compared with the slaughter of the open battlefield, yet it killed the archetypal innocents: women and children.[38] These were the victims needed to construct the image of the enemy as melodramatic villain. Gunners thus came to embody a force of distant and victimizing evil: they were the first symbol of war against humanity. This genre provided the French with a suitably clear-cut opposition between the forces of good and evil, which they could use to redefine themselves, not as aggressors but as victims.[39]

The slaughter of innocents, premeditated or otherwise, was not the only bone of contention between the French and the Prussians after the war. Each side accused the other of using forbidden weapons. Both countries had signed the 1868 St Petersburg Convention prohibiting explosive bullets. Ironically, this convention ignored much more destructive modern weaponry used during the war: steel Krupp guns shelled more accurately than had been thought possible in the past; the French *mitrailleuse* fired dozens of murderous 50 g conical lead bullets; the bullets of French rifles, with an effective range of over a mile, often caused incredible wounds.[40] While this modern weaponry was deemed regular, the outrage came to focus on the entirely mythical horror of exploding bullets.[41] Several army and Red Cross commissions launched enquiries into their supposed use, but none found any evidence to prove their existence,[42] nor that of the equally fanciful 'poisonous bullets'.[43] The most devastating wounds were more probably due to projectiles at the end of their useful firing range bouncing on bones within the body and tearing the flesh open. Even though these enquiries were unfruitful, the new codes of war and the international legislation that accompanied them made possible the battery of charges and counter-charges that followed the war.

Under these circumstances, the fact that the press and other observers could appeal to supposedly clear-cut rules of engagement, and supposedly clear-cut distinctions between combatants and non-combatants, made possible a whole new realm of atrocity. In effect, the advent of humanitarianism only made war the more horrible. Ironically, this new construal of war as organized brutality actually led to a popular appropriation of the motives of the war.[44] The barbarization of warfare was presented on both sides as a unilateral crime. French commentators made more capital than the invading Germans of this new sphere of cruelty and unnecessary violence in war, presenting the war as a conflict of civilization against barbarity, of ideas against strength, of humanist values against brutality. As a result, many French citizens forgot why France went to war in the first place, and rather found new reasons for regarding the war as legitimate. As one commentator put it: 'France will regain the certitude of representing what is Right in a struggle from which the winner, whatever it does, will appear only as the incarnation of strength.'[45]

The complex apportioning of responsibility thus boiled down to a banal story of good and evil. Indignation at isolated anecdotes of the violation of impossible rules served to cover up the mutual and multiple horrors of war. This had paradoxical results for the way the events of the war were perceived. On the one hand, questions of individual responsibility were passed over in favour of generalizations about national character. Thus German cruelty was condemned, but no German officer was ever singled out as a criminal.[46] This finer apportionment of blame was not carried out despite there being at least one famous American precedent. Captain Henry Wintz, commandant of Andersonville Confederate prisoner of war camp, had been prosecuted and sentenced to death under article 59 of the US General Order 100 after the American Civil War.[47] Six years later, however, neither the French nor the Germans actually thought of identifying brutal war action as the criminal behaviour of a few. On the other hand, the mass slaughters on the battlefield were neglected in favour of *faits divers*, of little scenes of anonymous human cruelty which readers and spectators could comprehend. War had not become any more brutal. Yet with the rise of the new humanitarianism, brutality had become a key concern around which civilian indignation and military aggression – themselves increasingly blurred and mutually self-reinforcing – could now be mobilized.

OFFICIAL MOVEMENTS

The history of the Red Cross is a familiar one, and Henry Dunant's *Souvenir de Solferino* remains a cornerstone of the history of humanitarianism.[48] The movement had its antecedents. Nineteenth-century French historians of humanitarianism looked back to eighteenth-century instances of neutrality at war and inscribed the Geneva Convention in a long sequence of enlightened progress.[49] Perhaps because of a misreading of the US experience, the American Civil War was often presented as the first occasion when a successful 'liberal', free enterprise system of administering help to wounded soldiers was instituted. Thomas Evans, Napoleon III's American dentist, introduced the American model to the French public as early as 1865. Evans's book ran to five editions between 1865 and 1867 and contributed to the promotion of medical neutrality at war.[50] He subsequently imported some American ambulance material for the Universal Exhibition of 1867, and eventually contributed to the creation of an American ambulance in Paris in October 1870.

The Geneva Convention dated from 1864 and had been first applied during the Prussian war against Denmark of the same year and, on a larger scale, during the Austro-Prussian War of 1866.[51] These short wars were merely semi-experiments, however, for only the Prussians had signed the convention and abided by its rules. The Franco-Prussian War thus came as the first full-scale application of the convention.

Symbolically linked with the text of the convention, but not strictly part of it, was the *Société de secours aux blessés des armées de terre et de mer.*[52] In 1870, a few months before the war, the *Société de secours* still looked unlikely to become operable in the foreseeable future. It was a rather informal club of medical men who had personally experienced war, like Chenu (the famous medical narrator of the Crimean War),[53] and benevolent aristocrats like Viscount de Melun. Benefiting from imperial patronage, it had become a tax exempt *association d'utilité publique* on 23 June 1866. Napoleon III insisted on a stand at the Universal Exhibition of 1867 and on an international congress. In the midst of this display of wealth, the congress delegates could do no more than air purely theoretical views about what it would do in the eventuality of war. The *Société de secours* had no funds. And in the absence of national war,[54] and under the patronage of the dictator who claimed his empire meant peace, it had no clear purpose. The 1870 war put an end to this uncertainty.

In July 1870, the *Société de secours* started canvassing for money, though with little result in the first month.[55] The public did not see a need to complement army services with civilian ambulances. Significantly, fund-raising only took off after the defeats early in August 1870. Equally significantly, during the first year, gifts from foreign countries, from Mexico to Japan, amounted to almost half the total income at the disposal of the French *Société*. In effect, the French *Société de secours* became at once an international investment fund in humanitarian causes and a form of surrogate diplomacy for neutral powers. As the Red Cross blossomed throughout Europe, it quickly came to serve a variety of political purposes ranging from the assertion of national identity on the European stage, as in the case of the Irish ambulance,[56] to gathering medical intelligence for foreign armed forces.[57] The British, Dutch, Italian, Austrian and Belgian committees sent ambulances to France to help the wounded and observe the effects of modern warfare; many of the staff of the British ambulances, for example, were on leave from the British Army.[58] Foreign observers subsequently published important analyses and medical observations of the effects of war; the Russians paid special attention to small calibre high-velocity bullets; the Italians cared about hospital trains, and so on.[59]

The Red Cross also elicited public donations that can be seen as a form of financial and sentimental investment in a 'civilising process', in Norbert Elias's meaning of the phrase. There was a clear shift in the kind of the philanthropy involved, from an individual aristocratic gesture to anonymous participation in corporate charity. This shift reflected the parallel growth of international media and finance. From the start the Red Cross involved highly complex financial tools, transferring large funds across Europe and the world into the heart of the conflict.[60]

At a national level, French conservative newspapers like *Le Gaulois* undertook to raise money for similar purposes. Public subscriptions started at the beginning of the war and soon gathered momentum: 352,141 francs by 21 July, 669,293 by 3 August; 1,000,637 by 21 August after the first heavy defeats and the battle of Gravelotte. Newspapers published patriotic lists of subscribers, street collections became a familiar sight, and coin boxes in Parisian shops gathered large public donations.[61] With the proceeds, the newspapers created a new organization called the *Comité de la presse*.[62] Although originally meant to be little more than a fund-raising group for the *Société de secours*, this organization soon came to see itself as a rival.[63] An editorial in *Le Gaulois* on 23 August signalled the break between the two organizations: 'Today we address to the Count of Flavigny, president of the International Society . . . a letter asking him to return to us the ambulance funded at our expense for this above mentioned Society. In this letter we warmly thank the Count of Flavigny and we regret withdrawing from his custody equipment that now needs to be used . . .'.[64]

The internal politics of the *Société de secours* were the cause of this split. The administration of the *Société de secours*, originally under the responsibility of

Nélaton, a high-class surgeon with a prominent university chair,[65] had recently been handed over to a group of aristocrats backed by Chenu. Major benefactors meant their names to be clearly associated with any action undertaken with the assistance of their money and their connections.[66] This significant seizure of power had two important effects. Firstly, non-medical men now entered the *Société de secours* as administrators or delegates,[67] frustrating medical hopes of complete independence in the management of 'their' ambulances. Secondly, funds were more liberally and indiscriminately distributed than had originally been planned.[68] The *Comité de la presse*, scandalized by the removal of Nélaton from his post, accused the Red Cross firstly of being unable to use their money, then a month later of wasting their funds. The most vociferous critic of the Red Cross was Léon Lefort who, according to Chenu, resented having lost the salary and status he had bullied out of the Red Cross in its earlier days. Lefort, for his part, declared that he had lost all faith in this amateurish aristocratic tea party.[69]

In the event, the two organizations unwittingly came to play complementary roles: the *Comité de la presse* used household names like Ricord to appeal for money on the domestic front, while the official *Société de secours* was able to call for foreign monies through the well-established networks of upper-class sociability.[70] This complementarity was never acknowledged, however, and there remained deep animosity between the two associations. The conflict was chiefly played out through competing claims to offer 'value for money'. As a result, the *Société de secours*, in particular, now sought to justify its existence by creating large numbers of ambulances. This was to a great extent a conscious move to associate the *Société* with the *levée en masse* and universal conscription. In choosing this route, however, the *Société* came to favour quantity of ambulances over quality. This required ever increasing funds, which had to be drawn from new and untapped civilian reserves. It also involved recruitment of an ever widening range of experts to join the original small and self-selected elite. As a result, relatively unknown members of the medical establishment now became heads of provincial field hospitals. This failure to conform to the niceties of scientific and social ranking encouraged medical men of high prestige to join the *Comité de la presse* rather than the *Société de secours*.[71] Besides, the *Comité de la presse* also provided high-profile newspaper coverage, the opportunity to obtain some surgical experience, and the public recognition of well-established status.[72]

Apart from the original split between the two main medical humanitarian organizations, there was also a deeper and more bitter division separating 'first and second class' medical men in both camps. At a time of grave political instability the *Société de secours* and its twin proved socially and politically useful for established medical men who owed their position to the rampant nepotism of the previous government. Voluntary organizations filled the political gap left by the collapse of the state, and provided an alternative institutional base for the identification of social élites. Consequently, 1870 became the golden age of voluntary movements, not least for medical men. Closing ranks against the lower medical orders, and often against more politically radical medical men, the *Société de secours* and the *Comité de la presse* covered their institutional prominence with the whitewash of war heroism, and provided a rare opportunity to obtain honours like the Légion d'honneur from whatever government might exist after the war.[73] 'This bright ribbon, that looks so good over a black coat, has become a mean of corruption, tempting vain and vulgar ambitions; it has become the price of the most shameful begging and the most revolting servitude, the mark of a lack of honour', wrote one medical journalist who failed to get one.[74] Some of the numerous war accounts used in this study prove, on closer examination, to be no more than dossiers compiled to justify an award.[75] When the coveted ribbon proved to be scarce, the commemorative medals of the *Société de secours* would do as second best. Being red and white, their ribbon could be woven with more red than white, making it easy to confuse them with the red Légion d'honneur. At best the *Société de secours* and the *Comité de la presse* thus served as a social ladder for those who had not yet achieved the highest prominence; at the very least they offered a social scaffolding which prevented leading men from falling with the Second Empire.[76]

As a result, there were obvious rivalries for acceptance into the voluntary ambulances, particularly of the *Société de secours*.[77] This rivalry became even more heated when the main Parisian ambulances published a list of 'authorised' surgeons of talent,[78] which excluded most medical volunteers from the lower ranks of the medical world.[79] Furious arguments dating from the Second Empire now boiled back to the surface of medical politics: 'We are the medical democracy, we want a medical republic and we will not accept that the revolution was won to favour privilege . . . No more oligarchy, no more princes of science, no more unfair and humiliating distinctions; let us leave to the clerics the privilege of their divided clergy.'[80]

VOLUNTARY MOVEMENTS

To begin to understand the complex relationships between organized voluntary movements, the army and the state administration, it is necessary to look at the chaos in which both the French state and army found themselves in 1870. In the political vacuum created by the war, voluntary associations offered a unique opportunity for free enterprise in humanitarianism and war mobilization. The *Société de secours* and the *Comité de la presse* had directly financed 217 ambulances in August 1870, including 3 gathered in Brussels, 31 regional ambulances, 11 or so 'flying ambulances' and 8 hospitals, with a total of 4,210 beds.[81] This compares rather poorly with the 1,291 other ambulances created in Paris alone.[82] The red cross emblem on flags legitimized the independent existence of hundreds of ambulances supported by religious orders, municipal authorities, businesses,[83] rich philanthropists like Wallace[84] or Rothschild,[85] Jewish, Protestant (748 beds)[86] and Freemason organizations,[87] or even by individuals. These Parisian ambulances together provided 25,182 beds, an average of 19.5 beds per ambulance.[88]

This proliferation of red cross flags[89] was largely uncontrolled.[90] The rationale behind their creation seems in many cases to have been more than a purely voluntary impulse.[91] The Geneva Convention explicitly protected ambulances and their personnel from requisitions and invading armies. While the French army was totally unaware of the benefits of the convention until late into the war,[92] civilians quickly came to appreciate that it could be used as a form of 'war insurance',[93] to supplement the protection of private and neutral property offered by more customary notions of *droit des gens*. The official Red Cross was quick to distance itself from such practices: 'These people do not calculate what a gaping wound or a broken limb may represent in terms of heroism or suffering, but [only] what they [the wounds] may confer in terms of protection against the advancing enemy and their requisitions. We will never, at any cost, become the society for the exploitation of the sick and wounded.'[94]

Not that the red cross could be relied upon to confer such protection. In the case of the particularly harsh occupation of Le Mans, for example, even the systematic conversion of almost the entire town into a hospital did not save homeowners from the invading army or their brutal exactions.[95]

This cynical approach to humanitarian work was not the only impulse behind the creation of ambulances, however. The proliferation of ambulances also called up a polyphony of specific and different humanitarian discourses. Charitable and religious agencies, for instance, used the red cross flag in their proselytizing.[96] Thus a Protestant preacher stated that 'beyond our care we had to remember the religious work we sought to carry on' through daily scripture readings.[97] Henri Monod candidly admitted that 'this spontaneous move [towards an ambulance] has been most helpful for the cause of Protestantism, because it powerfully undermined the prejudice, ignorance and ill-will against our faith'.[98] During the worst of the battles, local priests, unsolicited by their often hostile flock (when they were not Muslim Turcos), found in the ambulance a rewarding work which enabled them to satisfy their Saint-Sulpician sentiment for suffering and martyrdom while gently bending the ears of the patients. 'Only yesterday did I understand my true place in the ambulance', wrote one. 'I provide the patient with consolations and encouragement while his wounds are dressed. I elevate his soul to God, and then I lower it gently towards the consoling duties of a Christian.'[99]

Freemasons too acquired social visibility by integrating humanitarianism into their secularist philosophy. Notables gained social inviolability in the climate of civil war by practising charity in a new guise. Individuals avoided military service and requisition orders while still showing patriotism. Junior medical practitioners in the overcrowded urban medical market secured well-deserved custom out of their war effort.[100] Municipalities used ambulances to re-establish their political authority after years of repression. They also made occasional profits from donations.[101]

The government, meanwhile, was too feeble to do anything about marshalling this surge of sentimentalized war effort until the very end of December 1870, a month or so before the armistice. Even then, it did not have the power to assert much by way of control over the voluntary organizations. Thus at the end of the war the *Société de secours* was able to maintain its nominal independence from the army, giving it a total monopoly over humanitarian issues, sanitarian inspections (first attempted 20 October) and fund-raising.[102] Voluntary ambulances were simply registered by the *Société* which was then accountable to the army. In other instances the Red Cross stepped in to replace helpless local authorities.[103] The surge of civilian war effort thus overwhelmed the state, which could only react belatedly to this mobilization rather than sponsor or control it.

One of the legacies of the 1870 war, and especially of the collapse of state power and the enormous upsurge of voluntary effort that the war thereby unleashed in France, was thus the creation of unprecedented forms of institutionalized and militaristic humanitarianism. These new institutions would not enjoy their freedom from state interference for long, however. With the civil war the Paris Commune in 1871, they were quickly brought under stricter state control: as the Paris Commune nationalized the *Société* and incorporated it into the revolutionary army, the Versailles government, elected by the whole of France, moved to assert far more control over all areas of voluntary effort.[104] After a period during which it ignored the Red Cross movements it then militarized them to serve its own army. On the way to total war, the mobilization of resources which the Red Cross enabled became part of all European war machines. In 1878, for instance, the Prussian government subjected the Red Cross to military command.[105] In an age that increasingly inclined towards universal conscription and mass mobilization, free enterprise could not be tolerated.[106] In the early 1880s, French army administrators could thus confidently proclaim that 'the Red Cross has no longer any purpose'.[107] The conscription of medical practitioners through the reform of the military service in the 1880s seemed to justify this claim. The Red Cross did survive none the less, though now in ever closer partnership with the military. It did so because humanitarianism could serve the national war effort in other – primarily ideological – ways.[108]

IDEOLOGY

Though the *Société de secours* initially grew out of the soft Christian internationalism of the Geneva Convention, it did not long keep its roots there.

Rather, in the course of the war of 1870, it began to voice more robust forms of 'mobilising' discourse centred on the need to pursue national priorities. It did so in order to align itself with the popular calls to continue the war against the Prussians at all costs. Ironically, the professedly humanitarian *Société* owed its wealth and influence to the prolongation of the war. Moreover, this groundswell of bellicosity was rhetorically linked to a revival of the republican spirit of the people's war of 1792. Like that earlier revolutionary movement, it was legitimized by ideological statements about the national integrity of France and the need to defend liberty across Europe. The revolutionary government of 1870 thus continued an imperial war by giving it new meanings, and most importantly by invoking universal principles of human rights. In effect, ambulance work now became an integral part of a national-cum-republican revival. Medical authors clamoured: 'Salute gladly the return of Liberty and applaud this pacific revolution that will become, with our heroic national war, the greatest glory of our generation.'[109]

It might be argued that the display of generosity and the extravagant expenses incurred to establish ambulances were primarily morale-boosting measures. In besieged Paris, starved of any real news, ambulance activities provided a focus for an exuberant press. Journalists could eulogize the wounded heroes and the saintly nurses, from glamorous actresses like Sarah Bernhardt to more mundane semi-professional nurses belonging to religious orders or secularist movements.[110] The humanitarian sentiment behind such efforts went deeper, however, into the realms of ideology. The fact that the German forces were so often seen to violate the supposed rules of war[111] meant that this could itself be seen as a war of ideologies – a conflict between German *realpolitik* on the one hand and French civilizing ideals on the other.[112] And this in turn meant that the hitherto internationalist language of humanitarianism could itself be appropriated to the national purpose.

The interpretative frame of humanitarianism was in contradiction with the practices of modern warfare. Using the language of humanitarianism one could only conclude by emphasizing the growing barbarization of warfare. It built a self-perpetuating analysis. Humanitarianism needed war to be expressed, yet war was the negation of humanitarian feelings.[113] This vicious circle did not allow much space for internationalist humanitarianism or sympathy for the sufferings of the enemy. By creating a clear dichotomy expressed in moral and legal terms, the humanitarian ideology fed national hatreds among the protagonists. This appropriation of humanitarian principles worked on a purely national basis – the French vs. Barbarians – and went against transnational principles.

For a while it looked as though this nationalist appropriation of humanitarian sentiment, and the acrimonious debates that ensued in post-1870 Europe, would condemn the Red Cross movement. In the event, the Red Cross has nevertheless survived another 129 years. To explain this survival, most hagiographers of the

Red Cross seem to argue that international humanitarianism eventually won out over more nationalist perversions.[114] More critical observers, like Hutchinson for instance, point out that the more Utopian humanitarian discourse became autonomous in Geneva from the national experience.[115] In 1870 the picture is even more complicated by the fact, that, on a national basis, the humanitarian ideology served to justify the Franco-Prussian War while it lasted. Moreover, in the years after the war, that same ideology would be channelled, first into the conservative struggle against the barbarians within – namely the socialists and revolutionaries of Paris – and then into nationalistic efforts of reconstruction. The crucial role played by the *Société* during the 1871 Paris Commune civil war, and in subsequent efforts to mend the social fabric after it, did much to define the way that humanitarian action would be understood and practised thereafter.

It is significant that the first victim of the civil war between Paris and Versailles was a military doctor wearing the red cross band. This murder was subsequently used to justify the systematic execution of most Communards taken prisoner. The Red Cross movement, in its diverse forms, took sides during the civil war against Paris and joined forces with the government 'to whom our sponsors and donators called us to take our resources'.[116] To this end, Red Cross ambulances inside Paris hid soldiers who remained loyal to the government, and sheltered persecuted priests. In some ambulances, weapons were either destroyed or hidden.[117] Systematic sabotage, censorship, and betrayal of the Communard war effort was the norm in all Red Cross ambulances. The *Société de secours*, though nationalized by the Paris Commune, was the heart and soul of this resistance. Meanwhile, the Commune itself sought the protection of the new ideals of internationalist humanitarianism, and in mid-May claimed to have succeeded, after some difficulty, in becoming a signatory to the Geneva Convention, a claim which was not recognized abroad.[118] Nevertheless, it never managed to use the Red Cross personnel that remained under its control. Indeed, as the Communards now laid claim to the emblem of the red cross for their own use, those organizations that had hitherto served under that same emblem now promptly denounced it as a cover for espionage and for undesirable communication between the two sides. To avoid any Communard 'contamination' of their own staff and patients, the French *Société* and the foreign ambulances abandoned without hesitation the red cross on their identity cards.[119] Civil war imperatives took precedence over humanitarian ones. Humanitarianism did not apply to those now deemed subhuman. Consequently, far from being a Utopian ideology defending human rights, the humanitarian cause served to defend a social, political and cultural order against the chaos of civil war and socialist anarchy. The Red Cross movement had already become a vehicle for nationalistic ideology; now it made clear that it would not recognize a socialist nationhood. This first instance of civil war set the trend for all forthcoming internal conflicts in which the Red Cross movement later became involved.[120]

The ultimate form of national identification took place after the war when the Red Cross used some of its war dowry to establish itself as a 'patriotic and humanitarian institution' (in that order of priority) commemorating the fallen soldiers and pointing the path towards national reconstruction.[121] To state publicly their claims to be at the heart of this national reconstruction against both socialism and Germany, Red Cross officials organized a ceremony in January 1872 during which they stood alongside conservative leaders. During a long Roman Catholic funeral service they surrounded an empty coffin in the cathedral of Notre-Dame in Paris. The coffin symbolized 'the officers, non-commanding officers, soldiers, *gardes mobiles* and *gardes nationales* who died during the Franco-Prussian War'. The archbishop presided and a famous preacher underlined the meaning of the three-hour-long ceremony: 'Socialist utopians wanted to negate suffering; but one can find suffering even in the midst of our voluptuousness, above our wounded pride, below our unsatisfied greed, everywhere there is suffering even in pleasure . . . After each disaster France redresses herself through the [sacrifice] of martyrs' blood . . . France will not die, She will be again the soldier of God and Civilisation.'[122]

This Red Cross ceremony was the largest civic commemoration of the war in France, and it was not organized or paid for by the state. It celebrated the war victims but 'forgot' the Commune.[123] Books like Jules de Marthold's chronological account of the war suddenly bridge the gap by stopping their chronology at the Franco-German armistice in January 1870 and starting it again at the religious ceremony of Notre-Dame in January 1872. In occupied Lorraine, a similar ritual was to be enacted by the ladies of Metz under the patronage of Mgr Dupont des Loges on 8 September each year. These rites of commemoration and *revanche* – which the Red Cross initiated and to which it became so closely linked – ignored the civil war to concentrate on the war, past and future, against Germany.[124] After the political turmoil the humanitarian ideal was best expressed in celebrations of martyrdom and the commemoration of victims. The French then represented themselves as victims of Bismarck and German greed and as a wounded people, a bleeding nation amputated of two provinces (Alsace and Lorraine) in 1871. Until 1918, the statue of Strasbourg on the Place de la Concorde remained shrouded in black: 'Facing the Strasbourg statue veiled in mourning, a wounded but not dead people, thinking of what its past requires of present times, burning with hope, with all its undiminishing faith, honourable, their flag in mourning, can contemplate the future.'[125]

CONCLUSION

The Red Cross, the altar and the army formed an unholy trinity in the confusion of post-1870 France, and this social and ideological alliance prefigured the more organized and centralized mobilization of the civilian voluntary effort as a natural complement to the universal conscription reforms of the 1880s. The Red Cross, recognized and honoured at the end of the war, reflected faithfully the reactionary hierarchy which controlled France after the Commune. It differed, however, from M. Thiers's government in that it devoted itself to the preparation of the next European war.

During the war, the Red Cross provided a channel for mass mobilization independently of the state, and in so doing it created new institutional and social hierarchies that would endure after the war ended. In the process of the war and of the Commune revolution, however, the independence of the *Société de secours* and the substance of its internationalist ideology perished. In Comte de Beaufort's words: 'if the cause to which these societies contribute is international, their character is national'.[126] Even as it allied itself to the pursuit of nationalist projects, however, the Red Cross was able to ensure its survival by exploiting its international connections and developing its role as a channel for transnational corporate charity and surrogate diplomacy. It found new missions which relieved the state from such unpleasant duties as the repatriation of prisoners and refugees. During the conflict the Red Cross had used its international connections to publish, from October 1870, a regular list of wounded prisoners kept by the Germans.[127] The international agency in Basel especially played a major part in the repatriation of prisoners from Germany[128] and from the remains of the Bourbaki army detained in Switzerland.[129] The society also moved wounded Parisians to the provinces of France without any military involvement, negotiating almost independently with the German authorities.

Henry Dunant's Utopia had become the platform for the gradual integration of civilians into new forms of mass war. In doing so it helped to render the distinct categories of civilian and military meaningless. Moreover, the chaos of 1870 definitively linked the agenda of humanitarianism to national and military aims. The Red Cross thus served to blur the boundaries between war and peace – a function it would further fulfil by mobilizing, not just for war, but also for natural disasters like the Toulouse floods in the 1870s. By blurring these boundaries, the Red Cross became an integral part of the management of manpower in the age of the new mass armies. It thereby demonstrated the existence of a civilian 'push' towards total war before a military 'pull' could be organized.

After the war the Red Cross chose to develop two symbolic new activities: it created a permanent structure meant to train civilians to the requirements of a forthcoming war, and it set up a Red Cross museum. The latter institution was a constant reminder of the Franco-Prussian War and of German brutality. It opened in Les Invalides in Paris, in one wing of the palace that housed the tomb of Napoleon I.[130] This was a suitable location for more than one reason. Les Invalides symbolized at one and the same time the benefaction of the French monarchy to the wounded, the glory of the empire, and the centrality of the war in the making of the French state and nation.[131] In thus linking itself to one of the most resonant symbols of the belligerent conservatism of the empire, the Red Cross underlined its subversion of its founding ideal. From that time on, the words of one contemporary commentator have held good: 'during a war, the Red Cross can only be the servant and never the master'.[132]

Notes

1 Georges d'Heylli (ed.) *Télégrammes militaires de M. Léon Gambetta du 9 octobre 1870 au 6 février 1871* (Paris, L. Beauvais, 1871).

2 Stig Förster and Jörg Nagler (eds), *On the Road to Total War: The American Civil War and the German Wars of Unification, 1861–1871*, German Historical Institute (Washington, DC) Series (Cambridge University Press, 1997), pp. 8–16.

3 Carl von Clausewitz, *On War* (Ware, Wordsworth, 1997) book 1, pp. 1–24. See also M. Handel, *Masters of War: Sun Tzu, Clausewitz and Janini* (London, Frank Cass, 1992); Peter Panet, *Clausewitz and the State: the Man, his Theories and his Times* (Princeton University Press, 1985).

4 Raymond Aron, *Penser la guerre, Clausewitz* (2 vols, Paris, Gallimard, 1976), vol. 2: *L'âge Planétaire*, p. 31.

5 Von Moltke also referred to Clausewitz and thus linked directly the Franco-Prussian War to the theorist's views. Daniel Hughes, *Moltke and the Art of War* (Noveto, Periodic Press, 1993).

6 This despite the fact that Clausewitz's passage into more recent English literature was delayed by translation and misreadings. Christopher Bassford, *Clausewitz in English: The Reception of Clausewitz in Britain and America, 1815–1845* (Oxford University Press, 1994).

7 Daniel Pick, *War Machine: The Rationalization of Slaughter in the Modern Age* (New Haven, Yale University Press, 1993), pp. 88–114.

8 See for instance Keith Grieves, *The Politics of Manpower, 1914–18* (Manchester University Press, 1988); Jay Winter, 'Military Fitness and Civilian Health in Britain during World War One', *Journal of Contemporary History*, 15 (1980), 211–44.

9 Thomas J. Adriance, *The Last Gaiter Button: A Study of the Mobilisation and Concentration of the French Army in the War of 1870* (Westport, Conn., The Greenwood Press, 1987); François Roth, *La guerre de 1870* (Paris, Fayard, 1990); Stéphane Audoin-Rouzeau, *1870, la France dans la guerre* (Paris, Armand Colin, 1989); *idem*, 'French Public Opinion in 1870–1 and the Emergence of Total War' in Förster and Nagler (eds), *On the Road to Total War*, pp. 393–412.

10 Omer Bartow, 'The Conduct of War: Soldiers and the Barbarization of Warfare', suppl. to *Journal of Modern History*, 64 (December 1992), 32–45; George L. Mosse, *Fallen Soldiers: Reshaping the Memory of the World Wars* (Oxford University Press, 1990).

11 Michael Howard, George J. Andreopoulos, and Mark R. Shulman (eds), *The Laws of War: Constraints on Warfare in the Western World* (New Haven, Yale University Press, 1994); Geoffrey Best, *Humanity in Warfare: The Modern History of the International Law of Armed Conflict* (London, Methuen, 1983).

12 John F. Hutchinson, *Champions of Charity: War and the Rise of the Red Cross* (Oxford, Westview Press, 1996), pp. 105–49.

13 M. Huger and J. Picket, *Une institution unique en son genre: Le Comité International de la Croix Rouge* (Geneva, A. Paten, 1985), pp. 9–14.

14 Helen E. Hatton, *The Largest Amount of Good: Quaker Relief in Ireland, 1654–1921* (Kingston and Montreal, McGill-Queen's University Press, 1993), pp. 3–44.

15 William K. Sessions, *They Chose the Star: An Account of the Work in France of the Society of Friends War Victims Relief Fund from 1870 to 1875, During and After the Franco-Prussian War; Together with an Account of Bulgarian Relief Work in the 1870s* (London, Society of Friends, 1944, 2nd edn, York, Ebor Press, 1991), pp. 1–75. The London committee also distributed food to the municipal administration of Paris. Xavier Long, *Rapport au sujet de la répartition des secours faite par la société anglaise des Amis (Quakers), aux victimes innocentes de la guerre en France (1870–1871)* (Paris, n.p., 1872). See also in the Archives de la Ville de Paris (AdVP): VD6/1591/2.

16 Pick, *War Machine*, pp. 88–109.

17 Gerd Krumeich, 'The Myth of Gambetta and the "People's War" in Germany and France, 1871–1914' in Förster and Nagler (eds), *On the Road to Total War*, pp. 641–56.

18 '3: One who advocates or practises humanity or humane action, one who devotes himself to the welfare of mankind at large, a philanthropist. Nearly always *contemptuous*, connoting one who goes to excess in his humane principles.' *OED*.

19 T. Laqueur, 'Bodies, Details, and the Humanitarian Narrative' in L. Hunt, *The New Cultural History* (Berkeley, University of California Press, 1989), pp. 176–204. Best, *Humanity in Warfare*, pp. 31–74.

20 For an early example see Charles de Martens, *Causes célèbres du droit des gens* (2 vols, Leipzig, F.A. Brockhaus and Paris, Ponthieu & Cie, 1827). I am indebted to Andrew Jones for this reference. Individual rights were not discussed in an international convention until the Hague congresses of 1899 and 1907. See Donald A. Wells, *War Crimes and Laws of War* (London, University Press of America, 1984), pp. 44–5; James Brown Scott, *The Hague Conventions and Declarations of 1899 and 1907* (Oxford University Press, 1915). François Guizot, *L'église et la société chrétiennes en 1861* (Paris, Michel Lévy frères, 1861), pp. 109–12 which clearly states that: '*Hors du droit des gens, il n'y a que l'état révolutionnaire qui est la barbarie jetée au travers de la civilisation*' (p. 112).

21 For example, Archibald Forbes, *My Experiences of the War between France and Germany* (2 vols, London, Hurst and Blackett, 1871). On Naval warfare see Sir Francis Piggott, *The Declaration of Paris* (University of London Press, 1919).

22 *Circulaire du délégué du ministre des affaires étrangères aux agents diplomatiques de France* (29 November 1870) in *Recueil officiel des actes du gouvernement de la Défense Nationale pendant le siège de Paris du 4 septembre [1870] au 28 février 1871* (Paris, Librairie Administrative Paul Dupont, 1871), pp. 575–8.

23 For a critical appraisal of the so-called *levée en masse* see J.P.T. Bury, *Gambetta and the National Defense: A Republican Dictatorship in France* (London, Longman, 1936), pp. 179–273. Richard D. Challener, *The French Theory of the Nation in Arms, 1866–1939* (New York, Columbia University Press, 1965); Bertrand Taithe, 'Reliving the Revolution' in B. Taithe and T. Thornton (eds), *War: Identities and Conflict* (Stroud, Sutton Publishing Limited, 1998), pp. 141–56.

24 German occupants denied a military status to all *francs tireurs*. See in AdVP, VD6/1529 and in Archives Nationales [AN] F9/1348.

25 Soldiers were 'neutral', could be kept in ambulances and cared for, but remained prisoners. The Geneva Convention had not clarified this point. During the Italian wars of the 1850s the French had exchanged wounded prisoners with the Austrians and the 1870 practice seemed a regression in

this respect. Léon Lefort, *Oeuvres*, ed. Félix Lejars (2 vols, Paris, Félix Alcan, 1895), vol. 2, p. 20. François Louis Charles Amédée comte de Beaufort, *Étude sur la société française de secours aux blessés des armées de terre et de mer et sur la convention de genève* (Paris, Imprimerie Administrative Paul Dupont, 1870), pp. 37–48.

26 Jean Jaurès, *La guerre franco-allemande de 1870–1871* (Paris, Jean Rouff, Histoire Socialiste de la France, 1908; repr., Flammarion, 1971), ch. II.

27 Roger Cooter, 'War and Modern Medicine' in William F. Bynum and Roy Porter, *Companion Encyclopedia of the History of Medicine* (2 vols, London, Routledge, 1994), vol. 2, pp. 1536–73, at p. 1563.

28 Thomas Rohkrämer, 'Daily Life at the Front and the Concept of Total War' in Förster and Nagler (eds), *On the Road to Total War*, pp. 497–518.

29 Geoffrey Best, 'Restraints on War by Land before 1945' in Michael Howard (ed.), *Restraints on War: Studies in the Limitation of Armed Conflict* (Oxford University Press, 1979), pp. 17–39, at p. 33; Michael Howard, *The Franco–Prussian War: The German Invasion of France, 1870–1871* (New York, Dorset Press, 1990), pp. 251–2.

30 *The Times* (15 September 1870). E. Govoy, *Le service de santé militaire en 1870* (Paris, Lavauzelle, 1894), p. 21. Dr Weill, manuscript report, Archives du Service de Santé des Armées de Terre (ASSAT), box 64/30, 'à Stuttgart', p. 9. A meeting in Brussels in 1874 attempted to solve the vexed question of the status of irregular warfare. Peter Karsten, *Law, Soldiers and Combat* (Westport, Conn., The Greenwood Press, 1978), pp. 22–3.

31 A. Flamarion, *Le livret du docteur, souvenirs de la campagne contre l'Allemagne et contre la Commune de Paris 1870–1871* (Paris, Le Chevalier, 1873), p. 25. Dr Félix Bron, *Histoire d'une ambulance sur le champ de bataille* (Lyons, Vingtrinier, 1872), pp. 10–11.

32 Commandant Brice and Capitaine Bottet, *Le corps de santé militaire en France, son évolution, ses campagnes, 1708–1882* (Paris and Limoges, Berger Levrault, 1907), p. 375.

33 Dr Christot, *Le massacre de l'ambulance de Saône-et-Loire, 21 janvier 1871. Rapport du comité médical de secours aux blessés le 7 juillet 1871* (Lyons, Vingtrinier, 1871). For the German side, C. Lüder, *La convention de Genève au point de vue historique, critique et dogmatique* (Erlangen, Besold, 1876), pp. 231–3.

34 Dr Weill, 'Rapport', ASSAT, box 64/30.

35 A. Summers, *Angels and Citizens: British Women as Military Nurses* (London, Routledge & Kegan Paul, 1988), pp. 125–33.

36 Wachter, *La Guerre de 1870–1871*, p. 160. Brice and Bottet, *Le corps de santé militaire*, p. 404.

37 A.R. Allinson (ed.), *The War Diary of the Emperor Frederick III, 1870–1871* (Westport, Conn., The Greenwood Press, 1971), pp. 244–58.

38 Assimilation of civilian victims to soldiers; decree of 11 January 1871, *Recueil officiel des actes du Gouvernement de la Défense Nationale*, pp. 12–13.

39 Eric Carlton, *Massacres: An Historical Perspective* (London, Scolar Press, 1994), pp. 4–10.

40 William MacCormac, *Souvenirs d'un chirurgien d'ambulance*, tr. Dr Morachie (Paris, Baillière, 1872), p. 112.

41 See ASSAT, box 62/4, Baron Larrey's letter on explosive bullets to the French foreign office.

42 Service Historique de l'Armée de Terre (SHAT), Lu1, *Rapport sur le fonctionnement du service de santé militaire* (October[?] 1870), p. 13, on unexploded projectiles extracted from wounds at the battle of St Privat.

43 Jules E. Rochard, *Histoire de la chirurgie Française au XIX° siècle, étude historique et critique sur les progrès faits en chirurgie et dans les sciences qui s'y rapportent depuis la suppression de l'Académie Royale jusqu'à l'époque actuelle* (Paris, J.B. Baillière et fils, 1875), p. 860. Ernest Saint-Edme, *La science pendant le siége de Paris* (Paris, E. Dentu, 1871), p. 34.

44 A similar process of emphasizing German atrocities took place in 1914–15. See John Horne and Alan Kramer, 'German "Atrocities" and Franco-German Opinion, 1914: The Evidence of German Soldiers' Diaries', *The Journal of Modern History*, 66 (1994), 1–33; Ruth Harris, '"The Child of The Barbarian": Rape, Race and Nationalism in France during the First World War', *Past and Present*, 141 (1993), 170–206. Thomas Rohkrämer, 'Daily Life at the Front and the Concept of Total War' in Förster and Nagler (eds), *On the Road to Total War*, pp. 497–518.

45 A. Wachter, *La guerre*, p. 4.

46 Theodor Meron, *Human Rights and Humanitarian Norms on Customary Law* (Oxford, The Clarendon Press, 1989); Howard (ed.), *Restraints on War*; P. Bohannan, *Law and Warfare: Studies in the Anthropology of Conflict* (Austin, University of Texas Press, 2nd edn, 1980); Donald A. Wells, *War Crimes and Laws of War* (London, University Press of America, 1984), p. 65.

47 H.J. Schroeder (ed.), *Disciplinary Decrees of the General Councils* (London, Herder, 1937).

48 Henry Dunant, *Convention de Genève: un souvenir de Solférino* (Paris, Hachette, 6th edn, 1873).

49 Lüder, *La Convention de Genève*, p. 37; Moynier, *Le droit des gens*, pp. 38–9. On the same lines see Best, *Humanity in Warfare*, pp. 32–120.

50 Thomas William Evans, *La commission sanitaire des États Unis, son organisation et ses résultats avec une notice sur les hôpitaux militaires aux États Unis et sur la réforme sanitaire dans les armées européennes* (Paris, E. Dentu, 1865, 5 edns up to 1867); *idem*, *Essais d'hygiène et de thérapeutique militaire* (Paris, E. Dentu, 1867); *idem*, *History of the American Ambulances in Paris during the Siege of 1870–1871* (London, Baillière, 1873).

51 Mme William Monod, *La mission des femmes en temps de guerre* (Paris, Bellaire, 1870); *idem*, *Les héroines de la charité, Soeur Marthe de Besançon et Miss Florence Nightingale* (Paris, Bellaire, 1873).

52 The Red Cross was not mentioned in the convention. Although clearly associated, it needed flags and signs stamped by military authorities to be able to gain access to the battlefield. Only a revision of the convention in 1878 gave an almost complete monopoly to the Red Cross. Moynier, *La Croix Rouge*, pp. 46–7.

53 J.C. Chenu, *Aperçu historique, statistique et clinique sur le service des ambulances et des hôpitaux de la société française de secours au blessés des armées de terre et de mer sur le service médico-chirurgical des ambulances et des hôpitaux pendant la guerre de 1870–1871* (2 vols, Paris, Hachette, Dumaine, Masson, 1874); *idem*, *De la mortalité dans l'armée et des moyens d'économiser la vie humaine* (Paris, Hachette, 1870).

54 The situation was the same in most countries which had not yet experienced war. The 1870 war became a major challenge across Europe. On the measures taken in Belgium and on training schools established after the war see Zacharie Zéphirin Merchie, *Guerre de 1870–1871. Les secours aux blessés après la bataille de Sedan avec documents officiels à l'appui* (Brussels, Manceaux, Muquardt, Delahaye, 1876), pp. iii, 145.

55 Norbert Elias, *Über den Prozess der Zivilisation, Soziogenetische und psychogenetische Untersuchungen* (2 vols, Basel, Haus zum Falken, 1939). E. de Billy, *Rapport à la commission des finances à l'assemblée générale des fondateurs de la société de secours aux blessés des armées de terre et de mer* (Paris, Imprimerie Nationale, 1873), p. 7.

56 The Irish ambulance served complex nationalistic purposes and had a chaotic existence. Many of its orderlies joined the French army and the remaining ambulance was viewed with suspicion by the Germans and taken prisoner. *Report of the Irish Ambulance Committee of Dublin, Irish Ambulance Corps for the Service of the French Wounded* (Dublin, Browne and Nobu, 1871), pp. 5–27. John Fleetwood, 'An Irish Field-Ambulance in the Franco-Prussian War', *The Irish Sword* (1964), 137–48.

57 Merchie, *Guerre de 1870–1871*, ch. III.

58 For instance Capt Douglas Galton, Gen Vincent Eyre, Maj Jones, Capt Brackenbury, Capt Newill, Maj Wyatt et al., 'Opérations de la Société Nationale Anglaise pendant la guerre franco-allemande 1870–1871' in *Rapport des sociétés étrangères sur leurs activités durant la guerre de 1870–1871* (Paris, Société ABATM, 1873), pp. 56–78. Charles Alexander Gordon, *The Siege of Paris: A Medical and Chirurgical Study* (London, Baillière, Tyndall & Cox, 1872, tr. in French, Baillière, 1872). *Lessons on Hygiene and Surgery, from the Franco-Prussian War* (London, Baillière, Tyndall & Cox, 1873).

59 Osk Geifelieder, *Voienno Khirourgitscheskiïa Nablïoudeniïa vo Vremia niemiezko-franzousskoi voiny 1870–1871* (St Petersburg, 1873). E. Bellina, *I treno-ospedali della Germania nella guerra di 1870–1871* (Florence, 1872). On the latter see John H. Plumridge, *Hospital Ships and Ambulance Trains* (London, Seeley, Service and Co., 1975), p. 86. Twenty-one trains moved 90,000 casualties in France and Germany in 1870-1.

60 E. de Billy, *Rapport de la commission des finances à l'assemblée générale des fondateurs de la société de secours aux blessés de terre et de mer* (Paris, Imprimerie Nationale, 1873), pp. 11–12. Thirty sovereign nations including Japan and Mexico contributed to the Red Cross funds.

61 *Le Gaulois* (24 July–21 August 1870).

62 *Le Gaulois* (17 July 1870).

63 *Gazette médicale de Paris* (15 August 1870).

64 *Le Gaulois* (23 August 1870).

65 Auguste Nélaton (1807–73), was a high-class surgeon who had operated on Garibaldi in the past but was in 1870 mostly famous as one of Napoléon III's private surgeons.

66 The coup overthrew Nélaton and replaced him with a committee of founding members of the Red Cross composed of comte de Flavigny, viscomte de Melun for the aristocratic side and Dr Chenu for the medical side. Ambroise Tardieu, *Huitième ambulance de la société de secours aux blessés, campagne de Sedan et de Paris, août 1870–février 1871, rapport historique, médical et administratif* (Paris, Delahaye, 1872), p. 8; G. Wyrouboff, 'Les ambulances de la Société Française', *Philosophie Positive*, 6 (1875), 379–403, at p. 386.

67 A. Tardieu, *Huitième ambulance*, p. 91.

68 Emmanuel Domenech, *Histoire de la campagne de 1870–1871, et de la deuxième ambulance dite 'de la presse Française'* (Lyons, Imprimerie du salut public, 1871), p. 58.

69 J.C. Chenu, *Aperçu historique*, vol. 2, pp. x–xii.

70 Foreign appeals were under the elevated patronage of kings and queens in Italy, Belgium, the Netherlands and Britain – the main foreign contributors. The Lord Mayor of London led the subscription to help the Paris people, while Queen Victoria offered her patronage and financial contribution and the Prince of Wales presided over the society. *Rapports des sociétés allemandes et britannique* (Paris, Comité Français SSABMT, 1873), pp. 56–8; Dr Merchie, *Guerre de 1870–1871. Les secours aux blessés après la bataille de Sedan*, p. 140.

71 The main organizer of the committee was Philippe Ricord (1800–89), surgeon of Napoleon III and an extremely popular specialist of syphilis. C. Eginer, *Philippe Ricord, 1800–1889 sa vie son oeuvre* (Paris, Librairie le François, 1939); M. Guignard, 'Philippe Ricord, sa vie son oeuvre 1800–1889' (Thèse en Médecine, Paris VII-Lariboisière 1978).

72 Dr G. Bitterlin, *La Croix Rouge aux avant-postes de la Marne, 1870–1871* (St Maur, Vigot-Frères, 1912), pp. 17–18.

73 The government's decision of 28 October 1870 to limit the Légion d'honneur to military services provoked an uproar in the medical press. See *Recueil officiel des actes du Gouvernement de la Défense nationale*, p. 472; *Union médicale* (29 October 1870).

74 *L'abeille médicale* (26 December 1870) leader.

75 Eugène Delessert, *Épisodes pendant la Commune, souvenirs d'un délégué de la société de secours aux blessés des armées de terre et de mer* (Paris, Charles Noblet, 1872, private circulation), pp. 71–4.

76 Pasteur himself came under severe criticism for his stance at the end of the war: *Gazette médicale* (22 April 1871), p. 76.

77 The call to medical men took place in July to complement army ambulances paid for by the army itself. The Red Cross constituted its own ambulances later in July and in August, creating sedentary ambulances during the siege of Paris as late as January 1871 in the last month of the war. Michel Lévy, *Notes sur les hôpitaux baraques du Luxembourg et du Jardin des Plantes* (Paris, J.B. Baillière, 1871), pp. 5–6.

78 The *Commission d'hygiène et de salubrité* published a list of sixty-six authorized surgeons on 10 October 1870.

79 Conscripted *Gardes Nationales* elected their officers, including medical officers. Most medical officers elected were general practitioners with a limited number of second-class medical men called *officiers de santé* who were often discriminated against even by the least qualified doctors: Georges Carrot, 'La Garde Nationale 1789–1871, une institution de la Nation' (Thèse de Doctorat de 3° cycle, Université de Nice, 1979), pp. 222–4. Jacques Léonard, *La médecine entre les savoirs et les pouvoirs: histoire intellectuelle et politique de la médecine française au XIX° siècle* (Paris, Aubier Montaigne, 1981).

80 Printed in the radical periodical *Gazette médicale de Paris* 2, (October 1870), 541–2.

81 Auguste Cochin, *Le Service de Santé des Armées avant et pendant le siège de Paris* (Paris, A. Sauton, 1871), p. 41.

82 J.C. Chenu, *Aperçu historique, statistique et clinique*, vol. 1, pp. 101–267.

83 ASSAT, box 63/3, 'Rapport sur le service des ambulances pendant le Siège de Paris dans la 5ème section', par M. Barberet, Médecin Général, (unnumbered) p. 12(?).

84 Théodore Auger, *Le siège de Paris, rapport sur les services rendus par l'ambulance de feu le Marquis de Hertford* (Paris, Parent, 1871).

85 Dr Job, *Malades et blessés de l'hôpital Rothschild pendant le siège de Paris, 1870–1871* (Paris, A. Delahaye, 1871), p. 8.

86 H. Monod, *Rapport du comité évangélique auxiliaire de secours pour les soldats blessés ou malades* (Paris, Sandoz & Fichbacher, 1875), p. 7.

87 Félicien Court, *Louis Ormières (1851–1914), et l'ambulance du Grand Orient de France en 1870–1871* (Paris, Imprimerie Nouvelle, 1914). *Bulletin du Grand Orient de France*, 3ème série, 26 année, juillet-août 1870, pp. 380, 392.

88 ASSAT, box 63/1. Répartition des hôpitaux et ambulances de la ville de Paris.

89 George Holstead Boyland, *Six Months under the Red Cross with the French Army* (Cincinnati, Robert Clarke and Co., 1873), p. 232; Dr Chenu, *Aperçu historique, statistique et clinique*, vol. 1, p. xxxii; Flamarion, *Le livret du docteur*, p. 113; G. Peltier, *L'ambulance N°5* (Paris, Delahaye, 1871), p. 28.

90 Tardieu, *Huitième ambulance de campagne*, p. 18.

91 J.P. Bonnefont, *Ambulances internationales et privées* (Paris, Bureau de l'Union Médicale, 1871), p. 2.

92 SHAT, Lu1, memorandum (25 August 1870) from the Foreign Office to the Ministry of War following a reminder from the Swiss federal council on the terms of the convention of 20 July 1870.

93 John Furley, *Épreuves et luttes d'un volontaire neutre* (Paris, Jean Dumaine, 1874), p. 59.

94 SHAT, Lu1, *Circulaire au comité de la délégation de Tours* (4 February 1871), p. 514.

95 SHAT, Lu1, *Rapport de monsieur le conseiller de préfecture Boulanger à monsieur le comte de Flavigny, l'oeuvre du comité du Mans, 20 juillet 1871*, pp. 18–19.

96 Natalie Isser, 'Protestant and Proselytization during the Second French Empire', *Journal of Church and State*, 30 (1988), 51–70.

97 A.S. de Doncourt (*comtesse* Drohojovska), *Souvenirs des ambulances* (Lille, Lefort, 1872), p. 25. H. Monod, *Rapport du comité évangélique auxiliaire de secours pour les soldats blessés ou malades* (Paris, Sandoz, 1875), pp. 8, 65.

98 H. Monod, *Rapport du comité*, p. 17.

99 Archives Épiscopales de Paris (AEP) 5b2 10, weekly letter from Abbot Rincazaux to the Archbishop of Paris from the fort of Saint Denis, 2 October 1870. AEP 4 B244, André Belin, 'Les aumôniers de 1870: essai de reconstitution de l'ordre de bataille des aumôniers de l'armée et de la marine française pendant la guerre de 1870–1871', typescript, 1972.

100 Charles de Montesson, *Souvenirs d'ambulance, 1870–1871* (Le Mans, Monnoyer, 1885), pp. 80–2. J.C. Chenu, *Aperçu historique, statistique et clinique*, vol. 1, p. xxxii.

101 M. Ferré, *Rapport sur les services des ambulances municipales du troisième arrondissement pendant le siège de Paris* (Paris, Imprimerie Rigal, 1871), p. 33.

102 *Recueil des décrets, statuts, règlements et instructions concernant la société de secours aux blessés militaires* (Paris, au siège de la Croix Rouge, 1936), decree of 31 December 1870, p. 36.

103 François de Luze and Adolphe Labodie, *Rapport au comité départemental pour la Gironde* (Bordeaux, n.p., 1871), p. 13.

104 *Compte rendu des opérations du conseil d'administration siégeant à Versailles et du comité d'action depuis le 15 avril jusqu'au 31 mai* (Paris, Société de secours, 1872), p. 4. This nationalization provoked an international outcry, with the result that the French Red Cross doubled its income.

105 G. Moynier, *La Croix Rouge, son passé, son avenir* (Paris, Sandoz et Thuillier, 1882), p. 46.

106 *Le mouvement médical*, (15 October 1870), p. 543.

107 Edmond Delorme, *Histoire de la chirurgie de guerre* (2 vols, Paris, Felix Alan, 1888), vol. 2, pp. 342, 360.

108 Anselme Buchet de Chauvigné and M. Collet, *Rapport sur le service de l'évacuation des militaires blessés et malades présenté à Mr l'Intendant de Première Classe Guérin* (Paris, Lefebvre, 1875), p. 14.

109 *La gazette médicale de Paris*, (10 September 1870), p. 483.

110 H.A. Wauthoz, *Les ambulances et les ambulanciers à travers les siècles* (Brussels, Lebègue, 1872), p. ix. Baronne Ida de Crombrugghe, *Journal d'une infirmière pendant la guerre 1870–1871, Sarrebrück,*

Metz, Cambrai (Paris, H. Plon, 1872 and Brussels, Claessen, 3rd edn, 1871), p. 10.

111 Lüder, *La Convention de Genève*, pp. 227–63.

112 Lüder, *La Convention de Genève*, p. 18, on the hatred and fundamental opposition which arose during the second period of the war on both sides. Also see Elias, *Uber des Prozess der Zivilisation*, esp. vol. 1, chs I and II on the differences between German *Kultur* and Anglo-French *Civilisation*. On Elias see R. Robertson, 'Civilization and the Civilizing Process: Elias, globalization and analytic synthesis' in *Theory, Culture and Society*, 9 (1992), 211–27.

113 This vicious circle can especially be found in French or German propaganda which both use extensively medical evidence of war atrocities to sustain their analysis of the enemy. See for instance Hector de Condé, *La Prusse au pilori de la civilisation (crimes et forfaits des prussiens en France)* (Brussels, Devillé, 1871); anon, *Comment les français font la guerre. Recueil de faits pour servir à l'histoire des moeurs et de la civilisation au xixème siècle* (Berlin, C. Duncker, 1871) (simultaneously published in German and English and usually attributed to the Prussian Foreign Office); C.A. Daubant, *La guerre comme la font les Prussiens* (Paris, Plon, 1871); Amédée Marteau, *Le droit prime la force, page d'histoire de l'Empire d'Allemagne* (Paris, Librairie Internationale, 1876); *Recueil de documents sur les exactions, vols et cruautés des armées prussiennes en France* (Bordeaux, Férot et Fils, 1871); A. Vavasseur, *La paix honteuse ou le droit des gens selon les prussiens* (Paris, Lacroix, Verboeckhoven et Cie., 1871); Némésis, *Crimes, forfaits, atrocités et viols commis par les prussiens sur le sol de la France* (Paris, André Sagnier, 1871); *comte* Alfred de la Guéronnière, *La Prusse devant l'Europe* (Brussels, Office de Publicité, 1870).

114 P. Boissier, *Histoire du Comité Internationale de la Croix Rouge, de Solférino à Tsoushima* (Geneva, Institut Henry Dunant, 1978), pp. 353–83.

115 John Hutchinson, *Champions of Charity: War and the Rise of the Red Cross* (New York, Westview Press, 1996), pp. 150–7.

116 *Compte rendu des opérations du conseil d'administration siégeant à Versailles et du comité d'action depuis le 15 avril jusqu'au 31 mai* (Paris, Société de secours, 1872) pp. 5–6.

117 Louis Gallet, *Guerre et Commune. Impressions d'un hospitalier* (Paris, Calmann Lévy, 1898), p. 257.

118 *Journal Officiel de la République* (Édition de la Commune, 19 May 1871). In fact the Commune signed the convention on 13 May; A. Vidieu, *Histoire de la Commune* (Paris, Dentu, 1876), p. 336; *Rapport du comte de Beaufort, secrétaire général de la société de secours sur son administraion du 14 avril au 31 mai 1871* (Paris, Librairie Administrative Paul Dupont, 1871), pp. 27–8.

119 *Compte rendu des opérations du conseil d'administration siégeant à Versailles*, p. 7.

120 Moynier, *La Croix Rouge*, pp. 172–3.

121 *Compte rendu des opérations du conseil d'administration siégeant à Versailles*, p. 2. In the French it became an '*Oeuvre de Patriotisme et d'Humanité*'.

122 Dr. J. Grange, *Société française de secours aux blessés, compte rendu du service funèbre célébré à Notre Dame de Paris* (Paris, Chaix, 1872), p. 7. *Le Gaulois*, 16 January 1872 and 18 January 1872. Jules de Marthold, *Memorandum du siège de Paris, 1870–1871* (Paris, Charovay Frères, 1884), p. 305.

123 Many post-Commune sources show the need to forget which Ernest Renan discussed after the war and which is at the heart of Benedict Anderson's analysis of national identity. Benedict Anderson, *Imagined Communities* (London, Verso, 2nd edn, 1991), pp. 187–206.

124 François Roth, *La Lorraine annexée (1870–1918)* (Presses Universitaires de Nancy, 1976), pp. 99–100.

125 Jules de Marthold, *Mémorandum du siège de Paris, 1870–1871* (Paris, Charovay Frères, 1884), pp. 305–8.

126 Comte de Beaufort, *Étude sur la société française de secours*, p. 7.

127 SHAT, LT 28, *Liste des blessés français recueillis par les troupes allemandes* (Geneva, Georg, 1st list, 30 October 1870). This list completed the full list of wounded soldiers published by the national Red Cross committees since mid-August.

128 Stanislas Pietrowski, *Rapport général, campagne de 1870–1, armée de Sedan – armée de la Loire* (Paris, Imprimerie Centrale des Chemins de Fer, A. Chaix, 1871), p. 31.

129 SHAT, Lu1, Rapport du Pasteur Sohler à son excellence le ministre de la guerre sur l'ambulance du collège de Montbéliard.

130 Boissier, *Histoire du Comité International*, p. 287. The idea of a museum and of a permanent training ambulance had been discussed since 1867, only three years after the creation of the movement; J. Grange, *Rapport à Monsieur le Président de la société française de secours aux blessés, sur l'ambulance de Bougival, projet d'ambulance permanente de perfectionnement* (Paris, Chaix, 1871); E. de Billy, *Rapport à la commission des finances à l'assemblée générale des fondateurs de la société de secours aux blessés des armées de terre et de mer* (Paris, Imprimerie Nationale, 1873), pp. 62, 97.

131 Paul Triare, *Dominique Larrey et les campagnes de la Révolution et de l'Empire (1766–1842)* (Tours, Alfred Mame et Fils, 1902), pp. 717–23.

132 Lüder, *La Convention de Genève*, p. x.

3

STRIVING TO BE SEPARATE? CIVILIAN AND MILITARY DOCTORS IN CAPE TOWN DURING THE ANGLO-BOER WAR

Molly Sutphen

In their accounts of the 1901 outbreak of bubonic plague in Cape Town during the Anglo-Boer War, historians have neatly segregated themselves into two camps. Military historians have occupied one camp, where they have told one of two stories about the outbreak of bubonic plague.[1] Story one, which appears most often in accounts published soon after the war, details the success of the actions taken by the military authorities to control the disease. It is claimed that there were only 24 cases in the imperial forces, compared with 877 in the Cape Colony, a success they attribute to the Army's methods of disease control.[2] Story two, in contrast, alleges that the military was responsible for importing plague, and having introduced it, they left the messy job of coping with it to civilian authorities.[3] In both these accounts, however, the civilian authorities are shadowy figures; indeed, how the military coped with plague – what they actually did – is only briefly discussed.

Social historians, who tell a different kind of story, occupy the other historical camp.[4] Theirs is the story of the establishment of Ndabeni, a temporary segregation camp for black Africans that after the war was put on a permanent footing.[5] The actors in their accounts are the civilian doctors and colonial officials, while the military authorities are relegated to the shadowy margins.

A study of plague in Cape Town during the war provides a compelling reason for historians to desegregate these camps.[6] When the shadowy figures from each camp are allowed into the light, it is clear that military and civilian doctors interacted with each other to a significant degree in confronting the common problem of plague. Initially civilian and military doctors cooperated with each other, though after several months the bonds of cooperation frayed and snapped. At issue was whether civilian and military authorities might split the responsibilities for control of the disease. On the one hand the military proclaimed that it must maintain a campaign separate from the one civilians pursued. On the other hand civilian officials were equally adamant that civilian and military plague control should not be divided.

Although the ensuing fight appeared to boil down to little more than a spat over territory, the disagreement illuminates how military and civilian authorities struggled to shape their respective identities in a period of reform. The spat highlights tensions within the military over which hygiene and public health measures the newly formed Royal Army Medical Corps should adopt. The corps had been created through a series of Victorian Army reforms, and the second Anglo-Boer War was its testing ground. During the war members of the corps argued that plague – and sanitary work more generally – had to be dealt with in a particularly military way. On the civilian side, the spat reveals tensions within civil society over a new set of public health reforms. Just before plague broke out, new public health legislation had been passed giving significantly more power to a cadre of professional public health officers.[7] The dispute forced the public health officers to test the limits of their new-found power.

The dispute also sheds light on how civilian and military authorities viewed bacteriology, a talisman of a new, modern medicine. The plague broke out in a period and in areas where there were many debates over the value of laboratory medicine.[8] One key question at stake was whether methods of prevention, control, and diagnosis from the laboratory should change medical practices. The dispute in Cape Town reveals the extent to which civilian and military doctors were willing to change their practices.

THE OUTBREAK OF PLAGUE AND CIVIL MEASURES TO CONTROL THE DISEASE

In February of 1901, the Acting Medical Officer of Health for the Cape Colony, Dr A.J. Gregory, announced that bubonic plague had broken out among dockworkers in Cape Town. On his way to the docks to examine the suspected plague patients, he passed lines of military trucks in the streets and encountered troops parading around the city.[9] He also passed war refugees from the Transvaal and new immigrants from Europe, many of whom were looking for housing or jobs.[10] He found docks piled high with supplies and forage, with labourers there and at the nearby railway stations unloading while troops arrived or departed. Most of the labourers were black Africans from the Eastern Cape and the Transkei, who either travelled to the city in search of work or had been displaced during the fighting.[11]

Soon after this announcement, the Cape Colonial Secretary, T.L. Graham, took responsibility for the city's anti-plague measures.[12] One of the first things he did was to establish the Plague Advisory Board, asking a number of doctors and local government officials to join the board to give him advice on what steps were necessary to contain the disease.[13] Gregory was responsible for the day-to-day work of putting this advice into practice, while Major Wright of the Royal Army Medical Corps, was to be the liaison between the civilian and military authorities.

Soon after Graham established the Plague Advisory Board, the Cape government sought advice from outside the local community, hiring Professor William Simpson to travel to the city to supervise the control of plague. Simpson was already in South Africa, having been hired by the War Office in 1900 to study enteric fever in the troops fighting in the Transvaal.[14] When he embarked for South Africa, he had recently been appointed to the chair of Hygiene at King's College, London, and he taught tropical hygiene at the newly established London School of Tropical Medicine. Simpson's supposed expertise on plague was based on his experience as Medical Officer of Health in Calcutta in 1896–7, when he had claimed that plague had broken out. His work on plague was also familiar to Gregory, who had cited him in an article he had written in 1899 on how to recognize symptoms of the disease.[15]

Upon his arrival, Simpson immediately warned Cape Town of the dangers that he considered rats posed to the city. In doing this, he was following his own advice from a pamphlet that the Colonial Office had commissioned him to write in 1900.[16] In it, he proposed two means for the transmission of the disease: one was by rat fleas, and the other was by rats carrying the bacilli, which were then transmitted to humans. Simpson was not alone in his view that rats had something to do with the transmission of plague. Those who adhered to the rat school found support in the form of an 1898 article in the *British Medical Journal*, arguing that rats and humans spread plague through the intermediaries of parasites. The *Lancet* and the *Journal of Tropical Medicine* too had run several articles on the propagation of the disease by rats or other animals.[17]

While in Cape Town, Simpson pursued an aggressive campaign against rats. At his suggestion, and with Gregory's wholehearted approval, local authorities zealously pursued rat destruction. Ferrets were sent after the large rat population; rat-traps were set; poison was placed throughout the city; and officials offered rewards of 3*d* to 6*d* per rat.[18] The results, according to a 19 June 1901 report, were 19,108 dead rats.[19]

The military authorities also killed their share of rats. Within days of Gregory's announcement, Surgeon-General Wilson – the Principal Medical Officer for the Field Forces in South Africa – ordered the Director of Supplies to inform his officers that all mice and rats were to be killed.[20] At a meeting of the Plague Advisory Board, the Army's representative, Major Wright, claimed that he was seeking advice on how to gas rats.[21] He later reported that he had inspected the military forage sacks and found few traces of rats, though he claimed to have seen many in the storerooms. He asserted that the military was on the alert for rats and their destruction was proceeding apace.[22]

Another measure Simpson and Gregory pursued was plague inoculation with Haffkine's prophylactic. They established free inoculation stations, with separate times set aside for the city's different races.[23] At meetings of the Plague Advisory Board, Gregory strongly advised everyone to be inoculated, and urged that the public be encouraged to submit to the injections.[24] 'Unlike inoculation against small-pox,' Simpson told the readers of the *Cape Times*, 'it is not a living organism that is injected, and the prophylactic is perfectly harmless.'[25]

However, Simpson and Gregory were sharply disappointed by how few volunteered to submit to the injections.[26] This poor response to their inoculation campaign may have been due in part to Simpson's outsider status. The historian Elizabeth van Heyningen has argued that one theme in debates over public health matters in Cape Town in the 1890s was suspicion of Europeans newly arrived in the colony, especially those who claimed to be experts.[27] The reaction to Simpson and his syringes of Haffkine's prophylactic can be seen in a similar light. He was an outsider who was trying to convince South African doctors and members of the lay public to trust his medical judgement. During the previous decade South African physicians repeatedly noted that they lived in a unique place with weather and a population entirely different from Europe's.[28] Consequently, foreigners like Simpson, and foreign procedures like plague inoculation, may well have been deemed unsuited to control disease in the peculiar medical conditions of South Africa. Equally, of course, it may have been that those in Cape Town were simply unwilling to submit to a relatively new and much contested form of disease prevention.[29]

The civilian authorities also considered more familiar measures – usually used against infectious diseases – to be necessary. These measures included isolation of patients, suspects, and contacts, and the disinfection of where they lived. Gregory defined a contact as someone who had 'come into such close contact with an infected person, or with an infectious disease, that there was reasonable ground for believing that he was liable to take that disease'.[30] If a civilian or soldier was suspected of having plague, he or she was removed to a hospital in Maitland, a suburb just outside the city where the patient, contact, or suspect encountered a compound of temporary sheds and marquees with wards divided by race and gender.[31]

The policy of confinement was a controversial one, and not all in the contact camp were as enthusiastic as A.F. Thomas, who wrote a letter to the *Cape Times* on his confinement. A master furrier, who was in the camp and his son in the Plague Hospital, he gave 'grateful thanks for the very kind and generous treatment' during his twenty-five day stay. 'I must honestly confess', he wrote, 'that I do not for a moment regret my suspension from business, or my detention.'[32] Despite Thomas's enthusiasm, however, the colonial authorities clearly feared that other inmates might try to abscond: high fences surrounded the camps, and men on horseback patrolled the perimeters.[33] While Thomas and others of his class went to Maitland, there was also a class of contacts who

were allowed to remain in their homes. 'The removal of contacts', wrote
Gregory, 'has not been carried out in a few exceptional cases of better class
Europeans.'[34]

Another concern for both civilian and military authorities was how to keep
track of cases of plague both inside and outside the city. Municipal authorities
decided to inspect the persons and luggage of passengers who departed the city
from train stations and the docks, and they inspected all consignments of goods
for rats, both at the point of departure and the point of arrival. They also
telegraphed the authorities at passengers' destinations and asked that anyone
travelling from Cape Town be subjected to medical surveillance for twelve days.
Finally they prohibited black Africans from travelling to or from Cape Town by
any means.[35] The restrictions on black Africans had as much to do with keeping
plague confined as with keeping a steady supply of labour on tap.

Despite these measures, however, the epidemic among civilians continued to
spread. In March, Gregory reported to the Plague Advisory Board that the
virulence of the disease had generally increased, and the number of cases rose to
about five a day.[36] In response colonial authorities put in place a number of new
anti-plague measures. Most notoriously they decided to deport to a segregation
camp all black Africans living in Cape Town. Simpson and Gregory also decided
to institute compulsory inoculation for all black Africans, and by 20 March 1901
3,000 had been injected.[37]

As the historian Christopher Saunders and others point out, in the years
before the outbreak of plague, Cape authorities, members of the lay public,
doctors, and public health officers debated the advantages and disadvantages of
creating separate locations to segregate the city's black African population.[38] At
issue was the claim that black African labourers posed a serious danger to the
health of white Cape Tonians. One physician claimed that when a mix of races
lived together in unsanitary circumstances, they resembled 'in some respects
dynamite; harmless indeed under certain conditions', but a serious threat when
exposed to disease germs.[39] In his account of Cape Town, Vivian Bickford-Smith
reveals the dilemma the Cape government faced over how to protect whites from
the supposed health dangers that black Africans posed and how to maintain a
flexible and plentiful labour force.[40] Segregation was their answer.

A loose coalition of public health officers, doctors, and newspaper editors also
wanted to institute public health reforms, arguing that they would neutralize the
dangers black Africans supposedly posed to white society. The coalition lobbied
hard for a series of public health measures which after three years of wrangling
were finally passed in 1897. The measures included legislation to appoint a
medical officer of health for Cape Town and to introduce compulsory
notification of infectious diseases. This meant that local practitioners had to
report patients with certain classes of disease to the Medical Officer, and after
1899 plague was classed as an infectious disease. Once a disease was so classified,

the Medical Officer had to undertake measures to control its spread, and in the case of an epidemic introduced from outside the colony, the government would subsidize the full costs of controlling the disease.[41] These were the powers that the colonial and Cape public health authorities now invoked to segregate the black population.

THE DISPUTE

Until March 1901, when the virulence of reported cases increased, the military authorities and civilian officials collaborated with one another. Major Wright of the Royal Army Medical Corps went to the Plague Advisory Board meetings and listened to the civilian debates over inoculation and segregation. Civilians and soldiers agreed that rats played an important role in the outbreak, and they killed rats by the thousands. Initially too military officials went along with the civil authorities' policy of isolating patients and contacts. But they also took their own measures to protect their soldiers. In particular, they feared that troops arriving in Cape Town might be exposed to plague, and then spread the disease throughout the country, or those leaving South Africa might return to Canada, Australia or Britain with the disease. In response to these concerns, the military evacuated the troops in the area, and they instituted troop inspections at stations throughout the colony.[42]

As the epidemic worsened, however, the military grew increasingly suspicious of the measures the civil authorities pursued. Around the same time that Gregory and Simpson supervised the removal of black Africans from the centre of Cape Town, Sir W.D. Wilson, the Principal Medical Officer of the Field Force in South Africa, travelled to the city to survey the situation.[43] As did many civilians, he held that the racial mix of the city was dangerous. 'I very soon came to the conclusion', he wrote, 'that plague had come to stay as the bug had found in Cape Town a most congenial soil. The sanitation of the town is admitted to have been very bad. The population is of a most mixed character, and contains all shades of colour. Overcrowding is the rule not the exception.'[44] Wilson was not convinced that the civilian authorities had this dangerous situation under control, and he mistrusted their plague measures. He considered the segregation of contacts to be ineffective, as

> most . . . resent and avoid the stringent sanitary rules now in force, and I consider these rules, though, sound in theory, are most likely to defeat the object aimed at. As an instance of this I was told that a kaffir was found ill with plague. He was removed to Plague Hospital and about 20 kaffirs living in the same house were ordered to observation camp. These latter solved the difficulty by scattering themselves all over the town and so avoided going into segregation camp.[45]

Wilson found the policy not only ineffective but dangerous to the military's strength. He underscored how inappropriate he considered this civilian method of plague control to be when he noted one instance, a case of plague at the main barracks: 'It was proposed to send about 90 Ordinance and Army Service corps men out to Camp, but the Principal Medical Officer Base would not agree to paralyze two services at the base . . . so the men continued at their duties and were frequently inspected.'[46] From the Base Officer's and Wilson's point of view, it was unacceptable to put ninety men out of commission because they might have had contact with one case.

The civil authorities in turn considered the military lax in their policing of the epidemic. While Simpson and Gregory were segregating black Africans who lived in Cape Town, those who worked for the military, at least for a while, were allowed far more freedom. At a meeting of the Plague Advisory Board, the Mayor of one of Cape Town's suburbs, Mr Bradford, wanted to make sure that all black Africans stayed in camp.[47] He pressed the point the next week, saying that if the military authorities could not prevent black Africans from 'roaming about . . . at their own sweet will', then the government should do so. The military replied that all black Africans were now under guard.[48] If the military authorities were willing to go along with their civilian counterparts on matters such as putting black Africans under guard, they were less inclined to cooperate. They would not collaborate in civilian disinfection campaigns, Wilson noted, because 'we could not spare disinfectors for town use'.[49]

Soon after Wilson travelled to Cape Town, the military's Principal Medical Officer in Cape Town, Surgeon-General McNamara asked a civil surgeon with the South African Field Force W. Ramsay Smith to write a memorandum on his views of plague in Cape Town.[50] Like Simpson, Smith could claim an earlier experience with plague. Before the war he had reported to the Central Board of Health of South Australia on an outbreak of plague in Adelaide in 1900. And in certain respects the views he had expressed in that report were in keeping with the opinions of Simpson and Gregory. In particular, he suspected that rats and mice carried plague.[51] In his memorandum to the South African Field Force he reiterated these views, arguing that plague was a 'filth disease'. There was a chance, he held, that there was a relationship between outbreaks of plague among rats and its appearance in the human population.[52]

While Smith agreed with the civilian authorities on the aetiology of plague and on some practices to control the disease, he differed markedly from them on two scores. First, where Simpson and Gregory considered Haffkine's prophylactic to be one of the best methods of prevention for everyone, Smith held that it was of value in only a limited number of cases. 'If the serum', he wrote, 'had proved to be absolutely effective . . . and the danger of the disease be at the same time very great or almost certain, then there may be cogent reasons for urging inoculation with all its risks – not otherwise.'[53] He suggested that it might engender overconfidence or recklessness in those injected, and he argued that there was not convincing enough evidence that inoculation moderated the disease. Second, Smith agreed with Wilson that there was little reason to isolate contacts of alleged plague patients.[54]

But there was a matter brewing that whipped up even more contention. In late March 1901 Gregory became aware that the military wanted to establish its own Military Plague Hospital, and warned the Plague Advisory Board that the government would probably not look favourably on the suggestion.[55] Wilson related that the civilian authorities took issue with the separate hospital, which the military had set up on Cecil Rhodes's estate outside the city. 'They desired', he wrote, 'to have one central hospital for Civil and Military.'[56] Over the previous month the civilian authorities had renovated the Plague Hospital, turning it into a permanent hospital with four wards,[57] and the government bought from the military the Yeomanry Hospital at Mackenzie's farm, which was to be used for European patients.[58] After Wilson returned to Pretoria around 1 April 1901, he learned that the civilian authorities continued to object to the separation of military and civilian plague patients. He told the General Officer Commanding-in-Chief that 'it was likely that the Civil Authorities may not be able to accommodate the civil sick and that the only safe course for us to take is to look after our own'.[59] Wilson telegraphed back to the General Officer Commanding, Cape Town, saying that he approved of separate military hospitals and ordered him to evacuate Cape Town of all men who were not absolutely necessary. The plague camp outside Cape Town, he wrote, must be cleared of soldiers, and all troops arriving in the country should board their ships and trains immediately.[60]

The disagreement between military and civilian authorities worsened when Gregory informed the Plague Advisory Board that a 'suspicious case' was present outside Cape Town in Hermon, on the main military line, but that the civilian authorities could not investigate because the military would not allow patients to be removed.[61] In the middle of April the matter came to a head. The Cape Colonial Secretary, Graham, threatened the military with a high court action if the military went ahead with a separate hospital, on the grounds that by law, all plague cases were to go to the civil hospital.[62] Lord Milner, the High Commissioner for South Africa, agreed, and wrote to the commander of the British forces, Lord Kitchener, claiming that the dual administration would be inefficient. Kitchener refused to back down;[63] the military won. As a result, the Cape military authorities remained responsible for embarkation and disembarkation of all troops; they also secured clear authority to build separate accommodation for any soldiers allegedly afflicted with plague. They soon built a Military Plague Hospital about a quarter of a mile from the civil hospital and put Lieutenant Colonel David Bruce of the Royal Army Medical Corps in charge of it.[64]

CONCLUSIONS

'The great question with the military administrators,' remarked Smith just after
the war, 'was how to carry on operations without being subjected to all the
regulations that the civic and civil authorities deemed necessary to employ as
safeguards in the case of those under their jurisdiction; and, at the same time
how to conserve the interests of those others.'[65] Although they agreed on some of
the same measures, military and civilian authorities strongly disagreed on others.
Both the civilian and military officials engaged in a vigorous campaign to kill
rats, and both locked up black Africans, though the military authorities did not
do this as readily as civilian authorities did. Rat eradication was an
uncontroversial control measure, as was the segregation of black Africans. But on
other measures, such as the isolation of plague contacts, civilians and soldiers
took different paths. The military did not want to be shackled by the concerns of
civilian society: it would not share its disinfectors with the city, nor would it kill
rats on civilian property. And Wilson was unimpressed with the effectiveness of
the treatment civilian public health officers meted out. Part of his reluctance to
borrow from the civilian sphere stemmed from his lack of confidence in the
methods that Gregory and Simpson used. Wilson's and Smith's remarks on
civilian plague control indicated that they agreed with Simpson and Gregory on
what they considered to be the causes of plague, but they did not see the
measures civilians used as effective or as possible for the military.

The military's actions in Cape Town underscore a wariness about being pulled
into any civil public health programmes. The fear was that by meeting civilian
demands for cooperation, military strength would be leached away. The Army
was not interested in addressing the area of public health, simply because it was
public, and they did not want to be bothered with the problems of plague control
outside the military. The Army saw themselves as wholly separate and separable
from civil Cape Town.

Although military authorities endeavoured to keep their men and equipment
separate, the lines between civilian and military spheres nevertheless became
blurred, though not to the extent that they did in the First and Second World
Wars. Like colonial businesses, the military depended upon the labour that black
Africans supplied.[66] It was on the backs of donkeys and black Africans that the
tents, guns and supplies travelled. More to the point in Cape Town, it was black
African dockworkers, supervised by whites, who unloaded the food and forage on
which the Army depended. Both civilian authorities and military commanders
needed healthy populations of workers. The military commanders also looked to
civilians for moral support, and they must have been heartened by the *Cape
Times*'s generally favourable press on the military.[67]

As part of a programme to guarantee a robust workforce, Gregory laboured to
extend state health regulations into the lives of an ever widening circle of Cape

Tonians. Indeed, long before the war he had lobbied to extend the powers of the public health authorities over one stratum of society – black Africans. He and others finally achieved at least part of this programme when they created the temporary segregation camp, and later put it on a permanent footing, imposing severe restrictions on the lives of thousands. However, the rest of Cape Town remained more or less untouched by their efforts. Van Heyningen argues that after the plague subsided public health authorities forced squatters near the city's boundaries to leave their shacks, and some laws controlling common lodging houses were passed, but it was black Africans who bore the brunt of efforts to reform and modernize Cape Town's public health machinery.[68]

The military too extended its reach beyond soldiers in the name of modern warfare. It did so most dramatically and notoriously at the front, and in pursuit of professedly military aims. After November 1900, when Lord Kitchener took command of the British forces, he retaliated against the commando fighting style of the Boers with small units who burned farmhouses and crops, and they set up an extensive network of blockhouses for surveillance. The British also interned in concentration camps thousands of black Africans and Boer women and children, driving them out of their houses and huts by fire or blockading them.[69] To an extent, the military were prepared to extend their efforts into the civilian sphere by helping the civilian health authorities in Cape Town. Compared to previous epidemics in other parts of the world, however, that help was distinctly limited. In Hong Kong and in India, for instance, colonial authorities were able to call on the military to intervene in their plague prevention and control campaigns.[70] In both places soldiers and civilians barked out orders to Indians and Chinese to clean their houses, present themselves for inspection, and follow orders to go to isolation wards. The soldier and the sanitary inspector blended their methods, and they blurred the lines between civilian and military. During the outbreak of plague in Cape Town, though, the Army chose to leave civilians to their own devices, and pursued their own methods of disease control among their own troops. The civilian authorities, for their part, did not have the power to compel the military to put soldiers in civilian hospitals.

The disputes over practices of plague control in Cape Town need to be seen in the light of reforms designed to 'modernize' the late Victorian and Edwardian Army. One set of reforms concerned the officer corps, a group that upheld above all the ethos of the 'gentleman'; where honour, conformity, and character were paramount[71] and where personal animosities and rivalries flourished.[72] These rivalries and the ethos of the 'gentleman' were marks of a traditional approach to war, an approach that many reformers – from both within the Army and outside it – decried and tried to change. As a result, an officer corps that was traditional in outlook squared off with reformers who wanted to create a new kind of Army, one that was technologically well schooled, efficient and professional.[73] The period between the Anglo-Boer War and the First World War saw officers who were aware of modern weapons and the tactics that went with their use, but who maintained that character, intellect, discipline and willpower were far more important. They argued that a soldierly spirit conditioned through improved morale and tougher discipline would be a key bulwark against the stresses that the new firepower and tactics of modern warfare forced soldiers to endure.[74]

The disputes in Cape Town thus reveal how Wilson and others were trying to shape a soldierly rather than a scientific spirit in the Royal Army Medical Corps, a spirit uncontaminated by civilian influences. At least according to Wilson, Bruce, and others, corps men were to be military through and through, and they were to practise medicine untainted by civilian ideas. On the matter of isolation, for example, the military officials demarcated the type of sanitary work they would pursue, and the measures were supposed to be specific for the military, not universal ones borrowed from the civilian sphere. The historian Mitchell Stone argues that in this period Army doctors were trying to distance themselves from civilians as much as they could, in part to raise the low status many perceived they had in the Army. The Royal Army Medical Corps was a new division, having started in 1898, and not surprisingly the corps doctors wanted to prove their worth in a military hierarchy full of commanders wary of change and suspicious of doctors being 'soft' on their men.[75] Even the trappings of civilians, such as white coats over Army uniforms, were frowned upon.[76]

Bruce, Wilson and Smith were well aware of the new process of plague inoculation, but they considered the old-fashioned tactic of keeping tight control over their men to be of more value. The disputes over plague control reveal an Army that did not embrace the talisman of modernity: bacteriology. To a degree, the military were willing to support laboratory medicine, as they gave Bruce some space and equipment to conduct bacteriological studies. But mass inoculation was another matter.[77] By refusing to inoculate their men, the military signalled that they were not willing to run the risk of trying out a new practice that might confer immunity from plague, but also might possibly, they feared, leave their men incapacitated.

Not that support for laboratory medicine on the civilian side was much heartier. Simpson and Gregory clearly saw inoculation as representing all the possibilities of modern medicine captured in a tidy syringe. But most of Cape Town's doctors and the lay public looked at the 'new' medicine that bacteriology brought forth with much scepticism. Though the efficacy of Haffkine's prophylactic was hotly debated in Cape Town, neither statistical arguments nor calls to public duty convinced many to undergo the series of injections.[78] Gregory had neither the power to compel, nor the authority to persuade the population of Cape Town to accede to his favoured method of plague control.

Although Gregory had long argued that the state must wield more control over the public, in practice he found he only had authority over one portion of the population, black Africans. The Army might have had the power to help him extend that control more forcefully throughout Cape Town, had it chosen to take a more dominant role in the anti-plague measures. But while Gregory had the will to extend bureaucratic controls over all of Cape Town, the Army did not. Rather, the military authorities chose to circumscribe their powers of control to include only their men and the black Africans who laboured for the war effort. The military alone set up their bell tents, ordered their men inside, and closed the flaps.

Notes

1 Accounts of plague in the Anglo-Boer War are usually brief. Thomas Packenham did not mention the disease, nor did Leo Amery in his multi-volume account published just after the war ended. See Thomas Packenham, *The Boer War* (London, Weidenfeld and Nicolson, 1979); Leo Amery, *The Times History of the War in South Africa, 1899–1902* (London, Sampson Low, Marston and Company, 1909). In another of the large, multi-volume histories written soon after the war, Capt Maurice Harold Grant devoted half a page in an appendix to the disease, and other accounts were equally brief. Capt Maurice Harold Grant, *History of the War in South Africa, 1899–1902* (London, Hurst and Blackett, 1909), p. 69. See also Gen Sir W.D. Wilson, *Report on the Medical Arrangements in the South African War* (London, HMSO, Harrison and Sons, 1904), pp. 68–9; and Robert J.S. Simpson, *The Medical History of the War in South Africa: An Epidemiological Essay* (London, 1911), p. 178. The outbreak of plague has also not figured in histories of the Royal Army Medical Corps. See for example, Sir Neil Cantlie, who did not mention it in his 2 vol. history of the Army Medical Department. Lt Gen Sir Neil Cantlie, *A History of the Army Medical Department* (Edinburgh, Churchill Livingstone, 1974), or Lt Gen Sir Brian Horrocks, *The Royal Army Medical Corps* (London, Leo Cooper, 1972).

2 Simpson, *The Medical History*, p. 178.

3 See for example, Mitchell Stone, 'The Victorian Army: Health, Hospitals and Social Conditions as Encountered by British Troops during the South African War, 1899–1902' (Ph.D. diss., University of London, 1992), p. 17.

4 M.W. Swanson, 'The Sanitation Syndrome: Bubonic Plague and Native Policy in the Cape Colony, 1900–1909', *Journal of African History* 18 (1977), 387–410; Christopher Saunders, 'The Creation of Ndabeni: Urban Segregation and African Resistance in Cape Town', *Studies in the History of Cape Town* 1 (1979), 165–93; Elizabeth Boudina van Heyningen, 'Public Health and Society in Cape Town, 1880–1910' (Ph.D. diss., University of Cape Town, 1989); van Heyningen, 'Cape Town and the Plague of 1901', *Studies in the History of Cape Town* 4 (1984), 66–107.

5 For a valuable overview of the history of segregation in South Africa, see William Beinart and Saul DuBow (eds), *Segregation and Apartheid in Twentieth-century South Africa* (London and New York, Routledge, 1995). On segregation in Cape Town before the outbreak of plague see Harriet Deacon, 'Racial Segregation and Medical Discourse in Nineteenth-Century Cape Town', *Journal of Southern African Studies*, 22 (1996), 287–308; and Vivian Bickford-Smith, *Ethnic Pride and Racial Prejudice in Victorian Cape Town, Group Identity and Social Practice, 1875–1902* (Cambridge University Press, 1995).

6 Roger Cooter makes a strong case for historians not to 'separate the theatres of war and medicine from the social and economic contexts of which they are a part'. Roger Cooter, 'Medicine and the Goodness of War', *Canadian Bulletin for the History of Medicine*, 7 (1990), p. 155.

7 See van Heyningen, 'Public Health and Society,' ch. 5 and van Heyningen, 'Cape Town and the Plague of 1901', p. 86.

8 On debates over the value of laboratory medicine in the British Empire, see for example, Paul Cranefield, *Science and Empire: East Coast Fever in Rhodesia and the Transvaal* (Cambridge University Press, 1991). For other parts of the British Empire see John Farley, *Bilharzia: A History of Imperial Tropical Medicine* (Cambridge University Press, 1991); and Mark Harrison, *Public Health in British India, Anglo-Indian Preventive Medicine 1859–1914* (Cambridge University Press, 1994).

9 See Emily Hobhouse, *Emily Hobhouse: Boer War Letters*, ed. Rykie van Reenen (Cape Town, Human and Rousseau, 1984), p. 32.

10 Immigration of Eastern European Jews increased from 3,008 to 19, 537 between 1891 and 1904. M. Shain, 'Diamonds, Pogroms and Undesirables: Anti-Alienism and Legislation in the Cape Colony, 1898–1910', *South African Historical Journal*, 12 (1980), 13. The war refugees had started to arrive after mid-October 1899, having been deported from the Orange Free State and the Transvaal. Elizabeth van Heyningen, 'Refugees and Relief in Cape Town, 1899–1902', *Studies in the History of Cape Town*, 3 (1984), p. 64.

11 See Bickford-Smith, *Ethnic Pride*, ch. 7, esp. pp. 178–83.

12 Public Record Office (PRO), CO 48/551/11519, dispatch from the Governor of the Cape Colony to the Secretary of State, 13 March 1901.

13 *Cape of Good Hope Report and Proceedings, with Annextures, of the Cape Peninsula Plague Advisory Board, Appointed to Advise the Government on Matters Connected with the Suppression of Bubonic Plague* (Cape Town, W.A. Richards and Sons, 1901). The first meeting was 14 February 1901.

14 On being seconded by the War Office, see PRO, CO 48/551/7860, dispatch from the Governor of the Cape Colony to the Secretary of State, 1 March 1901.

15 A.J. Gregory, 'Notes on Some Recent Cases of Plague in South Africa', *South African Medical Journal* (1899), 85.

16 PRO, CO 854/36, W.J. Simpson, 'Memorandum on the Influence of Rats in the Dissemination of Plague'. This was sent to all colonies on 7 June 1900.

17 'The Plague, The Propagation of Plague by Insects', *British Medical Journal* ii (1898), 1906–7. In 'Notes from India', the editors of the *Lancet* relate that Waldemar Haffkine had attributed the spread of plague to animals; see 'Notes From India', *Lancet* i (1899), 337–8. For a longer discussion on plague transmission, see G.J. Blackmore, 'Some Notes on the Introduction and Spread of Plague', *Lancet* i (1900), 1789–91. The *Journal of Tropical Medicine* devoted several editorials to plague, for example, 'Plague', *Journal of Tropical Medicine* (1899), 247–8. Also Patrick Manson, *Tropical Diseases: A Manual of the Diseases of Warm Climates* (London, Cassell & Co., 1900).

18 PRO, CO 48/551/19672, dispatch from the Governor of the Cape Colony to the Secretary of State. The dispatch contained, 'A Memorandum by Acting Medical Officer of Health, Cape Colony' (12 May 1901). From 1896–1902 wages of the lowest-paid labourers at Cape Town's docks were 4s 6d per day. Bickford-Smith, *Ethnic Pride*, p. 179.

19 R.B. Low, *Local Government Board Reports and Papers on Bubonic Plague* (London, Darling and Son, 1902), p. 202.

20 Wellcome Institute for the History of Medicine, RAMC/ 2094, W.D. Wilson, *Diary of the Surgeon-General, Sir W.D. Wilson, K.C.M.G., M.B., Principal Medical Officer of the Field Force in South Africa, 8 November 1899 to 19 April 1901*, Wilson to the Director of Supplies 13 February 1901, p. 313. (Wilson's *Diary* contained letters he and others wrote to their commanders.)

21 Plague Advisory Board, *Report and Proceedings*, p. 12. The meeting was on 18 February 1901.

22 Ibid., p. 23. The meeting was on 20 February 1901.

23 For an example of an advertisement for free inoculations, see *Cape Times* (22 March 1901), 2.

24 See an account of one of the meetings, 'Plague Board', *Cape Times* (21 March 1901), 5.

25 W.J. Simpson, 'Inoculation', *Cape Times* (3 April 1901), 5. For a compact and informative analysis of Haffkine's work on the anti-plague vaccine, a devitalized vaccine, see Ilana Lowy, 'From Guinea Pigs to Man: The Development of Haffkine's Anticholera Vaccine', *Journal of the History of Medicine and the Allied Sciences*, 47 (1992), 300–3.

26 Molly Sutphen, 'Imperial Hygiene in Calcutta, Cape Town, and Hong Kong: The Early Career of Sir William John Ritchie Simpson (1855–1931)', (Ph.D. diss., Yale University, 1995), ch. 5.

27 Van Heyningen, 'Public Health and Society', pp. 248, 259.

28 See for example, Dr Hillier, 'Address At The Medical Congress, Kimberley', *South African Medical Journal* (1893), 2.

29 See correspondence in the *Cape Times* such as 'By a Doctor of Medicine', 'Inoculation. The Case For and Against', *Cape Times* (30 March 1901), 7.

30 'Plague Board', *Cape Times* (25 April 1901), 7.

31 T. Harrison Butler, *Bubonic Plague, With Special Reference to the Epidemic in South Africa in 1901, A Thesis for the Degree of Doctor of Medicine of the University of Oxford, 1902* (London, The Operative Jewish Converts' Institution, 1902), p. 53.

32 A.F. Thomas, 'Treatment at Uitvlugt', *Cape Times* (28 April 1901), 7.

33 PRO, CO 48/551/19672, dispatch from the Governor of the Cape Colony to the Secretary of State. The dispatch contained 'A Memorandum by Acting Medical Officer of Health, Cape Colony' (12 May 1901).

34 Ibid.

35 PRO, CO 48/551/19672, dispatch from the Governor of the Cape Colony to the Secretary of State (22 May 1901). The dispatch contained 'A Memorandum by Professor Simpson'.

36 With the exception of one report, dated 20 March 1901, the Governor reported to the Colonial Office that plague was on the rise throughout March and April. PRO, CO 48/551/11519, dispatch from the Governor of the Cape Colony to the Secretary of State (13 March 1901), 'Plague has increased'; PRO, CO 48/551/12220, dispatch from the Governor of the Cape Colony to the Secretary of State (20 March 1901), 'Plague has shown signs of diminution'; PRO, CO 48/551/13172, dispatch from the Governor of the Cape Colony to the Secretary of State (27 March 1901), 'Plague has somewhat increased'; PRO, CO 48/551/14042, dispatch from the Governor of the Cape Colony to the Secretary of State (3 April 1901), 'Plague has somewhat increased'; PRO, CO 48/551/15245, dispatch from the Governor of the Cape Colony to the Secretary of State (9 April 1901), 'Plague has somewhat increased'; PRO, CO 48/552/15656, dispatch from the Governor of the Cape Colony to the Secretary of State (17 April 1901), 'Plague is about stationary – about five cases a day are reported'.

37 'The Plague, On the Down Grade, Satisfactory Bulletin, Five Cases', *Cape Times* (20 March 1901), 7.

38 See for example, Saunders, 'The Creation of Ndabeni'; Swanson, 'The Sanitation Syndrome'; Bickford-Smith, *Ethnic Pride*.

39 C.F.K. Murray, 'Public Health Legislation in South Africa', *South African Medical Journal*, 1 (1893), 22.

40 Bickford-Smith, *Ethnic Pride*, pp. 81–4. See also Saunders, 'The Creation of Ndabeni', p. 168.

41 Van Heyningen has outlined how reformers tried to pass a comprehensive public health bill for the first time in 1894, and the opposition they encountered over the next three years. Public Health Amendment Act No. 23 was finally passed in 1897. Van Heyningen, 'Public Health and Society', pp. 246–51.

42 Wilson, *Report on the Medical Arrangements*, p. 69.

43 Wellcome Institute for the History of Medicine, RAMC/ 2094, Wilson, *Diary*, p. 351. This information is contained in a letter from Maj R.J.T. Simpson to the Director-General, Army Medical Service (19 March 1901).

44 Wellcome Institute for the History of Medicine, RAMC/ 2094, Wilson, *Diary*, Wilson to the Director-General, Army Medical Service (1 April 1901), pp. 379–81.

45 Ibid., p. 381. As Saunders and other historians have noted, the segregation and isolation measures Simpson and Gregory put in place were deeply unpopular, especially among black Africans. Saunders, 'The Creation of Ndabeni', pp. 176–9.

46 Wellcome Institute for the History of Medicine, RAMC/ 2094, Wilson, *Diary*, Wilson to the Director-General, Army Medical Service (1 April 1901), p. 381.

47 He also asked whether the military was taking any steps to disinfect the houses of black Africans who worked for the military at Green Point Camp. Plague Advisory Board, *Report and Proceedings*, p. 83. The meeting was on 3 April 1901.

48 Ibid., pp. 99–100. The meeting was on 10 April 1901.

49 Wellcome Institute for the History of Medicine, RAMC/ 2094, Wilson, *Diary*, Wilson to the Director-General, Army Medical Service (1 April 1901), p. 383.

50 W. Ramsay Smith, *Plague Administration (Military) on the Cape Peninsula* (Adelaide, Hussey and Gillingham, 1902), p. 5. This memorandum, dated 6 April 1901, was read before the Australasian Association for the Advancement of Science at Hobart, January 1902, and published as the pamphlet quoted here.

51 W. Ramsay Smith, *Central Board of Health, Report on Bubonic Plague* (Adelaide, C.E. Braistow, government printer, 1900), p. 7.

52 Smith, 'Plague Administration', p. 5.

53 Ibid., p. 6.

54 Ibid., p. 6.

55 Plague Advisory Board, *Report and Proceedings*, p. 56. The meeting was on 20 March 1901.

56 Wellcome Institute for the History of Medicine, RAMC/ 2094, Wilson, *Diary*, Wilson to the Director-General, Army Medical Service (1 April 1901), p. 381.

57 PRO, MH 19/261, dispatch from the Governor of the Cape Colony to the Secretary of State (23 April 1901).

58 Ibid.

59 Wellcome Institute for the History of Medicine, RAMC/ 2094, Wilson, *Diary*, Wilson to the Director-General, Army Medical Service (1 April 1901), pp. 373–5.

60 Ibid., p. 375.

61 Plague Advisory Board, *Report and Proceedings*, p. 83. The meeting was on 3 April 1901.

62 Maj R.J.T. Simpson, who was Principle Medical Officer of the South African Field Forces while Wilson was in Cape Town, related the débâcle to the Director-General of the Army Medical Service in London. Wellcome Institute for the History of Medicine, RAMC/ 2094, Wilson, *Diary*, Maj R.J.T. Simpson to Director-General of the Army Medical Service (19 April 1910), p. 399.

63 Van Heyningen, 'Cape Town and the Plague of 1901', pp. 84–5.

64 Wilson, *Report on the Medical Arrangements*, p. 69.

65 Smith, 'Plague Administration', p. 4.

66 Bickford-Smith, *Ethnic Pride*, pp. 64–5.

67 It was not simply that the war efforts of the British were chronicled, Afrikaans speakers were denigrated regularly. See headlines such as 'Boer Barbarity', *Cape Times* (6 October 1900), 5.

68 Van Heyningen, 'Public Health and Society', p. 348.

69 Peter Warwick, general introduction in Peter Warwick (general ed.) and Professor S.B. Spiers (advisory ed.), *The South African War: The Anglo-Boer War, 1899–1902* (London, Longman, 1980), pp. 60–1.

70 David Arnold, *Colonizing the Body: State Medicine and Epidemic Disease in Nineteenth-Century India* (Berkeley, University of California Press, 1994), p. 215. For Hong Kong see Elizabeth Sinn, *Power and Charity: The Early History of the Tung Wah Hospital* (Hong Kong, Oxford University Press, 1989), p. 164; and Sutphen, ch. 2.

71 See for example, Edward M. Spiers, *The Late Victorian Army, 1868–1902* (Manchester University Press, 1992), p. 103, or Tim Travers, *The Killing Ground: The British Army, the Western Front and the Emergence of Modern Warfare, 1900–1918* (London, Allen & Unwin, 1987), pp. 4–5. At home military leaders emphasized the gentlemanly approach the Army was taking toward Boer women and children. In justifying the concentration camps, the War Secretary in Britain, St John Brodrick, tried to seize the moral high ground when he used the language of protection, claiming that British forces were safeguarding Boer women and their children after being deserted by their unmanly men. The pro-government newspaper, *The Times*, took a similar line: Boer women had to be protected from the potential ravages black Africans might wreak on them. Paula M. Krebs, 'The Last of the Gentlemen's Wars: Women in the Boer War Concentration Camp Controversy', *History Workshop Journal*, 33 (1992), 44–5.

72 Travers, *The Killing Ground*, p. 16.

73 Ibid., pp. 4–5.

74 David Englander, 'Discipline and Morale in the British Army, 1917–1918' in John Horne (ed.), *State, Society and Mobilization in Europe During the First World War* (Cambridge University Press, 1997), pp. 125–6.

75 On Army reforms, see Stone, 'The Victorian Army', ch. 1.

76 Stone, 'The Victorian Army', p. 38.

77 Col D. Bruce, 'Military Plague Hospital, Maitland, Cape Town', *Journal of the Royal Army Medical Corps*, 2 (1904), 296.

78 On debate in Cape Town see Sutphen, 'Imperial Hygiene', ch. 5; and Sutphen, 'Rumoured Power: Hong Kong, 1894 and Cape Town, 1901', in Andrew Cunningham and Bridie Andrews (eds), *Western Medicine as Contested Knowledge* (Manchester University Press, 1997).

4

War as Experiment. Physiology, Innovation and Administration in Britain, 1914–1918: The Case of Chemical Warfare

Steve Sturdy

The first large-scale gas attack of the First World War took place at 5 p.m. on 22 April 1915 as part of the German offensive at Ypres. A light breeze carried clouds of gas from the German lines into trenches occupied by French and Algerian troops. Though there had been rumours of an impending gas attack, they had not been taken seriously, and the defending forces were unprepared for the effects of the new weapon. Half blind and choking, those who were not overcome by the gas itself were able to offer little resistance to the German advance which followed. A large breach was opened in the Allied lines, and the ground gained by the Germans was limited only by their failure to anticipate the success of the attack. Two days later, the Germans again used gas, this time against the adjacent Canadian trenches. However, the more experienced Canadian troops successfully resisted the new attack. Allied commanders were reassured that the strategic effects of gas when used against a well-disciplined defending force need not be overwhelming. Nevertheless, the Germans' deployment of a new weapon of mass destruction prompted widespread anger and consternation among the British public, and galvanized the War Office into a frantic search for ways of defending against further gas attacks, and for effective chemical weapons of their own.[1]

Two days after the first attack, Lord Kitchener summoned the respiratory physiologist J.S. Haldane to the War Office to ask him to visit France and report on the nature and effects of the German gas. Haldane was extremely well qualified to conduct such an investigation. Besides his research in academic physiology, he had worked closely with the mining industry, and had wide knowledge of the poisonous effects of mine gases and of the development of respirators for use in rescue operations. The following day Haldane set out for France where he examined soldiers injured by the German gas, and attended a post-mortem on a man who had recently succumbed to its after-effects. As a result, Haldane was able to identify the gas used as chlorine, and to demonstrate that it killed primarily by causing massive inflammation of the

lungs. His signed report appeared in the newspapers on 29 April. On his return
to England, Haldane and a number of his colleagues began to assist the War
Office in designing and organizing production of the first effective British gas
masks.[2]

Haldane's work for the War Office marked an important development for
British scientists, who had been trying for some time to convince the military
authorities that their professional skills might usefully be employed in war-related
research and development. That Haldane was the first to be officially recognized
in this way was probably due as much to personal connections as to his scientific
credentials. His brother was Viscount Haldane, the Lord Chancellor and one-
time Secretary of State for War, whose Army reforms had created the
Expeditionary Force that was now fighting in France. J.S. Haldane was also well
known to the Director-General of the Army Medical Service, Alfred Keogh, who
had helped to plan and supervise the medical aspects of Viscount Haldane's
Army reforms, and it may well have been Keogh who recommended Haldane to
Kitchener. Whatever the route by which he found his way into the War Office,
however, Haldane's entrance opened the door for others to follow, and growing
numbers of scientists would soon find themselves involved in research into
chemical warfare and a host of other military questions. Chemists were of course
prominent among these scientists. But physiologists too quickly found a place in
the rapidly expanding programme of military research and development. Indeed,
in many respects physiologists would come to play a more important role than
their chemical colleagues in building up and shaping that programme,
particularly in the field of chemical warfare.

This was all the more remarkable given that physiologists had not hitherto
played much of a role in the scientific campaign for official involvement in the
war effort, which was dominated by physicists, chemists and engineers. A handful
of physiologists had found employment in war-related medical research, notably
under the auspices of the government's Medical Research Committee (MRC).
But this was a very young organization – set up only in the year before the war
began – and it had yet to prove that it could contribute anything to the
development of medical care, even during peacetime. That it had anything to
offer to the War Office, whose first priority was to fight the war, not to engage in
fanciful medical experimentation, seemed unlikely. Nor was physiology
particularly highly regarded even within the medical profession. Over the
previous five decades it had come to be valued as part of the preclinical scientific
training of medical students; but the most eminent medical teachers commonly
regarded it as little more than a preparatory stage in the medical curriculum, and
not as something that had much to offer medical practice itself. Thus, though
firmly established as an academic discipline by 1915, physiology was remote
from any areas of practical endeavour that seemed likely to have any direct
impact on the pursuit of the nation's war effort.

In the course of the war, all that would change. Physiologists would move from the periphery of war-related research to its very core. Not least, the work of medical scientists, and especially of physiologists, would establish the MRC as a respected centre of scientific expertise within the machinery of government. One of the most important ways in which they would achieve this was through their activities in the field of chemical warfare research. By examining the role of physiologists in this field, we can begin to understand, not just how they managed to make themselves indispensable to the war effort of 1914–18, but also how they secured a new kind of authority for themselves as practical scientists, whose technical knowledge and skills in research might usefully illuminate the many medical problems with which governments had to contend in peace as much as in war.

PHYSIOLOGISTS AND THE OFFENSIVE AND DEFENSIVE ASPECTS OF GAS WARFARE

Early in November 1914, the Royal Society appointed a small War Committee, comprising some of the society's most distinguished physical and chemical fellows, in the hope that the government would call upon them 'to organize assistance . . . in conducting or suggesting scientific investigations in relation to the war'.[3] Only the Navy showed any interest, by referring a number of technical questions to the committee for investigation. Undeterred, the committee set about identifying specific areas in which it felt its expert assistance might be most urgently needed, and appointing subcommittees to deal with the relevant issues. One of these was the manufacture and supply of various fine chemicals, notably dyestuffs and pharmaceuticals, that had hitherto been imported from Germany. The War Committee accordingly appointed a Chemical Subcommittee to formulate recommendations for meeting the anticipated shortages, though in the event it would have only a relatively minor impact on the availability of drugs and other chemicals.[4] From early on, some of the Chemical Subcommittee's members also conducted research into the design and development of possible chemical weapons, chiefly tear-gas shells, but the War Office took little interest in this work.[5] The German gas attacks of April 1915, and Haldane's subsequent involvement with the War Office, provided the Royal Society with the entrance they had been looking for. Haldane was himself a Fellow of the Society,[6] and he was quickly co-opted onto the Chemistry Subcommittee, along with another physiologist, E.H. Starling.[7] At the subcommittee's urging, Haldane began conducting animal experiments to evaluate the poisonous effects of various chemicals and their potential effectiveness as weapons.[8]

At the same time, the military and public impact of the German gas attacks had convinced a number of government departments that they must make much more extensive use of the nation's scientific expertise, including expertise in physiology. At the War Office, Alfred Keogh quickly established an Anti-Gas

Department under the auspices of the Army Medical Service, to carry forward research into the design and production of respirators and other defensive measures. He looked to the Royal Society for advice and assistance, and on 24 June 1915, at Keogh's recommendation, the society's War Committee established a separate Sectional Committee on Physiology.[9] The Physiology (War) Committee was also invited to nominate two members to a Working Committee to supervise the research work of the Anti-Gas Department.[10] Some months later, towards the end of 1915, Starling was recruited into the RAMC to take charge of the anti-gas work, and subsequently brought in a number of other physiologists to assist him.[11] Under Starling's direction, the Anti-Gas Department was conspicuously successful in meeting its goal of developing effective respirators for protection against gas.

The War Office was not just interested in defensive work, however. Development and deployment of chemical weapons for use by the British forces was also seen to be of the utmost importance, and the Anti-Gas Department, despite its name, was also charged with conducting research into the potential offensive use of various chemicals.[12] The department also liaised with the research being undertaken by the euphemistically named Special Brigades of the Royal Engineers, that had been set up to take charge of the development and deployment of gas weapons in the field. The Special Brigades established their own Gas Services Central Laboratory at general headquarters in St Omer in June 1915. Though the work of the laboratory was chiefly chemical,[13] some medical scientists were also drafted in to advise on both the offensive and defensive aspects of chemical warfare. Among these was the respiratory physiologist C.G. Douglas.[14]

The chief responsibility for the development and production of chemical weapons fell not to the War Office, however, but to a new department of government. The Ministry of Munitions was set up in June 1915 in response to the difficulties encountered in supplying the Army with the huge numbers of artillery shells needed to meet the unprecedented strategic demands of trench warfare.[15] And from the start, it took a much more innovative approach to weapons development than had hitherto been adopted by the War Office. Lloyd George, the Minister in charge of the new department, was as keen to draw on the advice of civilian scientists as the War Office had been reluctant, and he too, like Keogh, turned to the Royal Society for assistance. Shortly after the ministry was established he set up a Scientific Advisory Group of scientists drawn from a variety of disciplines. Among them was a physiologist, W.B. Hardy, the Biological Secretary to the Royal Society.[16]

In his capacity as a member of the Scientific Advisory Committee, Hardy undertook to collect physiological data on the suitability of a wide range of chemicals for use as weapons. As one of the chemists involved in chemical warfare research observed: '[P]ractically no accurate information was available as to the physiological effects, the toxicity, etc., of chemical substances. Experiments had therefore to be at once put in hand in order to ascertain the lethal doses and the action of the various compounds which at that time were known to possess offensive properties, and might probably be of value in chemical warfare.'[17] This presumably included the research already under way in the Anti-Gas Department of the War Office, but a substantial amount of work also seems to have been conducted in the physiologists' own laboratories.[18]

Subsequently, the Ministry of Munitions also took responsibility for conducting its own physiological research into the offensive aspects of gas warfare. In June 1916 an Experimental Station was established at Porton Down, run by the Royal Engineers but serving as a field station for testing the experimental weapons developed by the Ministry of Munitions. Nine months later, in March 1917, a substantial physiology department was created there under the directorship of Joseph Barcroft; again, W.B. Hardy was responsible for nominating the scientists who were recruited to work there.[19]

As a result of such initiatives, physiologists were able to secure a very considerable degree of involvement in war-related research work. While welcoming this official involvement in the war effort, however, they harboured a deep dissatisfaction with the way it was organized. Officially, the Anti-Gas Department of the War Office had charge of the defensive aspects of gas work, while responsibility for offensive research and development resided primarily with the Ministry of Munitions, with some assistance from the Royal Engineers. This distribution of responsibilities reflected prevailing military suppositions about the different warfighting functions to be undertaken by different sections of the war machine. The tasks of fighting and killing, and that of protecting the health of soldiers, were generally regarded as quite separate from and even antagonistic to one another; consequently, it was assumed that responsibility for them was best allocated to separate departments of the military establishment.

As we have seen, however, this division of labour was not followed in practice. Nor did the physiologists think it should be. Their scientific knowledge and skills qualified them to advise on both the offensive and the defensive aspects of chemical warfare; detailed technical knowledge of the toxic effects of a particular substance, for instance, was useful both for evaluating that substance as a potential weapon, and for devising methods of protecting soldiers from it. Consequently, physiologists on both sides of the administrative divide applied themselves to both offensive and defensive questions. Still, the persistence of distinct chains of offensive and defensive command within the strongly hierarchical structures of the military administration tended to compromise the exchange of information between the various physiological research groups. As a result, the physiologists were fearful of duplicating one another's research, and of missing out on new developments that might be helpful to their own investigations. The regular meetings of the Physiology (War) Committee did much to fill the gap, by providing an unofficial but valuable means of coordinating the research effort across the organizational divisions of the military machine.[20]

The organizational rationality embodied in the work of the Physiology (War) Committee was officially endorsed with the restructuring of the Ministry of Munitions from mid-1917 onwards. The ministry had grown rapidly since its establishment; in the year from July 1916 alone, it had tripled the number of staff it employed, while departments had grown and divided in a largely ad hoc manner to number over fifty by early 1917. In July of that year, Winston Churchill was appointed Minister of Munitions, with the specific aim of imposing a more rational and efficient scheme of organization on this administrative jumble. He did so by creating ten new administrative divisions, each headed by an experienced ministry officer, and each comprising several functionally related departments.[21] Chemical warfare was identified as one of the functions that would benefit from this kind of rationalization, and in October 1917 the various offensive and defensive departments involved in such work – including the Anti-Gas Department of the War Office – were brought together to form a single Chemical Warfare Department of the Ministry of Munitions, with a single scientific advisory committee.[22]

The formation of the Chemical Warfare Department gave a considerable boost to physiologists' status and authority. Hitherto, their work had been to a great extent subordinated to the particular local concerns of quite separate branches of the military machine. Within the new department, by contrast, they were given a much greater degree of responsibility for determining how research into all aspects of gas warfare should be conducted. In effect, this reorganization presumed that the exercise of scientific knowledge and skill should be freed from the constraints imposed by older operational assumptions about the proper distribution of offensive and defensive functions, and should instead be given priority as one of the key activities around which the conduct of gas warfare in its entirety should be structured. Scientists were no longer simply employed to meet the disparate needs of pre-existing military services; rather, they now became directly involved in determining what those needs were and how they might best be met.

MEDICAL ASPECTS OF GAS WARFARE

In spite of this advancement, physiologists were ambivalent about their involvement in chemical warfare research. On the whole, it allowed them little scope to make use of the most distinctively physiological aspects of their scientific knowledge and skills. On the offensive side their work involved little more than a routine and theoretically unsophisticated screening of large numbers of chemicals for possible toxic effects.[23] Defensive work, meanwhile, revolved chiefly around the design and testing of respirators and other methods for protecting soldiers from contact with the various poisonous substances in offensive use. Such investigations related in only the most tenuous way to the researches that physiologists had pursued before the war, and to the theoretical elucidation of biological mechanisms that most engaged their interest. Thus W.M. Bayliss, one of the members of the Physiology (War) Committee, wrote in October 1915 to his friend C.S. Sherrington that 'Poison gas & such things, which I have had something to do with, are not attractive, although there are some interesting things about them.'[24] E.H. Starling applied himself purposefully both to the design of respirators and to the search for new chemical weapons, but his heart was not in the work, and in 1917 he resigned his RAMC commission and returned to civilian science.[25] And W.B. Hardy, though the only physiologist on the Scientific Advisory Group of the Ministry of Munitions, did not take more than a passing interest in gas warfare.[26] Indeed, some scientists feared that the military emphasis on gas warfare research would lead to physiological talent being diverted away from more interesting fields of investigation.[27]

Despite this official emphasis on offensive and defensive research, however, a number of physiologists continued to regard war gas poisoning as a subject of considerable scientific interest. J.S. Haldane, C.G. Douglas, Joseph Barcroft and Leonard Hill had all built their scientific reputations around research into the physiology of respiration, and they were keen to apply their specialist knowledge to the elucidation and possible treatment of gas poisoning. As a result of early examinations of gas victims, they quickly came to the view that the gravest danger in cases of poisoning by gases such as chlorine and phosgene was oxygen deprivation, caused by severe irritation and inflammation of the lung tissues. In many such cases, they reasoned, the immediate effects of poisoning might be mitigated by therapeutic administration of oxygen, and the victim kept alive until the inflammation subsided and normal lung function was restored.[28] The problem was, the physiologists had little opportunity actually to confirm this hypothesis clinically.

Both Barcroft and Hill made brief MRC-funded visits to France during the second half of 1915, the former to investigate the effects of asphyxia in gassed soldiers, the latter to try out a new oxygen administration mask.[29] But compared to the more pressing operational concerns of offensive and defensive chemical warfare research, the treatment of gas victims was of low strategic priority, and little came of their work. Haldane returned to the question of oxygen therapy in the autumn of 1916, when he began developing an apparatus specifically for the purpose of clinical oxygen administration. He sent a prototype to Douglas who was currently posted to the Gas Services Central Laboratory at St Omer, and who was in a position to conduct field tests on gassed soldiers. The results of Douglas's early trials were encouraging,[30] but his therapeutic investigations had to take second place to other responsibilities that fell on him as a Medical Officer to the Special Brigades. He had been appointed to this post primarily 'so as to be ready to study the gas casualties in the event of another attack', and especially because he was well qualified 'to recognize the appearance of any new chemical substances as soon as possible'.[31] These duties became particularly urgent when the Germans began deploying mustard gas and other novel chemicals from March 1917 onwards, and Douglas was quickly transferred from the Central Laboratory to the front line. Meanwhile, his therapeutic research had to be suspended. 'Of course now that I have left the laboratory I have practically ceased to have anything to do with protective work or with the medical aspect of gas poisoning,' he told Haldane in May. 'However, my position there was so unsatisfactory that I could really be of little use. After all if one is working at the medical aspect one must have authority to act in the matter.'[32]

By this time, though, military priorities were changing markedly. As the stalemate of trench warfare dragged on, and lives continued to be lost and soldiers wounded in staggering numbers, manpower issues came to the fore. Increasingly, the military and political leadership became preoccupied with maintaining an adequate supply of troops to the trenches, and with minimizing the sums that would have to be paid in pensions to disabled soldiers and to the dependants of those killed. Saving soldiers' lives, and if possible leaving them fit enough to return to the front, now became a matter of urgent military and political concern. In this setting, the possibility that physiologists might be able to provide an effective means of treating gas casualties assumed much greater importance. Consequently, in May 1917 the MRC began funding Haldane and a young Canadian clinical scientist, J.C. Meakins, to conduct research into the physiology and treatment of gas cases – many of whom recovered from the acute effects of their injuries but remained chronically disabled – at military hospitals in England.[33] Meanwhile, in the field Douglas's medical skills now came to be recognized and valued by his military superiors, and in July 1917 he was promoted to the new post of Physiological Advisor to the Gas Directorate, leaving him free to resume his investigations into the therapeutic administration of oxygen to gassed soldiers.[34]

Throughout this period, the Royal Society's Physiology (War) Committee again provided a forum where the results of these different lines of work could be discussed and evaluated. In the new climate of concern over manpower, the committee was also quick to capitalize on the therapeutic findings of its members and their colleagues. In September 1917 it issued a pamphlet, *Notes on the Effects of Pulmonary Irritant Gases*, intended for circulation to military Medical Officers. This publication clearly satisfied the authorities that the physiologists' medical skills, as much as their ability to devise new means of offence and defence, could make a significant contribution to the war effort. In January 1918, in consultation with the Chemical Warfare Department of the Ministry of Munitions, Keogh appointed all the interested members of the Physiology (War) Committee to serve on a new Chemical Warfare Medical Committee of the MRC. The physiologists' first action was to reissue their original pamphlet as the first official report of the committee, thereby conferring on it the authority of an official government publication. Three months later Keogh issued a memorandum to Medical Officers substantially based on this report. Meanwhile, the Medical Committee was using the resources at its disposal to develop a much expanded programme of physiological research into the medical and therapeutic aspects of chemical warfare.[35]

As a result of this work, the physiologists were able to develop a number of therapeutic innovations that clearly won them favour with the Army. Oxygen therapy was one such, and the Army Medical Service duly arranged for some 4,000 cylinders of the gas to be made available to Medical Officers in France.[36] The members of the Medical Committee also looked at the effects of mustard gas poisoning, and again were able to devise effective therapeutic responses. Douglas took responsibility for putting their findings into effect in France, with the result, as the Director of Gas Services noted with evident satisfaction, that the period of invalidism among troops affected by mustard gas was significantly reduced: '[E]ventually it was found necessary for only 25 per cent of the cases to be evacuated to England, while about 90 per cent of the remainder were dealt with at convalescent depots in France, from which they returned to duty within twenty-eight days. A great saving in manpower was effected in this way.'[37]

Once again, however, it is important to note that it was not just the physiologists' scientific knowledge and their ability to generate technical innovations that made them so valuable to the military. As in the case of their offensive and defensive work, so in their medical work they demonstrated a considerable capacity not only for organizing their own research, but also for coordinating developments in different departments of government. This was acknowledged, for instance, when Douglas was appointed Physiological Adviser to the Gas Directorate in the expectation that he would not only conduct his own medical investigations, but would also 'continue the close association of the defensive side of gas operations with the directorate of medical services'.[38] As the American physiologist W.B. Cannon noted with some envy, the British Army had been quick to recognize 'the values which the physiologist might have as a liaison officer between medical and gas interests'.[39]

Likewise, the creation of the Chemical Warfare Committee gave the physiologists a significant degree of authority to determine their own and others' research activities, even when they were employed in other departments of government. This was particularly clear in the case of Joseph Barcroft and his colleagues. Though still employed by the Chemical Warfare Department of the Ministry of Munitions, and ostensibly responsible for testing chemical weapons at Porton, they were nevertheless now able to devote a considerable proportion of their time to MRC-funded research into oxygen therapy at Cambridge.[40] Like the establishment of the Chemical Warfare Department itself, the creation of the Chemical Warfare Medical Committee further enhanced the physiologists' standing as key figures in determining the aims and methods of modern warfare.

WAR AS EXPERIMENT

Through their research into the offensive, defensive and medical aspects of chemical warfare, physiologists demonstrated their ability to generate technical innovations of immediate military value. In the course of the war, they successfully applied their scientific knowledge and investigative skills to the work of developing new methods of killing, new ways of protecting soldiers from being killed, and new ways of treating the injured and returning them to the fray. To an extent, in order to achieve these results physiologists had to tailor their investigative methodologies to the peculiar needs of war research. When Barcroft and his colleagues exposed animals to potential new chemical weapons at Porton Down, for instance, they recorded the results as 'severe or light casualties or non–affected'.[41] In effect, they modelled their methods of observation and accounting on those used by the military, and thereby turned the laboratory into an experimental analogue of the battlefield.

Physiologists were not the only ones to draw this analogy, however. Conversely, military commanders were beginning to think of the battlefield as a kind of laboratory. As C.H. Foulkes, the Director of Gas Services and the man responsible for deploying the new weapons developed and tested by the physiologists, put it: '[W]e had in the theatre of war itself a vast experimental ground . . . Human beings provided the material for these experiments on both sides of No Man's Land.'[42] What is evident from these remarks is a singular convergence of ideas among medical scientists and military thinkers; both groups were coming to share a view of the war itself as an experimental enterprise, in which new techniques of warfare were continually being developed and tested, and in which the line of demarcation between the laboratory and the battlefield was increasingly blurred.

It is important to recognize just how novel this view was within the British Army command at that time. Prior to the First World War, War Office officials had generally assumed that military research and development should be confined to the periods between armed conflicts; once war broke out, everything depended upon manufacturing and deploying existing weapons as efficiently and effectively as possible, and there could be little justification for making risky and potentially dangerous experiments with new weapons or new methods of warfighting. This attitude was evident in the early stages of the First World War itself, not least in the War Office's distinctly unenthusiastic response to the Royal Society's offer of scientific assistance, and in the very limited support given to the Chemistry Subcommittee's research into chemical weapons. However, as the conflict dragged on and it became clear that established methods of warfighting resulted only in an outrageous waste of lives and resources, military commanders and their political masters came to the opinion that success must depend upon the development of new weapons and new strategies.[43] The German deployment of gas weapons, though not strategically decisive, did much to reinforce this point of view; this was to be a war of invention, and victory would go to the side that first developed the technical means of breaking through the enemy's defences. By the closing years of the war, the British Army's offensive strategy was largely predicated on the development of new technical capabilities.[44]

In the course of the First World War, the British military came increasingly to the view that the development of new kinds of weapons and new forms of strategy, far from being wasteful or dangerous pursuits during wartime, were actually vital for the conduct of the war. Under the novel circumstances of trench warfare, experiment and innovation now became the key to military success. In effect, war itself now came to be seen as a grand experiment, whose outcome depended, not upon the deployment of tried and tested weapons and strategies, but rather upon finding new and unanticipated methods of overwhelming the enemy's defences, and upon being able to respond to and minimize the strategic effects of the enemy's own innovations.

To a considerable extent, this process of innovation came to be seen to depend upon the mobilization of new areas of technical expertise – including, perhaps most importantly, the knowledge and skills of scientists. But this too demanded innovation, this time of an administrative and organizational kind. Hitherto, relatively few scientists had sought or found careers in the military. During peacetime at least, their talents were far better employed in the universities, in civil government, and in industry. Moreover, as we have seen, the Army at least was generally reluctant to seek the advice of experts outwith its own establishment. Consequently, new administrative structures were needed that would effectively span the division between military and civilian life, and provide a conduit whereby scientific advice and expertise could be channelled into military affairs. To an extent, such structures had already begun to be put in place before the war, notably through the Territorial Army, set up in 1908 as part of Viscount Haldane's larger programme of Army reform.

The Territorials, established in parallel with the regular Army and under the same command, were intended above all as a means of mobilizing home resources to support the regulars, and effectively embodied Haldane's ideal of 'a nation in arms'.[45] But Haldane was particularly interested in building up the technical branches of the Army, and especially the Medical Service, which he saw as crucially important for the pursuit of a modern war. Consequently, in concert with Alfred Keogh, he took pains to ensure that the Territorial arm of this service was well organized. In particular, he ensured that it forged strong links with the universities and their pool of resident scientific experts. As we have seen, when war eventually did occur, Keogh and the Army Medical Service would be at the forefront of efforts to recruit civilian physiologists to the work of developing a British chemical warfare capability.

Perhaps the most important administrative development of the war, however – at least in terms of mobilizing civilian experts for war work, and in terms of fostering the assumption that the successful prosecution of the war effort depended upon both technical and administrative innovation – was the Ministry of Munitions. Under Lloyd George's aggressive leadership, the ministry quickly developed into a dramatically new kind of institution for channelling and managing national resources for the purposes of warfare. For one thing, the Ministry of Munitions made manifest a growing view that, in order to win the war, it was now necessary and justifiable for the government to exert far more extensive control over certain aspects of civilian life – in this case, the manufacture of munitions and other warlike materials – than had hitherto been judged acceptable. In effect, the ministry can be seen as a manifestation of the new era of 'total war', in which the prosecution of the national war effort came to depend as much on the mobilization of civilian as of military resources.

In this respect, it is significant that the Ministry of Munitions was itself a civilian organization, which marked a radical – and much contested – break with the long-standing supposition that matters of arms procurement should be left exclusively in the hands of the military. It also provided Lloyd George with what one historian has called the 'opportunity to implement his vision of a total war economy'.[46] During his time as Minister, he was able to secure control over 'virtually the entire process of armaments production: from research and development, procurement of raw materials and machinery, supervision of both private and State factories, to the provision to the War Office of finished guns, shells and other warlike stores'.[47] In so doing, he did much to blur the boundary, not just between military mobilization and civil administration, but also between the regulatory work of the state and the productive work of private industry.

Lloyd George was also highly innovative in the way that he turned to experts from outside the government to assist in the work of the new ministry. One such source of expertise was the business community. Lloyd George had long held the view that large areas of government administration might most effectively be delegated to private business, whose efficiency and competitiveness he greatly admired.[48] He accordingly recruited an unprecedented number of businessmen into executive and administrative positions in the Ministry of Munitions – an arrangement that, as Prime Minister, he would subsequently repeat in the creation of several other new departments, and that he liked to think of as his own personal 'experiment' in the conduct of government.[49]

The induction of civilian scientists, and especially physiologists, into war-related research was thus part of a more general reorientation of military and government thinking about how the resources of the nation should be mobilized for modern warfare. And central to this reorientation was the notion of 'experiment'. From the technical development of new forms of offence and defence to the reorganization of the machinery of government itself, victory in the war now came to be seen to depend upon a process of continual experimentation. Physiologists proved themselves to be adept at pursuing both kinds of experiment. In the laboratory, most obviously, they were quickly able to turn their technical skills to the business of generating innovations in *matériel* and in medical care. But they also revealed a considerable talent both for organizing their own work within the evolving structures of the wartime administration, and for showing how those structures might best be integrated and even reorganized so as to make the most effective use of their skills. It was this peculiar combination of skills that enabled physiologists to move so quickly into positions of unprecedented authority and responsibility within the military and in other organs of the state in the course of the war.

CONCLUSION

It remains to ask whether there might have been any intrinsic connection between these two sets of skills so ably deployed by physiologists: the one in the conduct of laboratory experiments, the other in the organization and administration of war-related research and development. In the first place, it should be observed that physiologists displayed a similar combination of talents in other areas of war work. In the field of industrial management, for instance, they drew on their technical knowledge of how the human body worked to recommend changes in the hours and environmental conditions of labour, in the design of factories, in the prevention of work-related illness, and in other aspects of industrial welfare. It is significant that this innovative approach to management was most enthusiastically taken up, once again, by the Ministry of Munitions.[50] Likewise, physiologists were also able to secure a role for themselves as expert advisers on matters of food policy with the creation of the Ministry of Food – another of Lloyd George's 'experimental' departments – towards the end of 1916.[51] They also conducted research into the treatment of some of the most urgent medical problems of the war, notably heart disease and surgical shock. In both these conditions they were able not only to develop new techniques of therapy and rehabilitation, but also to work closely with the Army Medical Service to ensure that these techniques were deployed as effectively as possible both at the front and in war hospitals.[52] Clearly, chemical warfare research was not the only area in which physiologists were able to make a contribution to the experimental war effort.

Indeed, it is notable that physiologists working in all these diverse areas of research continued to communicate and collaborate, not just with colleagues in their own particular field of practical application, but more generally. In particular, so close was the relationship between them that they increasingly inclined towards the view that almost all the conditions they investigated, from fatigue to wound shock and on to shell-shock, were little more than different manifestations of the same underlying physiological phenomena.[53] The physiologists' ability to develop this synoptic vision of war-related illness and debility was a reflection of the high level of theoretical and methodological coherence within their discipline. Over the previous three or four decades, scientists conducting detailed experimental research into a wide range of biological phenomena had nevertheless managed to articulate their work, by and large, around a shared body of theoretical issues. And the point that needs to be stressed is that this was as much an organizational as an intellectual or technical achievement. In developing their discipline and maintaining such a high level of coherence within it, physiologists had already developed considerable skills in organizing and integrating a diversity of specific and local technical activities towards the pursuit of common intellectual and practical goals.[54] They did so, above all, through their involvement in scientific bodies like the Royal Society.

It was surely this practical experience of organizing and coordinating their own technical work, that equipped physiologists to succeed so conspicuously both in meeting the technical demands of their war research, and in shaping the administrative environment within which they conducted that research. The experimental and organizational skills required for elucidating the complexities of normal organic function during peacetime also lent themselves to the pursuit of systematic investigations in a wide range of more or less related subjects during the war. The case of chemical warfare research, and the key role played by the Royal Society's Physiology (War) Committee in coordinating and integrating that research, illustrates this point particularly clearly.

It also makes clear the extent to which those skills acquired new value as the priorities of both military and civilian institutions changed during the First World War, from a prevailing commitment to the application of existing forms of warfighting technology and strategy, to a new concern with technical, strategic and administrative innovation. As a result, physiologists were able to carve out a new place for themselves within the machinery of wartime government. The Scientific Advisory Committee of the Chemical Warfare Department of the Ministry of Munitions is a case in point. From the vantage point of that committee, physiologists were able to survey the work of a particular government department, conduct such research as they considered relevant, and offer expert advice on the way the work of that department should be conducted. In this particular instance, the physiologists had secured only a temporary advancement; with the end of the war, the Ministry of Munitions was no longer deemed to have any place in the government of peace. But other gains were more permanent. Most important was the rise in status and authority of the MRC.

The MRC had been established just a year before the war began, as a research committee of the National Health Insurance Commission. Tucked away in this rather peculiar department of government, its remit was primarily to carry out research into medical conditions that had a bearing on the provision and cost of health care under the National Insurance Act of 1911. In the course of the war, however, it gradually acquired responsibility for initiating and coordinating research into a far wider range of medical issues, not least with the establishment of the Chemical Warfare Medical Committee in 1918. In effect, the MRC now assumed something of the independent and proactive character of the Royal Society's Physiology (War) Committee; indeed, as we have seen, the Chemical Warfare Medical Committee effectively was the Royal Society Committee in an official guise. Moreover, unlike the functions that the Ministry of Munitions had fulfilled, the style of scientific and administrative work the MRC established during the war was judged equally relevant to the pursuit of peacetime government. Consequently, in 1920, it was reconstituted, with a much increased budget, as a research council of the Privy Council.[55] Here it was no longer constrained by the particular concerns of any one department of government, but was free to pursue its own programmes of research, and to offer its advice and expertise wherever it saw fit. The war, in effect, was the making of the MRC as a centre of scientific authority in government and as a directing force in the development of medical science in Britain. The physiologists' role in the prosecution of chemical warfare played no small part in that making.

ACKNOWLEDGEMENTS

My thanks to Roger Cooter for comments on an earlier draft of this chapter, and to the Wellcome Trust for their funding and support.

Notes

1 L.F. Haber, *The Poisonous Cloud: Chemical Warfare in the First World War* (Oxford, Clarendon Press, 1986). Estimates of the number of casualties due to gas during the first two German attacks range between 7,000 and 15,000, including between 3,000 and 5,000 dead.

2 Haber, *The Poisonous Cloud*, pp. 45–6; S.W. Sturdy, 'A Co-ordinated Whole: The Life and Work of J.S. Haldane' (unpub. Ph.D. thesis, University of Edinburgh, 1987), pp. 278–86.

3 Royal Society War Committee Minutes (12 November 1914), Royal Society Archives, CMB 36. The committee initially consisted of ten members. As subcommittees were appointed to deal with specific subject areas, their co-opted members automatically became members of the parent War Committee, which grew rapidly to an unwieldly size as a result.

4 Royal Society War Committee Minutes (12 November 1914), and 'Sectional Chemical Committee. Report to December, 1917', appended to Minutes of War Committee (24 January 1918). See also Chemistry Subcommittee Minutes, Royal Society Archives, CMB 28.

5 The subcommittee's research was encouraged by the Inventions Branch (A41) of the War Office, but this small and purely advisory department was unable to persuade anyone higher up the chain of command that chemical weapons might be valuable. R.J.Q. Adams, *Arms and the Wizard: Lloyd George and the Ministry of Munitions, 1915–1916* (London, Cassell & Co., 1978), p. 145.

6 Moreover, he had been accompanied to France by Herbert Baker, one of the members of the Chemical Subcommittee who had worked on tear gas: Haber, *The Poisonous Cloud*, p. 23; J.F. Thorpe, 'Herbert Brereton Baker 1862–1935', *Obituary Notices of Fellows of the Royal Society*, 1 (1932–5), 523–6. Again, it may be that Keogh had a hand in Baker's selection for this mission. Baker was Professor of Chemistry at Imperial College, London, of which institution Keogh was Rector – the equivalent of a university vice-chancellor.

7 Royal Society War Committee Minutes (12 May 1915). Also co-opted onto the Chemical Subcommittee at this meeting were J.F. Thorpe and Colonel Louis C. Jackson of the War Office. Starling was already serving on the society's Engineering Subcommittee, where he was looking at the effects of severe acceleration on the human frame. This work was prompted by a query from the Navy, who were interested in the use of aeroplanes; Royal Society War Committee Minutes (19 November 1914).

8 Within a month, Haldane was testing the effects of hydrogen cyanide and N_2O_4 on mice and rabbits, with the assistance of J.G. Priestley and A. Mavrogordato. See his laboratory notes dated 23, 24 May and 7, 8 June 1915, in National Library of Scotland (NLS) MS 20233, ff. 170–7, 188–90; also 'Memorandum by Dr. Haldane. Capsicum for bombs', NLS MS 20234, ff. 125–8.

9 W.M. Fletcher, 'An account of the work done by the Physiology (War) Committee up to December 1917', Public Record Office (PRO), MUN 5/386/1650/13. The membership of the Physiology (War) Committee initially consisted of E.H. Starling (chair), W.M. Fletcher (secretary), W.M. Bayliss, A.R. Cushny, J.S. Haldane, Leonard Hill and F.G. Hopkins. Fleet Surgeon R.C. Munday of the Navy's Medical Department and Joseph Barcroft were added a month later. Royal Society War Committee Minutes (24 June, 25 July 1915).

The Physiology (War) Committee was appointed as part of a larger reorganization of the Society's system of war committees. On 5 June 1915 the Council of the Society discharged the original War Committee, which had grown unwieldy, and assumed that mantle for itself. It duly met as the War Committee on 24 June, when it redistributed the work of the earlier ad hoc and problem-oriented subcommittees among four new Sectional War Committees – for Engineering, Chemistry, Physics and Physiology respectively – that gave organizational and intellectual priority to the major fields of experimental science represented by the Society. Royal Society War Committee Minutes (24 June 1915). More pragmatically focused committees would later be reintroduced into the Society's idealized scheme of scientific organization in response to particularly urgent claims on its expertise.

10 Royal Society War Committee Minutes (15 July 1915). The physiologists were A.R. Cushny and Leonard Hill. The society was also invited to nominate two chemists to this Working Committee.

11 Starling was initially given two assistants, J.A. Sadd and E.F. Harrison. The latter was a pharmacist whose industrial experiences seems to have been crucial in coordinating the research programme. Starling subsequently brought in Lovatt Evans from his own department at University College, London, and H.S. Raper and H.W. Dudley from Leeds University. Raper later succeeded

Starling as Director of the Anti-Gas Department. See Haber, pp. 121–2; C.J.M[artin], 'Ernest Henry Starling 1866–1927', *Proceedings of the Royal Society, B*, 102 (1928), xvii–xxvii; Percival Hartley, 'Henry Stanley Raper 1882–1951', *Obituary Notices of Fellows of the Royal Society* 8 (1952–3), 567–82.

12 Indeed, it was offensive rather than defensive work that was specifically mentioned when the Royal Society nominated its physiological and chemical representatives to the department's Working Committee; Royal Society War Committee Minutes (15 July 1915). Starling's team was able to alert the Army to the offensive potential of mustard gas a full year before it was first deployed by the Germans, but the War Office only chose to act on Starling's recommendation after the Germans adopted mustard gas as one of their main chemical weapons; Haber, *The Poisonous Cloud*, pp. 116–17.

13 The laboratory was under the direction of William Watson, Professor of Physics at Imperial College, London. H.L.C., 'William Watson, 1868–1919', *Proceedings of the Royal Society, A*, 97 (1920), i–iii. Besides developing and testing gas weapons for Allied use, the laboratory also examined enemy gas munitions and devised appropriate protective measures.

14 D.J.C. Cunningham, 'Claude Gordon Douglas 1882–1963', *Biographical Memoirs of Fellows of the Royal Society*, 10 (1964), 51–74, at p. 58–9.

15 On the establishment and work of this ministry, see Adams, *Arms and the Wizard, passim*; and for a more critical assessment, Chris Wrigley, 'The Ministry of Munitions: An Innovative Department' in Kathleen Burk (ed.), *War and the State: The Transformation of British Government 1914–1919* (London, Allen & Unwin, 1982), pp. 32–56.

16 Hardy was apparently appointed at the suggestion of Christopher Addison, the Parliamentary Secretary to the Ministry of Munitions; J. Davidson Pratt, 'Memorandum on the organisation for chemical warfare research, December 1914–November 1918' (30 April 1919), PRO MUN 5/385/1650/8. Addison was himself a medical scientist, having been Professor of Anatomy at the University of Sheffield before he began his political career. The other members of the eight-man Scientific Advisory Group were all chemists, physicists or engineers, and all were members of the Royal Society War Committee or one or another of its subcommittees; Haber, *The Poisonous Cloud*, p. 122.

17 J. Davidson Pratt, 'Memorandum on the organisation for chemical warfare research, December 1914–November 1918', PRO MUN 5/385/1650/8.

18 Haber, *The Poisonous Cloud*, p. 121, mistakenly follows Pratt in implying that the Royal Society Physiology (War) Committee was established solely for the purpose of conducting this offensive research.

19 A.W. Crossley, 'The R.E. Experimental Station, Porton', PRO MUN 5/386/1650/14; Kenneth J. Franklin, *Joseph Barcroft 1872–1947* (Oxford, Blackwell Scientific Publications, 1953), pp. 102–3. The members of Barcroft's staff were R.A. Peters, A.E. Boycott, J. Shaw Dunn and G.H. Hunt. Research at Porton was the responsibility of the Trench Warfare Department of the Ministry of Munitions, which was seen as singularly successful in overcoming the rather fraught relationship that existed between the ministry and the War Office; Guy Hartcup, *The War of Invention: Scientific Developments, 1914–1918* (London, Brassey's Defence Publishers, 1988), pp. 61–93.

20 W.M. Fletcher, 'An account of the work done by the Physiology (War) Committee up to December 1917', PRO MUN 5/386/1650/13.

21 Adams, *Arms and the Wizard*, pp. 180–4; Wrigley, 'Ministry of Munitions', p. 44.

22 Pratt, 'Memorandum'; H.S. Raper, 'History of the Anti-Gas Department' (n.d.) in Anti-gas reports (II), PRO MUN 5/386/1650/13.

23 Haber emphasizes that this search for new gas weapons was largely uninformed by chemical or toxicological theory, and that 'scientists appeared to be working aimlessly and writing copiously'; *The Poisonous Cloud*, pp. 198–9. According to another authority, 'In Britain . . . much of the search comprised a compound-by-compound scanning of the myriad substances listed in *Beilstein's Handbook* for any suggestion of offensive properties, followed by laboratory experiment and field testing, the latter often being conducted on the battlefield itself'; Stockholm International Peace Research Institute, *The Problem of Chemical and Biological Warfare*, vol. 1: *The Rise of CB Weapons* (Stockholm, Almqvist and Wiksell, 1971), p. 38.

24 W.M. Bayliss to C.S. Sherrington (17 October 1915), University of British Columbia, Woodward Biomedical Library, Sherrington Papers I/2, No. 18. Bayliss was much more enthusiastic about the work on industrial fatigue in which Sherrington had recently become involved.

25 M[artin], 'Ernest Henry Starling', p. xxv. He resigned to take over what he considered to be the more physiologically interesting and administratively more valuable post of Chairman of the Royal Society's Food Committee.

26 Like Starling, he was more interested in the work of the Food Committee, and no mention is made of his chemical warfare connections by his Royal Society obituarists; F.G[owland] H[opkins] and F.E.S., 'William Bate Hardy 1864–1933', *Obituary Notices of Fellows of the Royal Society*, 1 (1932–5), 327–33.

27 When the Harvard physiologist W.B. Cannon began to study the physiological aspects of surgical shock, for instance, the physiologically inclined physician and consultant to the British Expeditionary Force, T.R. Elliott, urged him to tell the authorities that he was working on gas, while Bayliss urged him not to give in to pressure to conduct gas research; T.R. Elliott to Cannon (30 September 1917), Bayliss to Cannon (13 October 1917), both in Harvard University Countway Library, Cannon Papers, box 62, folders 822 and 812 respectively.

28 On the development of these views, and the reasons why they did not immediately find favour among clinicians in the field, see Steve Sturdy, 'From the Trenches to the Hospitals at Home: Physiologists, Clinicians and Oxygen Therapy, 1914–30' in John V. Pickstone (ed.), *Medical Innovations in Historical Perspective* (Basingstoke, Macmillan, 1992), pp. 104–123.

29 Sturdy, 'From the Trenches', p. 108.

30 Douglas to Haldane, 13 November 1916, NLS MS 20233, ff. 223–32, and 1 February 1917, NLS MS 20234, ff. 2–3.

31 Cunningham, 'Claude Gordon Douglas', pp. 58–9.

32 Douglas to Haldane, 14 May 1917, NLS MS 20234, ff. 9–12.

33 Sturdy, 'A Co-ordinated Whole', pp. 313–18.

34 W.G. Macpherson, *Official History of the War. Medical Services: General History*, vol. 2 (London, HMSO, 1923), p. 364; D.J.C. Cunningham, 'Claude Gordon Douglas 1882–1963', *Biographical Memoirs of Fellows of the Royal Society*, 10 (1964), 51–74. Douglas in effect replaced the pathologist S. Lyle Cummins, who from March 1916 had served in the post of Assistant Director for Defensive Gas Work, where his duties included testing the effectiveness of prototype respirators; obituary, 'S. Lyle Cummins', *British Medical Journal*, i (1949), 1054–5.

35 Sturdy, 'From the Trenches', pp. 114–18. Starling and Gowland Hopkins evidently chose not to sit on this committee, as they were more interested in other areas of war research. They were replaced by Meakins, the physiological pathologist A.E. Boycott, and Frank Sufflebotham.

36 Sturdy, 'From the Trenches', pp. 112–13.

37 C.H. Foulkes, *Gas! The Story of the Special Brigade* (Edinburgh, William Blackwood, 1934), p. 264.

38 W.G. Macpherson, *Official History of the War. Medical Services: General History*, vol. 2, p. 364.

39 Cannon to W.M. Fletcher, 12 April 1918, Harvard University Countway Library, Cannon papers, box 62, folder 825. He was comparing the British with the American field laboratories, which were dominated by chemical workers while physiologists occupied a distincly subordinate position.

40 Sturdy, 'From the Trenches', pp. 115–16.

41 A.W. Crossley, 'The R.E. Experimental Station, Porton' (28 May 1919), PRO MUN 5/386/1650/14. Physiologists and other scientists also frequently used themselves as experimental subjects, to test both the potency of new chemicals and the effectiveness of new forms of protection. In so doing, they often put themselves at considerable risk, sometimes unnecessarily. Some died as a result. It is tempting to suppose that on an emotional level too, they were inclined to consider the laboratory as a battlefield, where they had a duty to face equivalent dangers to those faced by their combatant colleagues, friends and family.

42 Foulkes, *Gas!*, p. 274. See also Haber, *The Poisonous Cloud*, pp. 119–20.

43 See e.g., Hartcup, *War of Invention*, p. 61.

44 By 1918 the Allied Command was planning strategy around the deployment of tanks that had not yet been developed but that were expected to become available in due course; see Keith Vernon, 'Science and Technology' in S. Constantine, M. Kirby, and M. Rose (eds), *The First World War in British History* (London, Edward Arnold, 1995), pp. 81–105, at p. 88.

45 Edward M. Spiers, *Haldane: An Army Reformer* (Edinburgh University Press, 1980).

46 David French, 'The Rise and Fall of "Business as Usual"' in Burk, *War and the State*, pp. 7–31, at p. 24.

47 Adams, *Arms and the Wizard*, p. 43.

48 The National Health Insurance scheme, established by Lloyd George as Chancellor of the Exchequer in 1911, represented an earlier expression of this view. The scheme was almost entirely run and administered through private insurance agencies, controlled by central commissions made up of the various interests involved, rather than by government departments as such; Bentley B. Gilbert, *The Evolution of National Insurance in Great Britain: The Origins of the Welfare State* (London, Michael Joseph, 1966).

49 Peter K. Cline, 'Eric Geddes and the "Experiment" with Businessmen in Government' in K.D. Brown (ed.), *Essays in Anti-Labour History* (London, Macmillan, 1974), pp. 74–104.

50 Richard Gillespie, 'Industrial Fatigue and the Discipline of Physiology' in Gerald L. Geison (ed.), *Physiology in the American Context 1850–1940* (Bethesda, MD, American Physiological Society, 1987), pp. 237–62; A.J. McIvor, 'Manual Work, Technology, and Industrial Health, 1918–39', *Medical History*, 31 (1987), 160–89; Antonia Ineson and Deborah Thom, 'T.N.T. Poisoning and the Employment of Women Workers in the First World War' in Paul Weindling (ed.), *The Social History of Occupational Health* (London, Croom Helm, 1985), pp. 89–107.

51 Mikulás Teich, 'Science and Food During the Great War: Britain and Germany' in Harmke Kamminga and Andrew Cunningham (eds), *The Science and Culture of Nutrition, 1840–1940*

(Amsterdam, Rodopi, 1995), pp. 213–34; Margaret Barnett, *British Food Policy During the First World War* (London, Allen & Unwin, 1985).

52 Joel Howell, '"Soldier's Heart": The Redefinition of Heart Disease and Speciality Formation in Early Twentieth-Century Great Britain', this volume; and on shock, Sturdy, 'A Co-ordinated Whole', pp. 331–45.

53 Sturdy, 'A Co-ordinated Whole', pp. 318–45.

54 Roger Cooter and I have developed a related point in a discussion of the role of laboratory science in the advancement of an 'administrative way of knowing' in modern medical practice; 'Science, Scientific Management, and the Transformation of Medicine in Britain, *c.* 1870–1950', *History of Science*, in press. Our key concern there is to argue that the laboratory-based medical sciences, including physiology, were adopted primarily as a means of pursuing a logic of diagnostic categorization, but we also consider how they were implicated in the development of medical 'team work'.

55 A. Landsborough Thomson, *Half a Century of Medical Research*, vol. 1: *Origins and Policy of the Medical Research Council (UK)* (London, HMSO, 1973).

5

'SOLDIER'S HEART': THE REDEFINITION OF HEART DISEASE AND SPECIALITY FORMATION IN EARLY TWENTIETH-CENTURY GREAT BRITAIN

Joel D. Howell

Social historians have clearly demonstrated how 'non-medical' factors such as race, class and gender are instrumental in defining diseases. However, less attention has been paid to how changing concepts of disease have interacted with political, military and economic forces to shape medical specialities. In this paper, I shall discuss how the disorder called 'soldier's heart' was redefined by British physicians during and shortly after the First World War. Heart disease in soldiers had been known by several names, including DaCosta's syndrome (referring to a set of symptoms described during the American Civil War), irritable heart and DAH (disordered action of the heart).[1] I will not attempt to answer definitively the question, 'What was soldier's heart?'[2] Indeed, I seriously doubt that the question even has an answer.[3] Rather, I will use soldier's heart as a window through which to examine changing disease definitions, the structure of medical research, and the development of specialized medical societies in the early twentieth century. I will argue that because heart disease in soldiers was the third leading cause of discharge from the British Army in the First World War, it became the focus of attention for military physicians in special hospitals set up to attempt to solve the problem.[4] These physicians redefined the disease. The new disease, the effort syndrome, was more consistent both with acute wartime exigencies and with an ongoing transformation of the concept of heart disease from static and anatomical to dynamic and physiological. In the second part of this chapter, I shall describe how the effort syndrome acted as a nidus for development of the Cardiac Club and the beginning of cardiology in Great Britain.

NINETEENTH-CENTURY IDEAS ABOUT HEART DISEASE IN SOLDIERS

Although the problem of heart disease among soldiers in the British Army was reformulated in the early twentieth century, the issue itself had been evaluated earlier within the anatomical, mechanical framework of nineteenth-century British medicine. Heart disease had first attracted official attention when soldiers from all parts of the world were brought to the Royal Victoria Hospital, Netley, which opened in 1863.[5] In 1864, a government committee was appointed to study heart conditions in the Army.[6] It met yearly from 1864 to 1868 and concluded that the commonly used kit, which weighed, for heavy marching order, somewhat over 60 lb, restricted the heart's action and thus produced heart disease. Army Medical School professors agreed, issuing a report on the appropriate type of pack, stressing the necessity for avoiding 'all impediments to the fullest expansion of the lungs, and to the action of the heart' (and noting the superiority of the Prussian pack).[7] They held that unnecessary chest compression led to cardiac hypertrophy, with resulting dilatation and valvular derangement, and the eventual appearance of a characteristic 'soldier's spot' on the inevitable post-mortem examination.

In 1870, the issue of the cause of heart disease in soldiers remained important enough for the Alexander Memorial Fund to select for its first prize essay 'the aetiology and prevalence of diseases of the heart among soldiers as compared with the civil populations of those countries in which they are called upon to serve, and the means of prevention or mitigation – due regard being had to the conditions in which the soldier is unavoidably placed'. The prize went to Assistant-Surgeon Arthur Myers, who recommended a simple remedy: allow the men to open their jackets. In his prize-winning essay, he admonished commanding officers for wanting their men to look 'smart and set up' at the expense of their health.[8]

Two years later, Francis Moinet looked for a cause of cardiac disease other than the soldier's clothing and gear. Reasoning from the mechanical relationships of the heart and aorta, Moinet argued that excessive rifle drills obstructed cardiac outflow. He pointed out that this argument explained the observed preponderance of aortic valve lesions in soldiers.[9] Surgeon Arthur Davy agreed that obstruction was the primary cause of heart disease in soldiers, although he thought the obstruction was due to the 'setting-up drill', which produced a dilated chest and therefore abnormal action of the heart.[10] The Irish Surgeon-Major, William Riordan, also rejected uniforms as the problem. However, he linked the hypertrophy of the soldier's heart with its displacement during position drills, labourers being more accustomed to a different way of standing.[11] For Riordan, the chief 'affectation' was palpitation. Palpitation increased the power of the heart, and this in turn produced aneurism. He advised the Army not only to change drill habits but also to pay more attention to personal comforts for the recruit in order to make him happier in his new, military surroundings.

These nineteenth-century studies of heart disease in British soldiers all shared a similar conception, that the problem was primarily hypertrophy, valvular lesions and aortic dilatation – all mechanical lesions that admitted only a mechanical cause, usually some form of obstruction to the heart's outflow. The only question was the aetiology of that obstruction – either stylish uniforms, poorly designed drills, compression of the thoracic cage by drill, or altered work habits.

These formulations, based firmly on a mechanical understanding of the heart, shared two other implicit characteristics. First, they were of no value in identifying an affected individual so that he might be treated or cured. Hypertrophy, valvular disease and aortic aneurism were permanent conditions. Once the diagnosis was made, there was little to be done for the individual soldier. The authors of these studies could only advise the Army to alter its treatment of all soldiers in the hope that fewer men would become ill.

Although all of these experts considered the role of vices, primarily tobacco and spirits, as possible underlying causes, they concluded that the increased incidence of heart disease in soldiers required some other explanation. This led to the second assumption: that on the whole recruits were healthy, and that therefore the cause of the disease lay somewhere in the Army's treatment of these men. Early in the First World War, the idea that heart disease was due to a static mechanical defect caused by the Army's training methods was to be severely questioned.

EARLY WAR WORK

In 1908 James Mackenzie, who would eventually play a pivotal role in developing ideas about soldier's heart, included some comments about the disease in the first edition of his *Diseases of the Heart* in the section on 'increased frequency of the heart's action'.[12] The disease was found not only in soldiers, Mackenzie claimed, but also in 'workpeople subject to severe muscular exertion', and was associated with free use of alcohol and a tendency to obesity. Sir Clifford Allbutt, Regius Professor of Physic at Cambridge, also thought that 'muscular exertion' was the determining cause of soldier's heart.[13] Although he considered that exercise need not lead to cardiac disease, he warned the 'overfed and self-indulgent person' against suddenly attempting vigorous physical activity. Allbutt saw the prognosis for soldiers as bad; most remained in hospital until invalided out of the service.

By describing the disease in this fashion, both Allbutt and Mackenzie rejected nineteenth-century theories linking soldier's heart with causative factors found exclusively within the Army. Although their descriptions reflected a shift in attitudes about soldier's heart, neither paid any special attention to the disease until the First World War. When German troops marched into Belgium in the summer of 1914, there was already significant literature on diseases of the heart in soldiers. Not that this seemed a particularly urgent problem at first. 'Home by Christmas' was the cry. But as the war dragged on, devastating new entities like poison gas, machine-guns and barbed wire presented physicians with hitherto unknown medical concerns. Heart disease first attracted serious attention following the August 1914 retreat from Mons, which saw many soldiers sent back to England with chest pain, dyspnoea, palpitations on exertion and tachycardia.[14] Heart disease eventually became the third leading cause of discharge from the British Army during the war.[15] ('Chest complaints' comprised the second most common cause for discharge, about the same order of magnitude as 'heart disease'.) Although falling far below 'wounds and injuries' in terms of absolute numbers, patients with heart disease seemed to constitute a group with which far more could be accomplished, both before and after enlistment.

Thus the war acted to focus official attention on the problem of soldier's heart. Eventually, that attention was to be directed to the soldier sent back from the front. The first problem the Army faced was how to assess the physical condition of recruits. Nearly a million men signed up in the initial burst of patriotic fervour, and no serious attempt was made to assess their medical condition.[16] Trauma was difficult to predict, but it became clear that the examining medical officer needed to evaluate carefully the cardiac status of any potential soldier. In so doing, he faced a serious practical problem. He could not admit someone with a manifestly damaged heart that was bound to fail, but did murmurs and irregularity always indicate severe damage? This problem, the 'superstition that a heart to be normal must be free from murmurs and irregularity', as Mackenzie put it, prompted the first organized medical attention to heart disease in the Army.[17]

The autumn of 1915 saw James Mackenzie's first memorandum on soldier's heart, a brief guide both distributed by the War Office and published by the *British Medical Journal*.[18] Mackenzie saw as the primary issue the '*functional efficiency*' of the heart (italics in original). Murmurs and irregularities were important only if they diminished the functional efficiency. If they did not, and this was to be ascertained either by asking the candidate how much exertion he was accustomed to or by observing him undergoing exertion without distress, then the candidate's heart was sound and he was fit for duty. Nowhere in this memorandum did Mackenzie use the term 'valvular lesions'.

This shift of focus from precise, anatomical lesions of the heart to general assessment of its global function was quite consistent with the 'new cardiology' of the early twentieth century. As would be expected, those who objected to Mackenzie's approach based their arguments on the importance of murmurs as indicators of valvular lesions. They quite clearly saw the primary cause for rejection as the mechanical defect, the abnormal valve, rather than the 'functional efficiency' of the 'new cardiology'. In opposing the 'new teachings of the past twenty-five years', some chose merely to republish their earlier, 1890 teachings.[19] However, Mackenzie and other proponents of the 'new cardiology' both defined the increasingly accepted intellectual approach and, perhaps most important, quickly came to control the organized, governmental approach to the problem of soldier's heart.

The autumn of 1915 also brought a worsening military situation. The failure at Gallipoli was well under way, and in September the disastrous attack at Loos resulted in an additional 50,000 casualties with very little gained. It was becoming obvious that the front would probably remain static throughout the winter and that the war would be a long one. In November, casualties sent back to University College Hospital, London, complaining of chest pain, breathlessness, palpitations, exhaustion, and giddiness prompted Thomas Lewis and his colleagues to write an urgent letter to the *British Medical Journal*.[20] This letter raised a different problem from that mentioned in Mackenzie's memorandum on the evaluation of recruits. Lewis had studied a group of soldiers sent from the front with 'cardiac strain' or disordered heart action. These men complained of chest pain, breathlessness, palpitation and fatigue. On examination, there was usually evidence of vasomotor instability. After excluding those who seemed likely to have structural heart damage by virtue of a past history of rheumatic fever, chorea or syphilis, Lewis and his colleagues identified a group in which the symptoms appeared to be caused by toxins produced by staphylococcal or streptococcal infections. Theirs was not to be the first wartime speculation on the cause of such symptoms in soldiers.

The *British Medical Journal* published several letters on the topic over the next few months. Most observers agreed that few soldiers did have clear-cut valvular disease seriously impairing the heart's action, and for the others the primary cause of cardiac symptoms and signs did not lie in the heart itself. Early ideas about the aetiology of 'irritable heart' reflected the most exciting developments in clinical medicine over the past decade or so: the discovery of circulating hormones and establishment of the new field of endocrinology, and the rapid progress of microbiology in identifying bacteria and associating them with specific human diseases. Some suggested that hyperthyroidism was the cause of the disease. Infections were sought in several locations and were postulated as the cause through a variety of mechanisms. The infection did not need to be coincident with the onset of symptoms. It could precede them by months or years, or it could be a smouldering invasion by micro-organisms, such as tuberculosis bacilli, that had yet to become apparent.

However modern new ideas such as excessive glandular secretions or infectious toxins may have seemed, they were of little help in dealing with the acute problem posed by the war and soldier's heart. The older theories, revolving around improper drill and poorly designed uniforms, at least held out easy, obvious approaches to prevention and treatment. Remove the inciting cause; change the constricting uniform; stop the offending drill. The newer theories were more consistent with changes in medical thinking, such as the 'new cardiology', but they made both prevention and treatment seem more difficult. It was not so easy to cure infections or hyperthyroidism. X-rays were a possible treatment for the latter, but few actually thought that more than a very small percentage of the soldiers being returned were suffering from hyperthyroidism.[21] Treatment for infections was limited to 'increasing the general health of the body in such a way as to increase the natural resistance to infection'.[22] This was fairly non-specific therapy, and unlikely rapidly to replenish casualties from the front.

Early in 1916 Sir James Mackenzie opened a session of the Section of Therapeutics of the Royal Society of Medicine with a paper on 'The soldier's heart'.[23] In it, he discussed the examination of some 400 soldiers invalided with heart disease. Mackenzie thought that the cases were overwhelmingly non-cardiac, the most likely aetiology being the strain and exhaustion of life in the trenches superimposed on some 'toxic influence' caused by infection. He declined to speculate on treatment of bacterial invasion (other than to suggest the possibility of vaccine therapy), but focused on uplifting the soldier's generally depressed mental and physical state through exercise. For officers in his private practice, Mackenzie advised 'fishing, riding, shooting, golf' (the last a particular personal favourite of Mackenzie's), and he urged the same kind of 'congenial exercise' for lower ranks. Lest his motives be misunderstood, he emphasized the need for 'not only the pleasure of the sideman, but so that the soldier may speedily regain his health and return the sooner to his duties'.

RESEARCH AT HAMPSTEAD AND COLCHESTER

Swift return to duties was the goal for most wartime agencies involved with invalided soldiers. With this priority, it is hardly surprising that the structure necessary to implement Mackenzie's suggestions was not long in coming. Once established, the wards, hospitals and groups started for one specific purpose developed a momentum and motivation of their own. Shortly after the onset of the First World War the War Office had set aside a few beds in the military wards at University College Hospital for research on soldier's heart.[24] In the winter of 1914/15, the energetic young London physician, Captain Thomas Lewis, took charge of these beds. Lewis's appointment probably was in large part due to the efforts of Mackenzie, his close friend and professional colleague. Mackenzie's earlier work with the polygraph had done more than make him a prominent figure in British medicine, one who could influence the War Department to establish a new hospital as well as to run it. He had also helped to popularize the use of graphic records, such as the polygraph, and the electrocardiogram (ECG), in the study of heart diseases. By so doing, he enabled Thomas Lewis, whose credentials lay primarily in the mastery of these instrumental methods, to be placed in charge of soldier's heart research. In February 1916 Lewis was appointed to the permanent scientific staff of the Medical Research Committee (MRC) to pursue clinical research.[25]

Although Lewis had been studying the heart since around 1906, lack of financial support for research obliged him to continue to see private patients. He received the first Beit Memorial Fellowship for Medical Research in 1910, and in 1911 was named honorary officer in charge of the Cardiographic Department at University College Hospital.[26] The honour of the title should not obscure the fact that Lewis still needed personal funds to purchase instruments, which he used in a basement broom-closet. While Mackenzie had a reputation as a master clinician, Lewis owed what medical standing he could claim to his work with the ECG. The ECG at first appeared to be a promising tool, and the MRC, which supported Lewis's work on soldier's heart from the beginning of the war, noted in its first annual report that cardiographic apparatus would be made available for the study of soldier's heart. But despite its early appeal, the ECG was to play no significant role in research on or treatment of heart disease in soldiers.

In 1915, Mackenzie had suggested to the War Office that a special hospital be established for treatment of patients with soldier's heart.[27] Near the end of that year, the War Office implemented this idea and transferred Lewis's work on soldier's heart from University College Hospital in London to Mount Vernon Hospital in Hampstead. The Hampstead hospital was directed by a distinguished advisory committee consisting of Sir Clifford Allbutt, Sir William Osler and Sir James Mackenzie. In September 1916, the War Office decided to have heart cases sent directly to Hampstead from France, not indirectly through other hospitals in Great Britain. By 1917, increased numbers of cases forced a move to larger facilities at Colchester.

Although one goal of the War Office was the rapid diagnosis and discharge of soldiers with serious heart disease, Mackenzie's work made them hope that this group of soldiers would constitute a relatively small proportion of those sent to the hospital. The hospital was intended instead for the larger group, those with 'true irritable heart'. The MRC and the War Office hoped that by bringing together a large number of these cases 'many (more) might be returned to duty more rapidly by treatment with suitable and graduated exercises, than when remaining as independent cases scattered through military and convalescent hospitals; and it was expected at the same time that the cases found not amenable to treatment should, without prolonged delay, either be sent to appropriate light duty or be permanently invalided'.[28]

By 1916, it was clear to the British government that the war was going to last a good deal longer than the few months anticipated at its onset. The increasing need for manpower led to conscription, an unprecedented and unpopular decision in a country which had previously seen little governmental influence on daily life.[29] Such a drastic move made the need for accurate medical evaluation seem all the more important. The diagnosis and treatment of soldiers with cardiac complaints was still in turmoil, and many military physicians had little patience with soldiers suffering from poorly defined complaints of any type.[30]

The goal of the staff at Hampstead was the swift differentiation of those soldiers who could be sent back to the front from those who should be quickly discharged. In pursuit of this aim, the hospital received not only an ample supply of soldiers with suspected heart disease but also generous resources and whatever technical and professional personnel were required. Establishment of this hospital also played a key role in furthering the career of Thomas Lewis, who, in turn, was to be a premier figure in the maturation of the postwar Medical Research Committee (called the Medical Research Council after 1920).

In February 1917, the MRC published an early summary by Lewis of its research findings.[31] This report was based on study of about 1,000 soldiers diagnosed as having soldier's heart. The crucial feature of this report is that the symptoms and signs that might once have been interpreted as pointing to structural change and *ipso facto* have been sufficient for an invalidity ticket, were now assessed in terms of the heart's total functional capacity. Primary symptoms of this disorder included breathlessness, pain, exhaustion, giddiness and fainting – a constellation of symptoms that were merely 'exaggerated manifestations of healthy responses to the effort'.[32] The MRC report therefore advocated the diagnostic term 'effort syndrome' for most of these cases. The report described evaluation by graded exercises, with the emphasis placed on establishing prognosis, not diagnosis, and one simple objective: rapid return to duty when possible, rapid discharge when the disease was too severe. The financial importance of the latter is obvious when one considers that soldiers invalided with heart disease spent an '*average period of nearly five and a half months in hospitals*'.[33] Graded exercises did more than merely serve a diagnostic function, they were therapeutic as well. By gradually increasing the intensity of the effort, and by rewarding a soldier's successful performance at each increment of exertion, 50 per cent of soldiers with effort syndrome could be returned to duty after an average stay of only 1.5 months in the Hampstead Hospital.[34]

Four observations can be made about this research on soldier's heart. Firstly, as intimated above, the economic implications of reclassification were never far from the top on a list of justifications for such research. The dramatic reduction in hospital stay, from an average of 5.5 months to an average of 1.5 months, saved approximately £50,000 a year, almost as much as the entire MRC budget.[35] Moreover, as will be discussed in greater detail below, the government anticipated early in the war the profound impact any method for establishing the level of disability would have on pensions assessment, and studies of soldier's heart explicitly reflected this need.[36]

Secondly, despite the early appeal of graphic methods to many who worked at the military hospitals, neither the polygraph nor the ECG was found to be valuable in sorting out soldiers with possible heart disease. Lewis thought his own ECG was of 'little or no value'.[37] This conclusion came despite the close connection many of those involved had enjoyed with medical instruments: Allbutt had introduced routine use of the thermometer and the opthalmoscope; Mackenzie had reached prominence in large part through his work with the polygraph; similarly Thomas Lewis and the ECG. For Lewis, the message was particularly clear. By 1914, he had attracted slight attention and very little financial support for ECG research; by the end of the war he was credited with saving vast sums of money, and, perhaps more important, he was in the full-time employ of the MRC to pursue his research. Thomas Lewis was knighted in 1921, not for his basic research on the ECG, but for his work during the war on the effort syndrome. If the clinical approach to breathless soldiers was to be easily incorporated into the contemporary medical system, it needed an easily appreciable, non-instrumental basis.

The third generalization about the entity, the effort syndrome, is that such a concept fits easily into the 'new cardiology' of the day. Physicians at Hampstead and Colchester directed attention away from local, particular valvular defects, de-emphasized the importance of murmurs and the stethoscope, and emphasized the global working ability of the heart. Whatever the cause (and infection of one sort or another was the most commonly proposed aetiology), the important final common pathway was failure of cardiac reserve.[38] While anatomical lesions could contribute to weakening of the heart, the actual state of the cardiac muscle could be ascertained only by observing the response to effort. The effort system therefore accurately reflected the physiological emphasis on cardiac function.

Finally, the research carried on at Hampstead and reported by the MRC falls naturally into two general categories. Firstly, there were empirical, clinical observations. These included studies on the response to carefully defined exercises, recommendations on the proper terminology (emphasizing the value of *not* using terms referring to heart disease), and speculating on the presence of malingerers, the effects of differences in class and occupation, and other practical points directly related to the wartime need to get soldiers either back to the front or out of the service. However, the hospital was to do far more than its supporters originally intended. It was to use the soldier's heart as a setting in which to apply all manner of physiological testing, and to serve as a first step in organized, centralized governmental support of medical research. Intermingled with practical observations was a second, more physiological group of studies. These used patients with soldier's heart to study such topics as buffer salts and their relationship to breathlessness, the effects of pilocarpine on sweating, the effects of atropine, adrenalin and apocodeine, and detailed studies of urinary composition. Here, investigators made little effort to relate the results of their studies to practical problems. It would appear that they were using the availability of funds and clinical resources to pursue basic research, with little effort made to link clinical findings with pharmacological or physiological ones. Out of wartime necessities came one of the first instances of organized support of basic science by the British government.

Two other diagnostic terms came into being during the war. One was 'shell-shock'.[39] Initially thought secondary to small cerebral haemorrhages, shell-shock was, by the end of the war, ascribed to psychological causes. Soldier's heart and shell-shock shared a number of medical and organizational features: both were marked by breathlessness and nervous instability, were less common in men previously accustomed to active, outdoor work, and regularly called into question the possibility of malingering. Both also led to the creation of special boards and special hospitals for study, and created postwar problems for the Ministry of Pensions. It is striking how frequently soldier's heart is discussed by those writing about shell-shock and how infrequently the reverse is true. The explanation may lie in the somewhat lower status accorded to psychological theories of disease than physiological or anatomical heart disease. Perhaps as a result, shell-shock was often equated with malingering or cowardice, and the remedy was too often the firing squad. While malingering was often an issue with soldier's heart too, these patients seem not to have faced capital punishment.

The same set of symptoms that was renamed the 'effort syndrome' in Great Britain was called 'neurocirculatory asthenia' in the United States.[40] A group of American physicians were sent to Colchester to make recommendations to the Surgeon-General about heart disease in the armed forces. They worked in the same military camps and at times saw exactly the same soldiers as their British counterparts who described these soldiers as having 'effort syndrome'. The entity 'neurocirculatory asthenia' occurred in American soldiers during mobilization in the USA, while the British soldiers usually became ill only after the stress of battle. Rather than advocating graded exercise and eventual return to duties, as was advised by the British, American soldiers with neurocirculatory asthenia were treated with rest and discharged to civilian life.[41] That the Americans chose to create a different disease with a different aetiology and therapy from the same set of symptoms supports the importance of social settings, military needs and national styles in the construction of systems of disease.

MINISTRY OF PENSIONS

Military, economic and political exigencies forced the MRC and the War Office to construct a wartime system of hospitals and physicians in order to deal with soldier's heart. Although this system was no less necessary after the cessation of hostilities, its function changed from concern with rapid assessment and return of soldiers to concern with postwar economic drain from thousands of pensioned soldiers. The Ministry of Pensions had been formed in December 1916; in February 1917 it took over the administration of disability pensions from the Admiralty.[42] Long before the war actually ended, British physicians and politicians appreciated the need for accurate assessment of disability and feared the impending financial pressure of soldiers' pensions.[43] Soldier's heart commanded attention as the third most common reason for disability, and the natural site for that attention was the Colchester Hospital.

By the war's end, Lewis was the obvious choice to guide the evaluation of soldiers pensioned with heart disease. He was named honorary consulting physician in cardiovascular disease to the Ministry of Pensions, and instituted 'intensive courses of instruction in pathology, diagnosis, treatment and prognosis for pension purposes' to train deputy commissioners for the ministry.[44] Some 150 deputy commissioners were trained in these courses, and after the armistice the War Office continued to send RAMC officers to Colchester. In addition to training examiners, until the spring of 1919, Colchester also functioned as a dispersal hospital for heart cases. Boards of discharge and dispersal sat assessing 'cardiovascular' cases for pension purposes almost constantly around the end of the war, in one period of intensive work evaluating some 150 cases per week.[45]

Britain's financial situation was precarious after the unexpectedly long war, and it rapidly worsened. Following the end of the war, the Ministry of Pensions expanded rapidly. By 1920–1, it employed a staff of approximately 18,000 and controlled a budget of £106 million, more than any other department of State.[46] By then, the national debt had risen to fourteen times the pre-war level and public expenditure had doubled, to 30 per cent of the national income.[47] With the slump of 1921, the search for economy reached 'panic proportions'.[48] Outside observers of the British pension system noted the very heavy financial burdens it placed on the country.[49]

Once again, attention was focused on soldiers with heart disease. However, rather than occupying hospital beds in wartime, these soldiers were receiving pensions for their disease. None the less, a soldier with heart disease had more chance of significant recovery than one of the many who had suffered penetrating wounds, or had required amputation of an arm or a leg. By the time all of the ex-soldiers had been assessed, over 1.3 million men were receiving pensions. Of these, about 9 per cent, or somewhat over 100,000, carried a diagnosis of heart disease. (The percentage diagnosed with 'heart disease' remained roughly constant from 1919 to 1928.) But, by the end of the war, the definition of heart disease had changed. Neither the constellation of symptoms that made up soldier's heart nor the presence of cardiac murmur alone was any longer sufficient evidence for disability (though to some practitioners not yet acquainted with the work at Colchester a murmur alone might still be considered sufficient evidence to label someone an invalid). The new diagnosis of cardiac incapacity was to be based solely on the observed response to effort. With these 'new methods of diagnosis and treatment', large numbers of soldiers were able to return to work and, presumably, would no longer require pensions.[50]

Who was to make the decisions regarding pensions? Paradoxically, despite nearly universal agreement by 1918 that the effort syndrome – whatever it was – was not primarily a disease of the heart, and despite the same unanimity that the word 'heart' itself should be studiously avoided in reference or even in proximity to the individuals in question, for fear of unduly alarming them and thereby impending recovery, it was to 'specialists in diseases of the heart' that the Ministry of Pensions turned for assistance in evaluating soldiers claiming to be victims of the disease. And it was to be this group of physicians who later formed the nidus for the development of British cardiology.

Lewis, honorary consulting physician in diseases of the heart to the Ministry, supervised the formation of a unified, rationalized and financially advantageous system for dealing with heart cases:

> Dr. Lewis's services have been made available at the request of the Ministry of Pensions for work in reorganizing the assessment of cases of cardiovascular disability. During the early part of 1919, he worked with the Resurvey Boards of the London region, and gave instruction to these boards by means of weekly lectures and demonstrations . . . on his appointment as Honorary Consulting Physician in diseases of the heart to the Ministry, he recommended that cardiac specialists should be appointed to carry on the instructional and assessment work at the Resurvey Boards under his supervision, and that all heart cases should be seen by the General Boards in special sessions. An outpatient clinic has been inaugurated at University College Hospital for reports upon and treatment of heart cases specially selected by officers of the Resurvey Boards. Recently, on his recommendation, beds have been set aside at the Ministry's hospital at Orpington as a convalescent unit for cardiovascular cases . . . The assessment and care of pensioners of the cardiovascular class in the London region has thus been organized in such a way that the assessments have been revised and brought to a uniform scale by officers specially trained for the purpose: facilities for special reports and special or convalescent treatment have also been arranged, and the various departments are now in full working order. A feature of the scheme is that all the departments, the Resurvey Boards, the special Cardiac Clinic and the convalescent unit are closely in touch with one another . . .
>
> It has been estimated that the annual saving upon cardiovascular assessments in the London region alone already amounts approximately to £46,000, and it is understood that the Ministry, acting upon Dr. Lewis's recommendations, have now appointed honorary consultants in diseases of the heart to supervise the work similarly in other regions of the country.[51]

This 1919–20 MRC report thus proposed an institutional apparatus much like that we have come to associate with a medical speciality: a group of physicians with special training in 'diseases of the heart', separate facilities, outpatient as well as inpatient, where patients with heart disease would be seen, close communication between all parts of the system, and a financial rationale for this systematic care of patients with heart disease.

The classic study for modern development of a medical speciality is George Rosen's work on opthalmology. The MRC system for dealing with heart disease describes three of the requirements Rosen postulated as necessary for specialty development: large groups of patients with specific diseases, specialized hospitals, and the financial resources to support a new group of specialists.[52] These three conditions held for at least the duration of war and the period immediately following the armistice. The fourth basis for speciality formation in Rosen's model, improved technology, appears, surprisingly, to have played little part in Lewis's plan. Despite his earlier advocacy for the ECG, the effort syndrome was diagnosed and treated by simple, non-technological open-air exercises. Certainly, some of the researchers at Hampstead and Colchester had used other technology, to measure blood pressure with the sphygmograph, heart size with the X-ray orthodiagram, the white blood cell count, the blood carbon dioxide. But these observations were not considered germane to the management of patients with the effort syndrome. They were interesting physiological observations, but not necessary for physicians taking care of patients. Machines belonged in laboratories; physicians, it was thought, should rely on their unaided senses.[53]

THE CARDIAC CLUB

Just as military needs brought together physicians in hospitals to work on soldier's heart during the First World War, economic pressures led the Ministry of Pensions to gather together British physicians interested in the heart. This group, the Cardiac Club, formed to address specific and (as we shall see) transient postwar problems, persisted long after the rationale for its formation was gone. It eventually became the leading British cardiology group, the Cardiac Society, and as such warrants attention as a case study in early twentieth-century speciality formation.

The honorary consultants Lewis proposed to aid regional directors in assessing cardiac cases were appointed in April 1920.[54] In 1921 they met for the first time in London, primarily to discuss technical and administrative matters pertaining to the Ministry of Pensions. However, more general matters were considered as well; the group felt that the discussion had been of value 'to themselves and perhaps to cardiac science' and that they should meet again under different auspices.[55] The first organizational meeting of the Cardiac Club was held at Oxford a year later, on 22 April 1922, and the first annual meeting was held at University College London, on 22 November 1922, with Sir Thomas Lewis in the chair. Until transformation into the Cardiac Society in 1937, the Cardiac Club met yearly on the day prior to the meeting of the Association of Physicians of Great Britain and Ireland.

Although they were, by the end of the war, the two physicians most associated with heart disease in Great Britain, neither Lewis nor Mackenzie played an active role in the Cardiac Club. In 1922, after organizing a group of cardiac consultants, Lewis declared 'the cream is off the top' and left cardiac research.[56] He never presented a paper at the Cardiac Club and did no further work for the Ministry of Pensions. When the new Cardiac Society founded the *British Heart Journal* in 1939, Lewis was asked to write the introduction to the first volume. He did so, but clearly from the perspective of an outsider.[57] Two years earlier, he had changed the title of his own journal from *Heart* to *Clinical Science*, a change in name that reflected a shift in the content of the journal.[58] Although he played a seminal role in the formation of the Cardiac Club, Lewis chose not to be a part of it. Why not?

Lewis perceived clinical research in a very different way from most Cardiac Club members. After early difficulty in obtaining support for research, since 1916 Lewis had been employed full time by the MRC. In the 1919–20 MRC annual report, the section on experimental medicine had been separated from the section on cardiovascular diseases. By 1922 he was director of the newly established clinical units at University College Hospital. Having cast in his lot with the MRC, Lewis was no doubt attuned to the wishes of his supporters within that organization. And it is clear that one of their priorities was practical results, findings that could be applied at the bedside by the average practitioner. A 1926–7 summary of Lewis's research praises his early work on the ECG and on soldier's heart, but then goes on to say: 'The work with disorders of the heart, an organ lying deep within the body, compelled the use of complex instruments and methods of great refinement, though happily it was found possible to translate almost all the discoveries so made into simple methods of observation for use at the bed-side.'[59] The most valuable experiments were those done on patients using simple equipment; the most worthwhile findings were those that could be applied at the bedside. Lewis turned his career to clinical research, leaving behind the heart and the ECG.

James Mackenzie, the only honorary member of the Cardiac Club, was a symbol of the club to many members. Some suggested that the Cardiac Club had been 'conceived in Burnley', Mackenzie's Lancashire home until 1907.[60] However, Mackenzie vigorously opposed the concept of a cardiac specialist. The same National Insurance Act that provided funds for Lewis through the MRC had also established the general practitioner in the centre of the health care system.[61] Mackenzie advocated a return to general practice and thought research by the general practitioner in 'places remote from hospitals and laboratories' was medicine's only hope for advancement.[62] He advised Lewis to take a post as a general practitioner in 1917 (Lewis did not); an American visitor wishing advice from the world-renowned heart specialist was surprised by Mackenzie's suggestion that his visitor should train for research by entering general practice for ten years.[63]

Mackenzie, 'the patron saint of the general practitioner', thought specialization was an affront to the essential unity of medicine,[64] calling it 'almost always a hindrance to progress. This is especially true in medicine. Moreover, a specialist is, by the nature of his calling, a man with a limited experience, and therefore he can have but a limited outlook.' Of men 'devoting themselves entirely to the study of affectations of the heart', Mackenzie thought that while this might appeal to the general public, it showed a 'complete misconception of the principles of medical practice'.[65] He thought no more highly of those who regarded laboratory devices, such as the ECG or his own polygraph, as the highest ideal. That conception was 'superficial and rudimentary'. He wrote to Lewis: 'If medicine is to make any progress at all, the symptoms of disease must be detected by the unaided senses.'[66]

In 1918, Mackenzie left London to found the St Andrews Institute for Clinical Research, based on his concept of research by general practitioners, in St Andrews, Scotland. In his later writings, Mackenzie attempted to define yet another 'new cardiology', one founded on early detection of disease and the principle of the reflex arc.[67] Neither this new line of research nor the St Andrews Institute long survived his death.[68]

But the Cardiac Club did survive. Moreover, it prospered; by 1935 no member had resigned and all were present for the annual meeting. Eventually, the club became the first British speciality group devoted to diseases of the heart. This seems quite remarkable. Firstly, the disease the club was formed to evaluate, soldier's heart, was widely believed to be non-cardiac even before the group was formed. Secondly, the problem that resulted in the group's formation, the financial crisis at the Ministry of Pensions, rapidly abated. From expenditures of £106,645,000 in 1921, expenses dropped to £81,500,000 in 1923 and £63,450,000 in 1927.[69] The club could not survive centred on a cardiac problem of soldier's heart.

Who were these physicians who gathered in 1922 to form the Cardiac Club? I have sketched their careers elsewhere.[70] Many had expressed a particular interest in heart disease even before the First World War.[71] Most were in their forties, many had early experience in pathology or anatomy, and many went on to hold chairs in their home institutions.

What was the source of cohesion for the Cardiac Club? If this was indeed an early speciality group, one might expect to see some common themes in their interests, perhaps in research, or some new technology, as Rosen suggested for the opthalmoscope. One can make three observations about the publications of Cardiac Club members. (I am excluding Lewis and Mackenzie from these generalizations.) Firstly, these were few. The entire production of John Cowan, the most prolific, was only 31 articles; by comparison, Lewis wrote over 250 articles and Mackenzie over 120. Secondly, they included almost no papers on animal research or experimental medicine, such as the research carried out at Hampstead and Colchester, or in Lewis's laboratories after the war.[72] Rather, Cardiac Club members mainly published an occasional case report. The third observation is that the articles covered a wide range of topics. Papers on the heart may be found, to be sure, and Thomas Wardrop Griffith published almost exclusively on cardiac diseases. However, for the rest, case reports on cardiac topics alternate with 'The treatment of acute lobar pneumonia' or 'Syphilis of the lungs'.[73]

On two occasions discussions at the yearly meeting of the Cardiac Club led to publication. Following Hay's discussion of the action of quinidine on heart disease in 1923 and Gibson's on anaemic necrosis of the heart in 1925, the members shared cases which were then published collectively in the *Lancet*.[74] These two efforts were clearly on cardiac topics. However, other than these case series, the members did not collaborate in investigations, and there is no evidence to suggest that shared research contributed to the survival of the club.

Nor was the primary source of cohesion an instrumental technology. One might think the ECG would have been ideal for that purpose. It was a new technology used to study an accepted cardiac problem, the irregular pulse. Furthermore, the ECG was supplemented by a theory that provided scientific legitimation for its use. But, while Cardiac Club members were frequently instrumental in bringing the polygraph and ECG to their own institutions, they based neither the club nor their own professional careers on such technology. Several members supervised cardiographic departments; none called himself a 'cardiologist'. ('Cardiographic' in the 1920s referred to graphic methods of analysing the heartbeat – the polygraph or ECG.) Over the fourteen years of its existence, the Cardiac Club heard thirty-four presentations. Of these, only five dealt with topics amenable to instrumental diagnosis, and only two of these presentations were made in the first ten years.

At their annual meetings, as in their publications, the members of the Cardiac Club addressed a wide range of topics. There was no central theme. Of the thirty-four topics discussed, there were five which dealt with instrumental methods, six on infectious diseases, six on the effect of drugs on the heart (including tobacco and alcohol), and sixteen (including the six on infectious diseases) on a heterogeneous group of conditions, such as the heart in pregnancy or in pneumonia.[75]

The Cardiac Club eventually became a true speciality group, the Cardiac Society. But, if the club had no unity of research, technology or practice, was the Cardiac Club itself a speciality group? Perhaps there was no hidden professional focus for the club. The members probably constituted a social group who enjoyed a yearly meeting in which the shared professional discussion was only a minor component. Three retrospective accounts of the club mention that 'friendship' was an especially important feature of the group.[76] While this may be only rhetoric, the fact that all three articles emphasize this point is suggestive.[77]

Soldier's heart may have been the catalyst that brought the Cardiac Club into being, but it was not the glue that held it together. If friendship was indeed the primary reason for the survival of the club, then this case study demonstrates how a group of physicians bound by social ties can act as the nucleus for later speciality formation. The case study also demonstrates how what was a minor clinical problem in the nineteenth century, heart disease in soldiers, became the focus of attention during the First World War, and how the disease of soldier's heart was redefined in military hospitals during the war.

For the British government, the redefinition of heart disease in soldiers was 'successful', meaning that it was consistent with national needs during the First World War, both economically – by reducing the number of days spent in the hospital; and politically – by increasing the number of soldiers already in the Army who could return to the front. During the redefinition of 'soldier's heart' as the 'effort syndrome', the aetiology was moved from factors controlled by the Army (uniforms and drills) to underlying weakness within the individual (occult infection). At the same time, the Hampstead and Colchester hospitals represented the beginnings of government support of basic scientific research.

The effort syndrome reappeared in the Second World War, but that is another story. From the late nineteenth century until the end of the 1920s, heart disease in soldiers serves as a window through which to view a changing medical world, a medical world that ultimately must include war, pensions and the yearly gathering of men who would, eventually, become cardiologists.

ACKNOWLEDGEMENTS

An earlier version of this essay was published in *Medical History*, supplement no. 5, 1985 (copyright The Trustees, The Wellcome Trust, reproduced with permission). The references have not been updated. I would like to thank Mary Fissell, Barbara Gastel, Janet Golden, Christopher Lawrence and Rosemary Stevens for their comments, and Alison Kraft for retyping the manuscript to disc. The research was supported in part by the Robert Wood Johnson Clinical Scholars Program.

Notes

1 Or a variety of other names. I will attempt to use the names appropriate for each period being discussed, but do not mean to imply that one or the other is 'correct'.

2 For an interesting perspective, see Charles F. Wooley, 'Where are the diseases of yesteryear? DaCosta's syndrome, soldier's heart, the effort syndrome, neurocirculatory asthenia and the mitral valve prolapse syndrome', *Circulation*, 53 (1976), 749–51; and 'From irritable heart to mitral valve prolapse: the Osler connection', *Amer. J. Cardiology*, 53 (1984), 870–4. Thomas N. James links soldier's heart and mitral valve prolapse through dysautonomia in 'Sir Thomas Lewis redivivus: from pebbles in a quiet pond to autonomic storms', *Br. Heart J.*, 52 (1984), 1–23.

3 John Gabbay provides an excellent synopsis of the problems inherent in attacking such a problem in his 'Asthma attacked? Tactics for the reconstruction of a disease concept' in Peter Wright

and Andrew Treacher (eds), *The Problem of Medical Knowledge: Examining the Social Construction of Medicine* (Edinburgh University Press, 1982), pp. 23–48.

4 Thomas Lewis, *The Soldier's Heart and the Effort Syndrome* (London, Shaw, 1918), p. 1.

5 W.C. MacClean, 'Diseases of the Heart in the British Army: The Cause and the Remedy', *British Medical Journal (BMJ)*, 1 (1867), 161–4.

6 R. MacNair Wilson, 'The Irritable Heart of Soldiers', *BMJ*, 1 (1916), 119–20.

7 MacClean, 'Diseases of the Heart'.

8 Arthur B.R. Myers, *On the Etiology and Prevalence of Diseases of the Heart Among Soldiers* (London, Churchill, 1870).

9 Francis W. Moinet, *A Treatise on the Causes of Heart Disease with a Chapter on the Reason of Its Prevalence in the Army* (Edinburgh, Bell & Bradfote, 1872), summarized in 'A Cause of Heart Disease in the Army', *Edinburgh Medical Journal*, 17 (1871), 505–11.

10 F. Arthur Davy, 'A Contribution to the Etiology of Heart Disease' in *Army Medical Department Report for the Year 1876*, vol. 18 (London, HMSO, 1877).

11 William E. Riordan, *The Causes of the Origin of Heart Disease and Aneurism in the Army* (Dublin, Fannin, 1878).

12 J.S. Mackenzie, *Diseases of the Heart* (Oxford University Press, 1908), p. 126. For biographies of James Mackenzie, see R. MacNair Wilson, *The Beloved Physician* (New York, Macmillan, 1926); Alex Mair, *Sir James Mackenzie, M.D. 1853–1925: General Practitioner* (Edinburgh and London, Churchill Livingstone, 1973).

13 T. Clifford Allbutt, 'Soldier's Heart' in Thomas Clifford Allbutt (ed.), *A System of Medicine by Many Writers* (London, Macmillan, 1905), vol. 5, pp. 851–5.

14 John Hay, 'Cardio-vascular Disorders' in W.G. MacPherson, W.P. Herringham, T.R. Elliot and A. Balfour (eds), *History of the Great War*, vol. 1: *Medical Services. Diseases of the War* (London, HMSO, 1923).

15 Lewis, *Soldier's Heart*.

16 Anthony Babington, *For the Sake of Example, Capital Courts-martial, 1914–1920* (New York, St Martin's Press, 1983), pp. 8, 204; A.J.P. Taylor, *English History 1914–1945* (New York, Oxford University Press, 1965), p. 20.

17 James Mackenzie, 'The Recruit's Heart', *BMJ*, 2 (1915), 807–8.

18 Ibid., pp. 563-4, also distributed as a separate sheet, 1693 (Army Medical Department 2).

19 James Kingston Fowler, 'Auscultation of the Heart of the Recruit', *BMJ*, 2 (1915), 744–5. For the debate over murmurs, the new cardiology, and the recruit's heart, see also Alexander Morison, 'The Recruit's Heart', *BMJ*, 2 (1915), 636–7; W. Gordon, 'Murmurs in the Recruit's Heart', *BMJ*, 1 (1916), 433–4; and Mackenzie, 'Recruit's Heart'.

20 Thomas Lewis, Thomas Cotton and F.H. Thiele, 'A Note on the "Irritable Heart" of Soldiers', *BMJ*, 2 (1915), 722.

21 There was a notable absence of support for James Barr's vitriolic writing on hyperthyroidism as the obvious cause for soldier's heart.

22 'The Soldier's Heart', *BMJ*, 1 (1916), 137.

23 Sir James Mackenzie, 'The Soldier's Heart', *BMJ*, 1 (1917), 117–19.

24 *Medical Research Committee Annual Report (MRCAR)*, *1914–1915*, 1, 44. There is no full-scale

biography of Thomas Lewis. The most complete obituary is in A.N. Drury and R.T. Grant, 'Thomas Lewis', *Obituary Notices of the Fellows of the Royal Society*, 8 (1945), 179–202. See also, Arthur Hollman, 'Thomas Lewis – The Early Years', *Br. Heart J.*, 46 (1981), 233–44.

25 *MRCAR*, 2 (1915–16), 17.

26 Drury and Grant, 'Thomas Lewis'.

27 Sir James Mackenzie to John Parkinson (3 December 1915), in Mair, *Sir James Mackenzie*, p. 63; W.R. Merrington, *University College Hospital and Its Medical School: A History* (London, Heinemann, 1976), p. 193.

28 *MRCAR*, 2 (1915–16), 58.

29 Although of tremendous symbolic importance, the draft actually failed to provide more men for the Army. Taylor, *English History*, p. 55.

30 Babington, *Sake of Example*, p. 60.

31 'Report Upon Soldiers Returned Cases of "Disordered Action of the Heart" (D.A.H.) or "Valvular Diseases of the Heart" (V.D.H.)', MRC *Special Report Series*, No. 8, 1917. No author listed, but Thomas Lewis cited as author in *MRCAR*, 3 (1916–17), 77.

32 MRC *Special Report*, No. 8, p. 7.

33 Ibid., p. 14, italics in original.

34 Ibid., p. 13.

35 *MRCAR*, 4 (1917–18), 53.

36 *MRCAR*, 3 (1916–17), 75.

37 Ibid., p. 38.

38 For a lucid description of the concept of failure of cardiac reserve see Lewis, *Soldier's Heart*, pp. 37–40, esp. fig. p. 39.

39 *Report of the War Office Committee of Enquiry into 'Shell Shock'* (London, HMSO, 1922); Martin Stone, 'Shell shock and the Psychologists' in W.F. Bynum, Roy Porter and Michael Shepherd (eds), *The Anatomy of Madness: Essays in the History of Psychiatry*, vol. 2: *Institutions and Society* (London, Tavistock, 1985).

40 Samuel A. Levine, 'The Origin of the Term Neurocirculatory Asthenia', *New Engl. J. Med.*, 273 (1965), 604–5; Harlow Brooks, 'Neurocirculatory Asthenia' in *The Medical Department of the United States Army in the World War*, vol. 9: *Communicable and Other Diseases*, prepared under the direction of M.W. Ireland by Joseph F. Siler (Washington, DC, US Government Printing Office, 1928), pp. 559–86.

41 Ibid., pp. 565, 582–4.

42 D.N. Chester, *The Organization of British Central Government 1914–1964* (London, Rosken House, 1968), p. 152.

43 *MRCAR*, 3 (1916–17), 75.

44 *MRCAR*, 5 (1918–19), 58.

45 Ibid., p. 57.

46 Sir John A.R. Marriott, *The Mechanism of the Modern State. A Treatise on the Science and Art of Government* (London, Oxford University Press, 1927), vol. 2, pp. 189, 193; 'Parlimentary Intelligence', *Lancet*, 2 (1922), 1255.

47 William Ashworth, *An Economic History of England 1870–1939* (London, Methuen, 1960), p. 389.

48 Ibid.

49 'Compensation for War Disabilities in Great Britain and the United States', International Labor Office, Geneva, *Studies And Reports*: series E, No. 4, 1921.

50 'Work of the Pensions Ministry', *BMJ*, 1 (1922), 68.

51 *MRCAR*, 6 (1919–20), 30–1.

52 George Rosen, *The Specialization of Medicine with Particular Reference to Opthalmology* (1944, repr. New York, Arno Press, 1972), pp. 28, 29.

53 For further discussion of British attitudes towards the ECG see Joel D. Howell, 'Early Perceptions of the Electrocardiogram: from Arrhythmia to Infarction', *Bulletin of the History of Medicine*, 58 (1984), 83–98.

54 John Cowan et al., 'Some Notes on the Cardiac Club', *Br. Heart J.*, 1 (1939), 97–103; Maurice Campbell, 'The British Cardiac Society and the Cardiac Club: 1922–1961', ibid., 24 (1962), 673–95.

55 Cowan, 'Some Notes', p. 98.

56 G.E. Pickering, 'In Memoriam, Thomas Lewis', *Clinical Science*, 6 (1948), 3–11.

57 Thomas Lewis, 'Foreword', *Br. Heart J.*, 1 (1939), 1–2.

58 The last volume of *Heart* contains the final publication of research on soldier's heart started at Hampstead Hospital. R.T. Grant, 'After-Histories for Ten Years of 1,000 Men Suffering from Heart Disease: A Study in Prognosis', *Heart*, 16 (1933), 276–381.

59 *MRCAR*, 13 (1926–7), 13.

60 Cowan, 'Some Notes', p. 97.

61 George Newman, *Recent Advances in Medical Education in England* (London, HMSO, 1923), p. 65; Rosemary Stevens, 'The Evolution of the Health Care System in the United States and the United Kingdom' in *Priorities for the Use of Resources in Medicine* (Washington, DC, US Government Printing Office, 1977), pp. 13–30.

62 Carter M. Smith sen., and Mark Siverman, 'A Letter from Sir James Mackenzie to Dr. Carter Smith (22 April 1924)', *Circulation*, 51 (1975), 212–17.

63 Mackenzie to Lewis, 25 December 1917, Contemporary Medical Archives Centre, Wellcome Institute for the History of Medicine, London; Wilson, *Beloved Physician*, p. 249.

64 Rosen, *Specialization of Medicine*, p. 63.

65 Sir James Mackenzie, 'The Role of Medicine at the Beginning of the Twentieth Century as Illustrated by the State of Cardiology', *New York Med. J.*, 65 (1922), 61–6.

66 Mackenzie to Lewis, 22 January 1919, Contemporary Medical Archives Centre, Wellcome Institute for the History of Medicine, London.

67 Sir James Mackenzie, 'A New Outlook in Cardiology', *BMJ*, 1 (1924), 1–5, 57–61, 104–9.

68 It is interesting that in the 1920s, although they were almost three decades apart in age, both Lewis and Mackenzie turned from the study of the heart by graphic methods to the study of human pain. Given their close personal relationship, that both should turn to this subject at the same time seems unlikely to be coincidental, although the reason for their doing so is unclear. Could this relate to the heightened Victorian sensitivity to pain, as discussed by James Turner, *Reckoning With the Beast: Animals, Pain and Humanity in the Victorian Mind* (Baltimore, Johns Hopkins University Press, 1980)? Alternatively, though related, could this be a reaction to the antivivisection forces that remained strong enough to draw public speeches from Lewis, as in *The Practitioner's Debt to Research*

(London, Research Defence Society, 1927)? Or did the human brutality and pain in the First World War play a role? The question remains unanswered.

69 *Annual Reports of the Ministry of Pensions* (London, HMSO, 1922), pp. 1924, 1928.

70 Unless otherwise stated, biographical information on members of the Cardiac Club is based on the following: Carey F. Coombs, *BMJ*, 2 (1932), 1126; *Bristol Med.-Chir. J.*, 49 (1932), 326–8; Thomas Cotton, *Br. Heart. J.*, 28 (1966), 137–8; J.G. Emanuel, ibid., 20 (1958), 579; John Cowan, ibid., 10 (1948), 1; A.G. Gibson: ibid., 13 (1950), 255; Wardrop Griffith, ibid., 9 (1947), 77; John Hay, ibid., 21 (1959), 573; Lord Horder, ibid., 18 (1955), 123; *St Bart's Hosp J.*, 6 (1957), 247–50; *Practitioner*, 70 (1963), 532–7; Sir William Errington Hume, *Br. Heart J.*, 22 (1960), 426; *Lancet*, 1 (1960), 117–18; *BMJ*, 1 (1960), 132–3; John E. MacIlwaine, *Lancet*, 2 (1930), 428; Sir John Parkinson, *Br. Heart J.*, 38 (1976), 1105–7; William T. Ritchie, ibid., 7 (1945), 207; Hubert John Starling, ibid., 13 (1950), 2581; Kenneth Douglas Wilkinson, *Br. Heart J.*, 14 (1951), 556. The relevant details are tabulated in Joel D. Howell, '"Soldier's Heart": The Redefinition of Heart Disease and Speciality Formation in Early Twentieth-century Great Britain', *Medical History*, suppl. no. 5 (1985), 34–52, at p. 52.

71 Christopher Lawrence, 'Moderns and Ancients: The "New Cardiology" in Britain 1880–1930' in W.F. Bynum, C. Lawrence and V. Nutton (eds), *The Emergence of Modern Cardiology, Medical History*, suppl. No. 5 (1985), pp. 1–33.

72 Experimental medicine was thus defined by Lewis: 'In experimenting we make observations, not upon events that are happening quite spontaneously (observational method), but upon events that are provoked or influenced by the interference of the experimenter.' This remains a reasonable definition today. 'The Relationship of Clinical Medicine to Physiology From the Standpoint of Research' in *Research in Medicine and Other Addresses* (London, H.K. Lewis, n.d.).

73 John Hay, 'The Treatment of Acute Lobar Pneumonia', *BMJ*, 2 (1927), 477; H.J. Starling, 'Syphilis of the Lungs', *Quart. J. Med.*, 32 (1939), 381.

74 John Hay, 'The Action of Quinidine in the Treatment of Heart Disease, Based on the Experiences of Certain Members of the Cardiac Club', *Lancet*, 2 (1924), 543–5; Alexander George Gibson, 'The Clinical Aspects of Ischaemic Necrosis of the Heart Muscle', *Lancet*, 2 (1925), 1270–5. Cary Coombs chose to publish separately, along with Geoffrey Hatfield, 'Ischaemic Necrosis of the Cardiac Wall', *Lancet*, 1 (1926), 14–15.

75 To what extent the same variety was represented in the hospital practice of club members cannot be established without examining members' case books.

76 Creighton Bramwell, 'John Hay and the Founders of the Cardiac Club', *Br. Heart J.*, 27 (1965), 849–55; Cowan, 'Some Notes', p. 98; Campbell, 'British Cardiac Society', p. 685.

77 Evidence for social interactions might be found in the Minute Book of the Cardiac Club and personal papers of the members.

6

PHYSICIANS AND CITIZENS: US MEDICAL WOMEN AND MILITARY SERVICE IN THE FIRST WORLD WAR

Kimberly Jensen

Modern warfare presents nations with the tremendous challenge of mobilizing complex human and economic systems including supply, combat, and medical resources. During the First World War American army recruiting posters that featured Uncle Sam and his now famous 'I Want You for the US Army' focused on the political obligation of men to fight for their country. The posters would have been more accurate had they featured Uncle Sam appealing to civilians and military personnel, women as well as men, and admitting 'I *Need* You to Win the War'. For many of the approximately 6,000 women physicians in the United States the nation's need for their medical skills was a crucial part of their campaign to be commissioned as officers in the army's medical corps. With the work of several generations of women physicians providing a foundation and with the national campaign for woman suffrage in its concluding phase, they hoped that the First World War would be the final chapter in their efforts to achieve professional and civic equality. During the war male colleagues and military officials provided limited support for opportunities for medical women to serve, and there was temporary support of an expanded role for the female citizen during wartime. Yet these women did not achieve their goal of commissions and officer status in the medical corps. Such status would have represented the achievement of a lasting equality in both profession and nation, not a temporary 'equality' born of wartime need that could be removed as easily as a uniform after the Armistice. While it did not comprise the final chapter, as they wished, the struggle of US women physicians to achieve officer status in the medical corps is none the less an important chapter in the history of women and medicine, citizenship and the military.

As individuals and through organized groups such as the American Women's Hospitals sponsored by the newly formed Medical Women's National Association, women physicians struggled to claim a place in military medical service through petitions, resolutions, war service registration, contract practice and medical service close to the battlefront during the war. Their purposeful work was not only part of a continuing struggle for equality within the profession, but also part of a larger movement of women to define the meaning of female citizenship. As the war placed the medical profession on the public stage they made a claim for equal opportunity within military medicine, hoping for professional equality during the conflict and also in the postwar medical world. The growing momentum of the national campaign for woman suffrage, and the fact that women had achieved the right to vote in many states by 1917, provided the context for their claims of expanded citizenship rights that included military medical service. At this convergence of an unprecedented mobilization of government and civilian resources to win the war and the movement for expanded female citizenship, women physicians believed they could make a practical as well as an ideological case for equal acceptance as officers in the medical corps. Their story is a vivid illustration of the resiliency of the resistance to women's military service, the enduring boundaries of gender in the medical profession, and the determination of a group of women to press their claims for equality in spite of the limits of wartime need and postwar retrenchment.

Women physicians made their wartime claims for equal opportunity in the context of a broader history of struggle for access to educational, professional and organizational opportunity in the field of medicine, as well as the struggle for women's rights.[1] The first decades of the twentieth century were optimistic times for many medical women. As the nation entered the war, women physicians could point to progress in educational opportunity and in occupational variety. In 1910 women physicians reached a peak of 6 per cent of the medical profession. And a 1916 study showed that 1,313 American women physicians in active practice were specializing, two-thirds in what were considered women's specialities such as obstetrics and gynaecology, and one-third in fields considered to be male territory.[2] But there were still many reforms to be made, especially in access to medical education for African-American women and other women of colour, and in internship and professional opportunities for all women.[3]

In addition, medical women constructed their case for a place within the military medical corps at the same time that male physicians were waging their own battle with the military for increased rank and authority. This wartime legislative campaign, led by medical leaders under the direction of Dr Franklin Martin of the General Medical Board of the Council of National Defense and waged for almost the entire length of the war itself, was finally successful when the Owen–Dyer Bill was passed in both houses of Congress in July 1918. Officers in the medical corps were then given the same status as other officers and increased authority in sanitary regulations and recommendations.[4] Women physicians wished to take their equal place in the wake of these important reforms.

In June 1917, three months after the United States entered the war, the members of the Medical Women's National Association (MWNA) assembled at their second annual meeting in New York City. A purposeful audience unanimously approved a resolution by California women physicians to be sent to

Secretary of War Newton D. Baker, calling for acceptance of women in the military medical corps on equal terms with men. In this atmosphere of enthusiasm for the possibilities of medical women's war service, the members present also supported the creation of a War Service Committee which they hoped would translate their desire for service and recognition into concrete plans and positive results. New York surgeon Rosalie Slaughter Morton, who had visited and served at the war front, was chosen to chair the committee. She gave it a new name, 'the American Women's Hospitals' (AWH), linking the new group to the strength and accomplishment of the Scottish Women's Hospitals already in service at the front. Morton's leadership role for medical women was strengthened when she also accepted the chair of the Committee of Women Physicians for the General Medical Board of the Council of National Defense.[5]

Leaders of the American Women's Hospitals believed they might prepare the way for acceptance in the medical corps by conducting a nationwide survey to determine the numbers of medical women who could serve and the specific skills they possessed. Such a census would demonstrate concretely to officials in Washington that medical women were ready for wartime service. They also believed that whoever controlled such information would be recognized as authoritative by military medical men, and would be called upon to set policy and oversee the wartime activities of women physicians.[6] The registration was both a practical and political measure, in effect a petition to the government on behalf of medical women. Under the auspices of the American Women's Hospitals and several affiliated groups, medical women across the country received registration blanks that were to be filled out with their preferences for wartime service. In late 1917 and early 1918 they returned the completed registration forms to AWH headquarters and to the Washington offices of the Committee of Women Physicians, both headed by Morton.

War service registration did not lead to the acceptance of women into the medical corps as officers, yet the individual act of registration and its cumulative effects had political meaning. Registration could demonstrate that women physicians were ready to be full citizens through war service, and that they wished to claim equality with male medical colleagues. Some women viewed registration as a strategic organizational step in preparation for full participation in the military medical corps. Rosalie Slaughter Morton also knew that some medical women 'as a matter of principle and precedent' refused to register for war service unless they were first commissioned in the military medical corps.[7]

The results of the registration, with other information on 5,827 women licensed to practice medicine in the United States, were published by the AWH and the Committee of Women Physicians as the *Census of Women Physicians* in 1918.[8] According to the *Census*, almost one-third (1,816 or 31 per cent) of the medical women of the country in 1917/18, active and retired, signified through registration their willingness to provide medical war service. The significance of this percentage is amplified when we realize that this one-third does not simply reflect those medical women who believed in the principle that women physicians should have the opportunity to participate in war service, but those who were personally willing to register for such service. And it does not include those who refused to register to protest against the lack of commissions for women physicians.

A commitment to medical professionalism was an important factor in the war registration of women physicians. Forty-one per cent of medical women who were members of the American Medical Association registered for war service; 59 per cent of the members of the Medical Women's National Association registered; and 63 per cent of those women who were members of both the AMA and MWNA registered. The last of these figures was twice the percentage seen for the *Census* as a whole.[9] Only 24 per cent of the women with no professional affiliation registered for war service. These figures indicate that those medical women who were most concerned with women's professionalism, those who were active in organizations and who perhaps believed that they had the most to gain in a bid for equality with male colleagues, registered for war service.

The war service registration rates of the medical women of the *Census* compare significantly with the war service numbers of male colleagues. According to the army's Surgeon-General's office there were 30,591 male physicians in the medical corps at the time of the Armistice in November 1918, which means that approximately 20 per cent of the male physicians in the country were in military service in 1918.[10] Another contemporary listing, *The Physicians and Surgeons of Chicago* (1922), gives information on the military and civilian war service for 1,507 Chicago medical men. Almost half of this group (734 or 49 per cent) reported no war-related service, civilian or military. Twenty-six per cent reported some form of civilian war service, and 25 per cent reported military service in the First World War.[11] These figures suggest that medical women committed themselves to war service through the avenues open to them in substantial numbers in favourable relation to the service rates of male colleagues.

As the registration of women physicians got under way in the summer of 1917, officials in Washington received numerous letters and other enquiries regarding women and the medical corps, and many women sent their applications for acceptance to the army's Medical Reserve Corps (MRC). Some physicians made personal visits that summer, and prominent non-medical women and men urged Surgeon-General William Crawford Gorgas and Secretary of War Baker to admit women physicians to the corps on equal terms. At the same time, medical men were developing their own campaign for increased status within the military. Pressure from many sides mounted. What would the military do about women physicians?

One official avenue for women's military service existed. Before 1917 several women had served as contract surgeons, including Dr Anita Newcombe McGee, who later became the head of the Army Nurse Corps. Yet most women physicians opposed such work. For Philadelphia surgeon Caroline Purnell, contract work 'would mean our ability to be under the cook, the head nurse, or others, and be ordered around'. Following a trip to the West, Chicago physician Martha Whelpton reported that very 'few of the Coast women, and few of the Colorado women also, will go as Contract Surgeons. They object with all their might.' Chicago medical women believed that their 'professional dignity' was at stake, and 'absolutely opposed' contract service.[12]

For these and other medical women across the country, contract service in the military represented acceptance of inferior status based on gender. Physicians in the American Civil War had been employed as contract surgeons performing 'part-time work, the individual doctor so employed maintaining his own private practice at home and at the same time giving some hours of each day to his Army hospital duties'. Since the civil war male physicians had achieved increased rank and status within the medical department and were struggling for more, and the position of contract surgeon was weak in comparison, lacking rank, professional prestige, or the authority to command deference.[13] The Surgeon-General still had the power to appoint as many contract surgeons as might be needed in 'emergencies', and 'at places which did not justify the expense involved by the detail of a medical officer'. Only two men served with the American Expeditionary Forces as contract surgeons; the other 887 men employed during the war years as contract surgeons served on the home front in part-time, limited capacities. Chicago neurologist Peter Bassoe, for example, contracted with the army to teach a course in neurosurgery.[14]

Yet in response to pressure from women physicians and their supporters the US government reinterpreted medical contract work to create a special, limited category for women's wartime medical service. In August 1917 Acting Judge Advocate General Blanton Winship handed down his interpretation of military regulations regarding contract surgeons. 'The statute does not prescribe that contract surgeons shall be males', he wrote, 'and, in the absence of such a limitation, I am clearly of the opinion that it is allowable by law to appoint female physicians as contract surgeons in the United States Army.'[15] For many medical women this was nothing more than an attempt to create a separate and unequal category of military service for women physicians. The regulations dealing with service in the medical corps contained the same phraseology as those outlining the qualifications for contract work. Yet that same month the Acting Judge Advocate General interpreted these medical corps regulations as pertaining solely to men.[16] It seemed that while women would be accepted only as vulnerable 'day labourers' men would be given the status, rank and pay of officers in the medical corps.

Caroline Purnell, for one, did not believe that contract practice was a step along the road to equality in military service. 'As a woman and as a physician and as a surgeon, I think our days for crawling are over,' she said. 'I cannot see why women should demonstrate their patriotism in any different way from men. If the men respect themselves and demonstrate their patriotism according to their training and experience, why should not women do the same thing? Why should we have to have a different way when our ability is just the same? We would be more self-respecting if we should stand upon this . . . Our brains are not in our sex.'[17] Apparently the majority of medical women in the country agreed. In the autumn of 1917 Dr Caroline Towles of Baltimore surveyed medical women's opinions on contract service. In response to the question 'As the only manner of serving, would you consider contract practice if this form of service can be made less objectionable?' most medical women answered 'No.'[18]

Some women held notions of patriotism and professionalism that allowed them to see contract service with the military in a more positive light. Such service would make it possible for them to use their professional skills to serve their country, the wounded and the sick without delay. Some believed that if contract service was the place where women could push at the boundaries of military service then they would join and push. And a few women found contract service to be the only way that they could circumvent military restrictions and still serve as members of the hospital units that they had joined for overseas work. These units, formed in anticipation of the war, were converted to army base hospitals as the United States entered the conflict. Physician Esther Pohl Lovejoy, who later compiled their history, summed it up: 'They were without commissions', she wrote, but 'they were on the job.'[19]

The army's Surgeon-General asked Emma Wheat Gilmore, who became chair of the Committee of Women Physicians of the General Medical Board of the Council of National Defense in 1918, to recommend women for contract service. Over the course of the war, 55 medical women engaged in contract service with the US army, all, apparently, with her approval. They came from all parts of the country – 19 of the 55 from the East, 23 from the Midwest, 7 from the South, 5 from the West, and 1 from Puerto Rico – and from urban areas like Brooklyn, Boston, Memphis and San Francisco as well as smaller towns and rural communities from Kalamazoo, Michigan to Gilmore City, Iowa. They had been educated at both large and small medical institutions. And although more than half graduated from medical school after 1908 they represented a range of age groups. The average length of service for the group was seven months, with two women serving only one month and one serving longer than eighteen months. It appears that most of these women served as pathologists, anaesthetists and did laboratory work.[20]

Eleven women served as contract surgeons overseas. Frances Edith Haines of Chicago worked as an anaesthetist with her medical unit at Limoges, France.[21] Cincinnati physician Elizabeth Van Cortlandt Hocker entered the army as a contract surgeon in May 1918 and served until August 1919. She was particularly proud that after the Armistice she was placed in charge of two hospital wards of forty-two beds each that were for women personnel of the army at Savenay, France.[22] Forty-four women contract surgeons (80 per cent) performed their military duties while remaining in US territory, some serving in administrative posts and others at military hospitals, many caring for convalescent soldiers.[23] Physician Dolores M. Pinero received her medical degree in Puerto Rico and was practising in the town of Rio Piedras when the war began. She became a contract surgeon with the army in October 1918 and was immediately assigned to the base hospital at San Juan, the only woman serving in the army in Puerto Rico. She did anaesthesiology and laboratory duty and helped to open a 400-bed hospital in a school in Ponce during the influenza epidemic that autumn.[24]

While these medical women accepted the terms of contract service, other women physicians wished to provide immediate war service overseas without the onus of contract work, and volunteered with the Red Cross and other civilian organizations in Europe. They made individual contracts with these organizations, and their work ranged from service in private hospitals to service in civilian communities and in locations near the front. These women provided medical and surgical care and worked in public health with civilians and refugees. By November 1918 there were at least seventy-six medical women serving abroad with various organizations. They came from all regions of the country – 49 per cent of them were from the East, 21 per cent from the West, 17 per cent from the Midwest and 13 per cent from the South. When we compare the average graduation year for these women who went overseas to that of women physicians in the 1918 *Census of Women Physicians* in general we find that this overseas group was younger: for all medical women the average year was 1899, and for these seventy-six overseas women the average year of graduation was 1904. Sixty per cent of the overseas women had graduation dates from 1902 to 1914.[25]

Voluntary service with organizations other than the United States military was more accessible to medical women of colour, and most African-American women physicians worked within their communities to provide wartime health care. Records show that two African-American women physicians served overseas. One of them was Dr Mary L. Brown who received a commission from the Red Cross to serve in France. A graduate of Howard Medical School who had received advanced training in Edinburgh, Brown was living in France when she received her assignment in the spring of 1918.[26] Dr Harriet Rice of Newport, Rhode Island, an 1891 graduate of the Women's Medical College of New York, was living in France with her brother at the outbreak of the war. Rice distinguished herself by her work in a French military hospital where she served for most of the war. In August 1919 she received the Reconnaissance Française for her meritorious medical service with the French wounded.[27]

Physician Jessie W. Fisher wrote to her friend and colleague Kate Campbell Mead from Paris in May 1918 while with a group of medical women with the Red

Cross 'loafing around Paris waiting for our papers to different stations'. Her detailed letter shows that this type of war service raised questions about the broader issues of women's status and position in the war. Fisher wrote to her colleagues that there were 'lots of good places to be filled in the civil work where you could do a lot of good and would be invaluable', and that the Red Cross was willing to pay a good salary. Yet, she warned, 'we are in a very anomalous position'. Women physicians in Fisher's situation were not saluted, they had no standard uniform, and the authority accorded to them and the treatment they received depended upon circumstance and the inclinations of the men with whom they worked. 'It is most embarrassing,' Fisher wrote. She found the older men in the Red Cross and the army to be 'as courteous as at home', but younger men were a problem. 'I struck [slapped?] a young medical officer the other day who made me feel my lack of rank,' she reported. 'I think we are usually taken for army chauffeurs and of course the soldiers do not have the proper respect for us.'[28]

Fisher's comments underscore the vulnerability of women involved in wartime service without official military status. In her relations with men both socially and professionally she had much the same difficulties as did army nurses serving without definite rank. And her solution was similar: medical women must gain equal status as officers for professional integrity and especially to enable them to control their social and professional relations with men. 'My advice to you, and to all women M.D.s', she wrote, 'is to *stay* in the U.S. and fight for commissions for the women.' The demand for medical women was strong, she believed, and 'if the women will refuse to come without commissions they will be compelled to give them to us'. Her first-hand experiences with these issues gave authority to her recommendations. And she was emphatic in her conclusion: 'Now *stay at home* and fight tooth and toe nail for those commissions.'[29] The message was clear. Unless they had officer status and rank, women physicians would be extremely vulnerable in their working and social relationships with men in the military.

At least two groups of women, and many others as individuals, sought to gain these commissions by direct application, taking the position that they were the citizens that were eligible for service as stated in military regulations.[30] Their strategies were similar to those used by Susan B. Anthony, Virginia Minor and other late nineteenth-century suffrage activists who presented themselves at the polls as citizens eligible to vote under the protection of the Fourteenth Amendment, which established the definition of citizenship as 'all persons born or naturalized in the United States'.[31] As Susan Anthony declared to audiences prior to her 1872 trial for attempting to vote, 'in voting, I committed no crime, but simply exercised my "citizen's right", guaranteed to me and all United States citizens by the National Constitution, beyond the power of any state to deny'.[32] Now these medical women, many of whom lived in states that granted women the right to vote by 1917, continued the cause of defining women's citizenship rights and obligations. It was as citizens that they challenged their exclusion from military medical service to the state.

In September 1917 the newly formed Colorado Medical Women's War Service League created a Committee on Recognition of Medical Women. Mary Elizabeth Bates, a prominent Denver gynaecologist, officer of the Medical Women's National Association, suffrage activist, community organizer and secretary of the league, chaired the new committee. Her charge was to 'take up the question of the appointment of women physicians in the Medical Reserve Corps of the U.S. Army'.[33] The committee had two tasks: firstly, to identify and study the regulations governing the service of physicians in the Medical Department of the army; and secondly, to recommend and implement the actions necessary for women physicians to gain equal access to the Medical Reserve Corps.

Bates and her committee members began an investigation of the status of the regulations concerning service with the Medical Reserve Corps. Section 37 of the National Defense Act of 3 June 1916 prescribed the following qualifications for appointment in the Officers' Reserve Corps: 'such citizens as, upon examination prescribed by the President, shall be found physically, mentally and morally qualified to hold such commissions'.[34] No restriction based on gender was in the language of this Act. The *Manual For The Medical Department* required applicants for the medical corps to be 'between 22 and 30 years of age . . . a citizen of the United States, [who] must have a satisfactory general education, must be a graduate of a reputable medical school legally authorized to confer the degree of doctor of medicine, and must have had at least one year's hospital training, including practical experience in the practice of medicine, surgery and obstetrics'.[35] The requirements for service in the Medical Reserve Corps were similar: commissions were to be given 'to such graduates of reputable schools of medicine, citizens of the United States [who shall be found] physically, mentally, and morally qualified to hold such commissions'. Such officers were also required to be between twenty-two and forty-five years of age and to be qualified to practise medicine in their state or territory of residence.[36]

Gender was not an explicit category for acceptance in any of these regulations, and there were hundreds of women who could meet the professional and physical qualifications necessary for service. Based on their examination of military regulations, Bates and her committee concluded that 'the word "citizens" must include women, since women are citizens', and that it would not be 'necessary to seek the enactment of a law to permit the appointment of women'.[37] Unlike nurses who needed to get new legislation passed to allow them as a professional group to gain officer status, medical women had to deal with the interpretation of laws that, in explicit language at least, were not gender specific, and already granted officer status to their professional group.

Yet the interpretation of a law could be just as powerful as the absence or presence of a law. On 30 August 1917, Acting Judge Advocate General S.T.

Ansell had written an official interpretation of military regulations regarding the service of women physicians in the Medical Reserve Corps. After quoting the National Defense Act of 1916, which stipulated the service of 'citizens', Ansell referred to an opinion of the Massachusetts Supreme Court in a case dealing with the appointment of women as notaries. This decision in turn employed as precedent another Massachusetts court decision that raised the question of whether or not women could serve as justices of the peace. 'There is nothing in the Constitution which in terms prohibits women from being appointed to judicial offices, any more than from being appointed to military offices, or to executive civil offices, the tenure and mode of appointment of which are provided for in the Constitution. It was the nature of the office of justice of the peace, and the usage that always had prevailed in making appointments to that office, that led the justices to advise that it could not have been the intention of the Constitution that women should be appointed justices of the peace . . . In our opinion the same considerations apply to the office of notary public.'[38]

Claiming these rulings as precedent, Ansell concluded: 'For similar reasons it is the view of this office that it is not allowable by law to appoint female physicians to military office in the Medical section of the Officers' Reserve Corps of the Army.'[39] In the body of his decision, the Judge Advocate General stated four main reasons why, in his opinion, women physicians should not be commissioned as officers in the Medical Reserve Corps. Women physicians could not serve in the Medical Reserve Corps because they had not done so in the past; soldiers were specified as 'men' in other regulations not affecting the Medical Department; as women they would not be physically capable; and they were not to have the status of officers, by which they would command men.

To test the medical corps regulations that called for the appointment of 'citizens' Bates and her committee developed a plan that, Bates wrote, would 'achieve the result desired with the minimum amount of trouble for the War Department'.[40] They would select from six to twelve women physicians who would apply as a group for service with the Medical Reserve Corps. The medical women in this test case would come from states that granted women the right of suffrage, presumably because women in these states had already crossed an important conceptual boundary of citizenship. They would be professionally prepared and have all of the qualifications necessary to 'make good' if appointed to the Medical Reserve Corps. Along with the standard documentation of education and accomplishments, the medical women would secure recommendations from 'prominent and influential persons'. Senators and representatives from home states would be enlisted to present the applications with Colorado Senator John Franklin Shafroth and Representative Edward Keating who already 'enthusiastically endorsed the plan'.[41]

The Bates Committee selected eight women physicians to present their applications to the Surgeon-General and Secretary of War for service in the

Medical Reserve Corps.[42] By February 1918 the applications were in order and the test case was put in motion. A group of eleven members of Congress, led by Shafroth, went to the office of Surgeon-General Gorgas.[43] Anita Newcombe McGee, who had served as a contract surgeon in the Spanish–American War and had been appointed head of the Army Nurse Corps at its creation in 1901, accompanied the delegation. As the woman physician most closely associated with actual experience in military medicine, McGee's presence was both symbolic and practical. In her account of the proceedings, McGee reported that the application of Mary Bates was included with those of the other eight women, and all were presented to the Surgeon-General for his approval.[44]

By all accounts Gorgas was sympathetic with the movement. McGee reported that he told her he personally favoured commissions for women physicians. But he was bound, he said, by the decision of the Judge Advocate General opposing women in the Medical Reserve Corps. He suggested that the next step for the group was to take the matter up with Secretary of War Baker. McGee believed that if Baker could be persuaded, then 'the Judge Advocate General's Office would doubtless reverse its decision, and the Surgeon-General be given a free hand'.[45]

On 4 February this same group met with the Secretary of War, who had already publicly expressed his views on women in military service. In a letter to the House and Senate military committees, which were considering a bill to commission women in the Signal Corps, Baker had written that he did 'not approve of commissioning or enlisting women in the military service'.[46] The group presented the women's applications to Baker, read the decision of the Judge Advocate General, and explained their position on the matter. Baker replied that 'his main thought was to win the war, and that he did not think that commissioning women physicians would contribute to that end, nor did he want to make any unnecessary innovations now'. Shafroth and McGee both argued that there was a need for the service of women physicians, McGee stating that the Surgeon-General wanted them especially for work as anaesthetists and pathologists. Baker terminated their conversation, saying that he believed that women physicians were not needed by the military but that he would consider the matter further.[47] The test case was at a standstill, with the applications shelved in the office of the Secretary of War, a man opposed to women's military medical service.

Other women made their claims for eligible citizenship status through local action. Four women physicians from Portland, Oregon drove to the Vancouver, Washington training facility for medical officers in the spring of 1918 to present themselves as eligible physicians desiring commissions as medical officers. Drs Katherine Manion, Mae Cardwell, Mary MacLachlan and Emily Balcom came representing many other women physicians of the area. 'There is no word in the war department regulations that bars women', one of them told a reporter for the Portland *Journal* after their attempt, 'and away we went to the [medical] officers' training camp'. They presented themselves to an astonished major in charge of the camp, 'ready and armed to take the examinations, don the uniforms and salute the privates'. The four women stated their intentions, arguing that in their community women had full suffrage, that they were citizens, and ready to meet the professional and other requirements necessary for acceptance into the Medical Reserve Corps. They brought with them the necessary documents. After checking these, the major told the group that he could not examine them because 'it hasn't been done'. After more discussion he asked them if they wouldn't like to go overseas as nurses. They replied firmly that they would not, and asked the male physician/officer, 'Would *you*?' The major finally said that he would telegraph Surgeon-General Gorgas for an answer, and the negative reply came from Washington the next day.[48]

Medical women also mounted a campaign to bring the question of women's entrance in the medical corps to the formal attention of the American Medical Association, after which they hoped that the association would act to support commissions for women physicians. They were successful in achieving a voice, although it was a voice filtered through male allies, at the AMA National Convention in Chicago in June 1918. Here resolutions supporting commissions for women physicians were introduced and made their way to committees. Three resolutions on behalf of women physicians were introduced: one by Dr H.G. Wetherill, a Colorado colleague of Mary Bates in gynaecology; another which specifically reflected the views of the Medical Association of the State of California by Dr George Kress, a California physician active in tuberculosis work and professor of hygiene at the College of Medicine of the University of California; and a third by Dr E.O. Smith, professor of urology at the University of Cincinnati.[49]

The language contained in these three AMA resolutions reveals a great deal about the way in which medical women and their allies constructed a case for women's service. In a broad sense, medical women employed the same two arguments that Aileen Kraditor identified as the basic rationales in the call for woman suffrage: expediency and justice.[50] According to the AMA resolutions, it would be expedient for the government to commission women physicians; they were 'fitted and equipped' to provide 'valuable service', they were graduates of medical schools and qualified to practise medicine, and 'most if not all of them have signified their readiness' for service. With the demands of war, all available skill should be utilized, and commissions would 'further the utilization of women physicians in service'.[51] The resolutions also called for women's entrance into the medical corps based on the idea of justice. Women physicians in all fields, including surgery, one resolution emphasized, 'render service as efficient and valuable as can be rendered by men'. Medical women already serving overseas with such groups as the Red Cross had 'performed invaluable services', and demonstrated their loyalty, employing, in the words of another resolution, 'their skill and energy in our common cause'. For these reasons, the resolutions called upon the Secretary of War to bring women physicians into the medical corps 'in full standing' with the same rank and pay as male medical officers.[52]

Medical women also addressed objections to service based on a supposed physical weakness or unsuitability for military service. American women physicians serving in the war zone with the Red Cross and other organizations, and women physicians from other nations, one resolution stated, 'have demonstrated that it is possible for women to endure the hardships of life in the war zone and still do creditable work'.[53] Here, as well as in the other aspects of their argument, they made the implicit claim for service as citizens who were equal in their abilities to serve the state, even while facing the dangers of the war zone.

The resolutions were forwarded to the Reference Committee on Legislation and Political Action for the AMA. This committee returned an opinion that appeared to be both supportive and cautious, and drew the line for women's service at the boundary of 'soldiering'. The 'very character of military service and women's natural limitation for such service must require wise discrimination in their employment in war work', the committee members wrote. Women physicians, in other words, were not to be front-line soldiers due to the 'natural limitations' of sex. However, they continued, the 'principle of equal rank and pay for equal service is inherently just without regard to sex, and the committee feels this should be unhesitatingly approved by the House [of Delegates of the AMA]'.[54] According to this AMA committee, women physicians could serve in the military without actually being soldiers, and therefore they avoided the issue of women's military service as combat service, a threshold most Americans were unwilling to cross. Yet by denying them soldier status, the AMA also perpetuated a less than equal place for women in the medical corps.

In her study of the relationship between male and female workers in the auto and electrical industries in the Second World War, Ruth Milkman demonstrates that male union members supported female workers' claims for equal pay during wartime. In her analysis, such support for women's 'equality' by male workers was directly linked to their own self-interest in promoting standards and pay for jobs that they believed would return to the hands of men following the war.[55] The decision of the AMA committee to support the principle of 'equal rank and pay for equal service' follows the same pattern. As we have seen, male physicians were fighting their own battles for increased status and authority in the military. They were interested in strengthening and maintaining the military status of their profession both during and after the war, and could stand on such principles as 'equal pay for equal work' without conceding much overall ground to women. This was especially true when the disclaimer regarding the 'natural limitations' of women's military service was included in their resolution. Caroline Purnell believed it. 'The men are not just ready to give us the ground yet,' she told her colleagues. 'They got in on the ground floor first; they are going to get all out of it that they can for the sacrifices they have made.'[56]

Delegates recommended the resolutions to the AMA for action, but before that could take place the war was over, taking with it many of the expediencies that had made the arguments for women's service possible. Like the applications of the women brought to Secretary of War Baker by the Colorado coalition, the resolutions, petitions and other calls for legislative action were not formally acted upon before the end of the conflict, and yet they helped to set new definitions for what was possible. Officially buried, they lived in the memories of the women and men who had made their claims until another war broke out in Europe twenty years later.[57]

Full citizenship, service to the state and professional opportunity during wartime involved complex issues for medical women. Some believed that as medical professionals they could ameliorate the effects of war by saving lives, thus placing themselves outside the boundaries of responsibility for war. Perhaps this philosophy allowed pacifist medical women such as Alice Hamilton to register for war service. Dr Alice Wakefield believed that she 'could not bear the war' if she were not working 'purposefully every hour' in wartime medical service. Some believed that the war had a larger political purpose. 'If we had not believed in the ideal of the war for the establishment of international peace,' Rosalie Slaughter Morton recalled, 'we could not have gone forward, planning, organizing, so strenuously.'[58] And many medical women believed, from sad experience, that it would take a catastrophe such as war to change the way that they were viewed by male colleagues and others in American society. They did not welcome the war, but when it came they claimed the right to be civic and professional equals with men. Dr Frances van Gasken of the Medical College of Pennsylvania used the metaphor of Pandora's box to explain such views. Although the war let loose a host of disasters when it was opened, she believed that it also brought hope in the promise of equality and opportunity for medical women.[59]

From what we can see from the activities and reports of medical women themselves, and from their characteristics as revealed in the *Census of Women Physicians*, service in the First World War represented a claim by many women physicians for full membership and participation as women, as citizens of the state, and as members of the medical profession. Almost one-third of medical women registered for war service. Along with the four Portland women, the members of the Colorado Medical Women's War Service League, the hundreds who sent in applications and enquiries, and the thousands who signed petitions to Washington officials, they seem to have agreed with Colorado physician Mary Bates that the real question – or perhaps the all-encompassing question – was 'the rights of citizenship as applied to women'.[60] The juxtaposition of their campaign for wartime service with the final stages of the suffrage campaign allowed these medical women to link their professional and civic arguments for equality. But gendered boundaries in the military and in medicine prevented them from achieving full and lasting equality with male colleagues in spite of the wartime need and the ideology and momentum of the women's rights movement supporting them. Such issues make their story an important one in the history of war, medicine and modernity.

ACKNOWLEDGEMENTS

An earlier version of this chapter was published in vol. 67 (1993) of the *Bulletin of the History of Medicine*. This chapter appears with permission from the editors of the Bulletin.

Notes

1 For background on these issues in medicine, see Regina Morantz-Sanchez, *Sympathy and Science: Women Physicians in American Medicine* (New York, Oxford University Press, 1985); Mary Roth Walsh, *Doctors Wanted: No Women Need Apply: Sexual Barriers in the Medical Profession, 1835–1975* (New Haven, Yale University Press, 1977). For the context of the campaign for women's suffrage, see Marjorie Spruill Wheeler (ed.) *One Woman, One Vote: Rediscovering the Woman Suffrage Movement* (Troutdale, Oregon, New Sage Press, 1995); Nancy Cott, *The Grounding of Modern Feminism* (New Haven, Yale University Press, 1987).

2 Mary Sutton Macy MD, 'The Field for Women of Today in Medicine', *The Woman's Medical Journal (WMJ)*, 27 (March 1917), 49–58. These figures do not include those women physicians who were *de facto* specialists, who were not traceable in official records. Undoubtedly many more medical women specialized in these years.

3 The US census for 1910 reports that 84 per cent of the women physicians in the country were white and born in the United States, 12 per cent were white and born outside the US, 4 per cent were African-American, and less than 1 per cent were Native American, Asian or of other racial/ethnic origin. US Bureau of the Census, *Thirteenth Census of the United States Taken in the Year 1910*, vol. 4: *Population 1910, Occupation Statistics* (Washington, DC, Government Printing Office, 1914), p. 428; see also Morantz-Sanchez, *Sympathy and Science*, p. 234.

4 Senate Bill 3748, House Resolution 9563. See also 'The Evolution of the Medical Department' in Col Charles H. Lynch, *The Surgeon General's Office*, vol. 1 of *The Medical Department of the United States Army in the World War* (Washington, DC, Government Printing Office, 1923); Franklin H. Martin, *Fifty Years of Medicine and Surgery: An Autobiographical Sketch* (Chicago, The Surgical Publishing Company, 1934), esp. pp. 379–82. There was vigorous editorial comment in the medical journals. See 'Giving the Medical Officer the Rank to Which He Is Entitled', *Journal of the American Medical Association*, 69 (28 July 1917), 292–4, and 'Rank and Authority of Medical Officers', *Journal of the Iowa State Medical Society*, 7 (September 1917), 352.

5 See the typescript report 'American Women's Hospitals, Organized by War Service Committee of the Medical Women's National Association', box 1, folder 1, American Women's Hospitals Records (1917–82), accession No. 144, Archives and Special Collections on Women in Medicine, the Medical College of Pennsylvania, Philadelphia (hereafter AWH Records); 'Origin of the American Women's Hospitals', in box 1, folder 1, AWH Records; Bertha Van Hoosen, *Petticoat Surgeon* (Chicago,

Pellegrini and Cudahy, 1947), p. 202; Rosalie Slaughter Morton, *A Woman Surgeon: The Life and Work of Rosalie Slaughter Morton* (New York, Frederick A. Stokes Company, 1937), pp. 270–94. For additional information on the origins of the MWNA, see Ellen S. More, 'The American Medical Women's Association and the Role of the Woman Physician', *Journal of the American Medical Women's Association*, 45 (September/October 1990), 165–80. More also discusses the leadership style of Morton and the activities of women physicians in the war in '"A Certain Restless Ambition": Women Physicians in World War I', *American Quarterly*, 41 (1989), 636–60.

6 Information about registration may be found in various reports, especially in box 30, folders 292, 293, AWH Records.

7 See Morton, *A Woman Surgeon*, p. 283, and Emma Wheat Gilmore, 'Report of Committee, Women Physicians, General Medical Board, Council of National Defense', *WMJ*, 29 (July 1919), 146–7.

8 The information that follows is taken from my analysis of the database I created from the *Census of Women Physicians* (New York, The American Women's Hospitals, 1918).

9 By 1918, members of the MWNA were also required to be members of the AMA (to avoid the appearance of separatism). But in 1918 there were women who had joined the MWNA from the time of its organization in 1915 who were not AMA members.

10 Lynch, *The Surgeon General's Office*, p. 138 and *American Medical Directory* (Chicago, American Medical Association, 1918).

11 *History of Medicine and Surgery and Physicians and Surgeons of Chicago* (Chicago, Biographical Publishing Corporation, 1922).

12 Caroline M. Purnell MD, 'The Work of the American Women's Hospitals in Foreign Service', *Transactions of the Forty-Third Annual Meeting of the Alumnae Association of the Woman's Medical College of Pennsylvania* (Philadelphia, Alumnae Association of the Woman's Medical College of Pennsylvania, 1918), p. 97; Martha Whelpton to Rosalie Slaughter Morton, New York City, 26 November 1917, box 2, folder 14, AWH Records; and see *Bulletin of the Medical Women's Club of Chicago* (*MWCC Bulletin*), 6 (September 1917), 5.

13 Lynch, *The Surgeon General's Office*, p. 42.

14 Lynch, *The Surgeon General's Office*, p. 151; Colonel Joseph H. Ford, MC, *Administration, American Expeditionary Forces*, vol. 1 of *The Medical Department of the United States Army in the World War* (Washington, DC, Government Printing Office, 1927), p. 102; see the entry for 'Peter Bassoe' in *Physicians and Surgeons of Chicago*, p. 395.

15 US Judge Advocate General's Department (Army), *Opinions of the Judge Advocate General of the Army*, vol. 1 (1 April 1917 to 31 December 1917) (Washington, DC, Government Printing Office, 1919), p. 126; Blanton Winship, Acting Judge Advocate General, to the Surgeon-General of the United States (13 August 1917), in Anita Newcombe McGee MD, 'Can Women Physicians Serve in the Army?' *WMJ*, 28 (February 1918), 26–8.

16 See my discussion of these interpretations in the text below.

17 Purnell, 'The Work of the American Women's Hospitals in Foreign Service', p. 97.

18 'Women in the Medical Reserve Corps', *MWCC Bulletin*, 6 (September 1917), 5.

19 Esther Pohl Lovejoy, *Women Doctors of the World* (New York, The Macmillan Company, 1957), p. 303.

20 Lovejoy discusses Gilmore's role and other aspects of contract service in *Women Doctors of the World*, pp. 302–4. I have gathered information for this profile on women contract surgeons from a five-page typewritten list dated 13 November 1919 entitled 'Women Contract Surgeons, U.S. Army, Who Served During the War With Germany', box 17f, folder 142, AWH Records. At the end of the list is the typewritten notation: 'CHAIRMAN OF COMMITTEE OF WOMEN PHYSICIANS, Emma Wheat Gilmore, M.D.' I have also used information from the *Census of Women Physicians*, and individual sources listed below to augment the information in the 1919 list for this profile.

21 See 'Haines, Frances Edith, Memoirs of War Service', accession No. 103, Archives and Special Collections on Women in Medicine, Medical College of Pennsylvania, Philadelphia, Pennsylvania.

22 Elizabeth Van Cortlandt Hocker, MD, 'The Personal Experience of a Contract Surgeon in the United States Army', *MWJ*, 49 (January 1942), 9–11. See also 'Women Contract Surgeons', p. 2.

23 Ford, *Administration, American Expeditionary Forces*, p. 102.

24 See 'Contract Surgeon: Dolores Mercedes Pinero, MD', *MWJ*, 49 (October 1942), 310, 324. Lovejoy, *Women Doctors of the World*, pp. 275, 303, and also 'Women Contract Surgeons', p. 4.

25 The overseas women are listed in *WMJ*, 28 (November 1918), 247. The figures come from the information on these women in my *Census of Women Physicians* database.

26 Information on Mary Brown may be found in *The Crisis*, 16 (May 1918), 26.

27 Sara W. Brown MD reports on the achievements of Harriet Rice in 'Colored Women Physicians', *Southern Workman*, 52 (December 1923), p.583.

28 The typescript copy of this letter from Jessie W. Fisher in Paris, dated 12 May 1918, is addressed to 'Dear Lady', but on the top is written 'Kate Campbell Mead, M.D'. Evidently copies were passed around the community of women physicians to spread Fisher's message. The typescript is in box 30, folder 295, AWH Records. The sexual tension with younger officers is a strong feature of her report.

29 Fisher to 'Dear Lady'.

30 The regulations for both the Medical Corps and the Medical Reserve Corps included the term citizens without explicit reference to gender. When most women talked about military service they referred to service with the Medical Reserve Corps – in other words service for the duration of the war and not career service with the regular Medical Corps of the army. This was the type of service of most male physicians in the war. Sometimes women used the terms interchangeably, or referred to their right to service in both organizations. For the specific requirements, see 'Article I – The Medical Department, Its Organization and Personnel' in the 'Manual for the Medical Department' repr. in Lynch, *The Surgeon General's Office*, pp. 762–7.

31 A number of cases of such direct action in relation to voting under a Fourteenth Amendment claim may be found in Elizabeth Cady Stanton, Susan B. Anthony and Matilda Joslyn Gage (eds), *History of Woman Suffrage* (1881, repr. edn New York, Arno Press, 1969), pp. 586–755. See also Ellen Carol DuBois, 'Taking the Law Into Our Own Hands: *Bradwell, Minor* and Suffrage Militance in the 1870s' in *One Woman, One Vote*, ed. Wheeler, pp. 81–98.

32 *History of Woman Suffrage*, pp. 630–1.

33 'A Most Interesting Report of Work of Colorado Medical Women's War Service League', *WMJ*, 28 (February 1918), 39. See also Kimberly Jensen, 'Western Women and the "Open Way of Opportunity": The Case of Colorado Women Physicians, Women's Rights and World War I', *Western Historical Quarterly*, 27 (1996), 327–48.

34 McGee, 'Can Women Physicians Serve in the Army?', p. 26.

35 'Manual for the Medical Department', p. 763.

36 'Manual for the Medical Department', p. 766. These regulations also illustrate the extent to which the professionalization of medicine had been encoded in the army.

37 'A Most Interesting Report of Work', p. 39.

38 The case in question for justice of the peace is 107 MA 604, and for notaries 165 MA 599. Quotation appears in *Opinions of the Judge Advocate General*, pp. 126–7.

39 *Opinions of the Judge Advocate General*, p. 127.

40 'A Most Interesting Report of Work', p. 39.

41 'A Most Interesting Report of Work', p. 39.

42 They were: Myra L. Everly of Seattle, an 1893 graduate of Northwestern Medical College; Julia P. Larson of San Francisco, an 1898 graduate of the Medical Department of the University of California at Berkeley; Mary McKay of Macon, Georgia, an 1897 graduate of the Women's Medical College of Baltimore; Mabel A. Martin of Livingston, New York, a 1912 graduate of Cornell Medical College; Regina M. Downey of Beaver Falls, Pennsylvania, a 1914 graduate of the Woman's Medical College of Pennsylvania; Marion H. Rea-Lucks of Philadelphia; M. Jean Gale of Denver, an 1889 graduate of the Woman's Medical College of Pennsylvania; and Helen Craig of Denver, a 1913 graduate of Rush Medical College of Chicago. All were from suffrage states except for McKay of Georgia and Downey and Rea-Lucks of Pennsylvania, who, it appears, were chosen to round out the group's regional and institutional representation. I augmented the information on these women given by Bates in 'A Most Interesting Report of Work' with information from the *Census of Women Physicians*.

43 The group included Senator McNary of Oregon; Senator Calder of New York; Senator Jones of Washington; Senator Phelan of California; Senator Knox of Pennsylvania; Senator Smith of Georgia; Representative Nolan of California; and Representatives Keating, Taylor and Timberlake of Colorado, led by Senator Shafroth of Colorado. See 'A Most Interesting Report of Work', p. 39.

44 McGee, 'Can Women Physicians Serve in the Army?', p. 28.

45 'A Most Interesting Report of Work', p. 39, and McGee, 'Can Women Physicians Serve in the Army?', p. 28.

46 This is quoted in McGee, 'Can Women Physicians Serve in the Army?', p. 28.

47 McGee, 'Can Women Physicians Serve in the Army?', p. 28.

48 This event is reported in the Portland *Journal* (5 May 1918) and is reprinted in *WMJ*, 28 (July 1918), 155–6.

49 The 'Proceedings of the Chicago Session: Minutes of the Sixty-Ninth Annual Session of the American Medical Association, Held at Chicago, June 10–14, 1918', *Journal of the American Medical Association*, 70 (16 June 1918) contains an account of the resolutions and the action taken; see pp. 1855, 1858. See also 'Resolutions Pertaining to Women Physicians as Recommended to the A.M.A. by Legislative Committee', *WMJ*, 28 (June 1918), 138–9. For Wetherill see *Who Was Who in America* (Chicago, Marquis-Who's Who, Inc., 1968), vol. 1, p. 999. For Kress see *Who Was Who in America*, vol. 3, p. 490. For Smith see *Who Was Who in America*, vol. 1, p. 1139.

50 Aileen Kraditor, *The Ideas of the Woman Suffrage Movement, 1890–1920* (New York, Columbia University Press, 1965).

51 The resolutions may be found in 'Proceedings of the Chicago Session', p. 1858.

52 'Proceedings of the Chicago Session', p. 1858.

53 This was part of the Smith resolution. For a discussion of the late twentieth-century debate about these same issues, see Linda Bird Francke, *Ground Zero: The Gender Wars in the Military* (New York, Simon & Schuster, 1997) and Jeanne Holm, *Women in the Military: An Unfinished Revolution* (Novato, CA, Presidio Press, 1992).

54 'Report of Reference Committee on Legislation and Political Action', in 'Proceedings of the Chicago Session', p. 1858.

55 Ruth Milkman, *Gender at Work: The Dynamics of Job Segregation by Sex During World War II* (Urbana, University of Illinois Press, 1987).

56 Purnell, 'The Work of the American Women's Hospitals', p. 98.

57 Their actions provided precedent as another generation of medical women prepared for an assault on barriers to military service in the Second World War. *The Woman's Medical Journal* for 1941 and 1942 contains numerous reminiscences and biographies of women who served as contract surgeons and with medical units in France during the First World War: tales of the past with hope for the present and future. And Emily Dunning Barringer, a member of the Executive Committee of the American Women's Hospitals during the First World War, became the leader of the successful fight for commissions for women in the medical corps during the next 'war to end all wars'. See Emily Dunning Barringer MD, *Bowery to Bellevue: The Story of New York's First Woman Ambulance Surgeon* (New York, W.W. Norton and Company, 1950).

58 For Hamilton's registration, see *Census of Women Physicians*, p. 27. For the other views, see Morton, *A Woman Surgeon*, p. 276.

59 Van Gasken was speaking to students and faculty in September 1917 at the opening of the first college session since the US entry into the war. See Frances van Gasken MD, 'Introductory Address, Woman's Medical College of Pennsylvania', *Bulletin of the Woman's Medical College of Pennsylvania*, 68 (December 1917), 3–4.

60 'A Most Interesting Report', p. 40.

7

MALINGERING IN MODERNITY: PSYCHOLOGICAL SCRIPTS AND ADVERSARIAL ENCOUNTERS DURING THE FIRST WORLD WAR

Roger Cooter

As a means of exploring the relations between war, medicine and modernity, malingering during the First World War seems unpromising. After all, malingering (by that or any other name) long predates 'modernity', as the example of 'mad' Ulysses sowing his fields with salt to escape military service confirms. Moreover, the practice was never the concern only of the military; as testified by an abundance of pre-1914 publications, malingering was one of the preoccupations of industry and the civil state once workmen's compensation and health insurance schemes came into operation. More to the point, little appears to have emerged from the wartime medical involvement with malingering – little, that is, that could be deemed 'modern'. In relation to the vital issues of manpower, morale and pensions, the prevention of malingering was perceived by the military as the primary duty of medical officers; yet there is little evidence of rationalizing medical manoeuvres around it comparable to those associated with orthopaedics, physiology, cardiology, dentistry or neurology, which were stimulated by the same wartime concerns with efficiency.[1] The nearest such action was that taken by the United States Office of the Surgeon-General which in 1918 sought to systematize the medical knowledge on malingering it had obtained from medical officers in the home forces.[2] But that effort was exceptional – more of a résumé after the fact than a plan for action or the development of special expertise. Unlike within the medical specialisms mentioned above, no one was heard later to proclaim that the war had been good for the art of medical sleuthing, let alone that, as a result, it had been scientized, professionalized, managerialized, or generally 'modernized'. No one ever claimed the war a 'milestone' or a 'watershed' in the medicalization of malingering.

But might they? Was not the medical interest in malingering during the First World War affected by the processes of modernity? This chapter seeks to answer these questions in the affirmative, but submits that the material for doing so is recalcitrant and that, for a number of reasons, the record has been obscured. The first part of the chapter therefore explores why the history of malingering in general, and its First World War medical history in particular, has largely failed to reach the agenda of historians.[3] The second part turns to the issue of medicalization itself, illustrating how some doctors did indeed bring malingering under their command – through its psychologization. The third and final part is devoted to exposing the limits to, and constraints upon, this endeavour. The dynamics of medicalization, I suggest, may be less significant historically than the adversarial contest with the state within which, for most doctors, the medical encounter with malingerers transpired and took meaning. Thus, just as the medicalization of malingering might be interpreted as a radical denial of the realities of power against which soldier malingerers fought with their bodies (their only available resource in the situation), so a history of wartime malingering written entirely in terms of its psychologization eclipses the wider politics of professionalization existing in the power relations between doctors and the state. In so far as the history of malingering during the First World War offers a window on these wider politics and power relations, it provides a means to rescue the history of doctoring from the enormous condescensions of a 'modernist' posterity which has too often been scripted in psychologistic terms. One of the purposes of this chapter is to expose that scripting. A further purpose is to signal the limits of medical modernity in war. At least in these respects, I submit, the medical engagement with malingering during the war does indeed hold promise.

BLINKERS AND LENSES

To a degree, it is the malingerers themselves who have obstructed the historical analysis of medicine and malingering. The general perception of their activity as grounded in 'human nature' has tended to detract from (or at least has not encouraged) historical focus on malingering in concrete historical contexts. What the pioneer of scientific management, Frederick Taylor, referred to in 1911 as 'soldiering'[4] – and what soldiers themselves referred to, variously, as 'sodgering', 'swinging the lead', 'funking', 'feigning', 'shamming', 'shirking', 'skulking', 'scrimshanking', 'stuffing the doctor', 'wheezing', 'goldbricking', becoming a 'hospital bird', 'working your ticket' and suffering from 'gang-plank fever' – has suggested only the timelessness of the behaviour of those seeking a ready way to better their immediate lot in life or, more especially, to escape relentless 'obedience and industry'. Medical writers have willingly endorsed this ahistoricity and universalism. Typically, John Collie, the leading British expert on malingering during the first two decades of the twentieth century, spoke of the feigning of disability from injury or disease as having 'occurred in every age, in every country and in every class of society'.[5] This 'timeless aspect of malingering' has also been emphasized by at least one medical historian in order 'to give comfort . . . to the modern physician [in contending with] . . . this ever-present problem'.[6]

Now it may well be that malingering is a common human response to certain intolerable situations, real or imagined – 'a melancholy commentary on human nature', in the words of a contributor to a Dublin medical journal in 1917.[7] And it may also be that doctors – humans too, after all – have habitually felt a need to unmask those patients who appeared to be deceiving them. At least since the time of Galen (to judge from a text anachronistically translated in 1929 as 'How to Detect Malingerers'),[8] some doctors have sought to call the bluff of those who may have been seeking to outsmart them. It hardly follows, however, that the medical playing of this game of cat and mouse has been timeless, consistent over time, or embedded only in individual doctor–patient relations. The bulk of the medical literature on malingering in fact dates only from the Napoleonic Wars when French doctors working for the military were compelled to deal with the evasion techniques of conscripted soldiers.[9] Moreover, then and since, most of the medical writing on the 'contest of wits' with malingerers has implicitly or explicitly sought to flatter the profession's skills at sleuthing, thereby obscuring the contextual political significance of such representations of skill.

It is true that we know little about the history of malingering: how soldiers and sailors acquired their knowledge; how it was transmitted over oceans, between ships and across the barbed wire of no man's land;[10] how it may have been transformed in the process; and how it may have varied in practice between classes, nations and ethnic and occupational groups. But we know at least this: that malingerers were often wise to the latest technologies of detection. Indeed, an intriguing history of popular medicine might be written around their evident mastery of the clinical signs and symptoms of disease and the changing techniques of detection at any one time. By the First World War such knowledge could include that on tendon reflex tests, Babinski's (or Oppenheim and Strumpell's) sign for true hemiplegia, Heilbronner's sign for the spread of muscles among the truly paralysed, Schüller's test for the gait of the paraplegic,[11] Lian's test for arterial pressure to measure the functional efficiency of the heart, Wassermann's reaction for syphilis, and (post-1917) the Felix-Weil test for typhus.[12] Insofar as some of these tests were devised and later routinized specifically with a view to detecting and deterring malingerers and to bypassing individual narratives of illness, it is possible to conceive of another history here, too, or rather the rewriting of a more conventional one. Instead of thinking of medical 'progress' through disinterested discovery, one might conceive of it in terms of expedient reactions to malingerers – much as one might write a history of car security technology in terms of the industry's reactions to the tactics of ever-more-clever car thieves. For example, microchemical analysis had to be devised during the war in order to detect such things as pus from abscesses artificially induced by turpentine, egg albumin in urine, and jaundice caused by the ingestion of picric acid.[13] Techniques such as complete or partial etherization, electric shock and a variety of tricks to test visual and aural acuity were also refined during the war in the effort to unmask malingerers.[14]

Such events in the history of the medical detection of malingerers can be incorporated into a broader history of detective work in medicine generally. While physicians had long acted as diagnosticians (with or without the help of patients' own accounts of illness),[15] an increasing amount of medical work by the late nineteenth century was cast within a forensic frame which had no dependence on individual understandings or narrations of illness. The shift that the historian John Pickstone has delineated in science and medicine from the 'biographical' or individualized way of knowing to the 'analytical'[16] can be traced through the increasing use made of analytical techniques and institutions such as public health laboratories, and even through the rise of psychoanalysis towards the end of the century, informed as these often were by detective fiction. In the medical unmasking of malingering by the First World War the detective trope was widespread. 'The examiner assumes disguises of face and voice in trying to plumb the depths of the suspects's mind,' explained one doctor; 'He may give the idea of being extremely casual, or fussy, uninterested or absurdly inattentive. Deliberate clumsiness with his papers or a sudden break-off to chat with another medical officer: these are the phases designed to distract or bewilder the suspected soldier, and to leave him in doubt as to whether the examiner is a fool to be hoodwinked or a man who stands no nonsense.'[17]

This doctor was not alone in perceiving such 'detective work' as a 'kind of professional sport', a gladiatorial encounter 'of man to man, and brain to brain'.[18] But for others, the detection could be more environmentally or community orientated. Since the mid-nineteenth century, the example of John Snow and William Budd hunting down cholera by retracing the 'scenes of the crime' had provided a model for public health doctors. In fact, for several decades prior to the famous tracking of the carrier 'Typhoid Mary' in 1906,[19] Medical Officers of Health had prided themselves on the subtlety of their epidemiological sleuthing. By then their language was also suffused with the combat metaphors of bacteriology. Thus some military medical officers spoke of malingering as a contagious 'virus which has to be reckoned with', for the 'microbe of insubordination may rapidly permeate a battalion'.[20] This is not the place to elaborate on such metaphors, nor to enter into the broader 'detective' enterprise of public health, except to say with regard to the latter, that it was partly on its basis that new justification was lent to the compulsory notification of certain diseases. The importance of this to the present discussion may be twofold. Firstly, notification constituted a part of the routinization of detection and surveillance by the state in the interest of a more 'fit' population. And secondly, because saving the community (or the state) took precedence over individual relations between doctors and patients, ordinary general practitioners were compelled to cede authority to public health officials or the state's 'medical police'.[21] Significantly, it was a doctor employed by the state (in the Royal Army Medical Corps) who, at the outset of a 1911 paper on malingering, drew attention to the fact that 'observation followed by correct deduction is the basis of all clinical medicine. We should therefore welcome the malingerer who, as it were, takes us on a staff ride in clinical observation.'[22]

Thus the medical detection of malingering around the time of the First World War, or at least the medical interest in it, need not be regarded merely as the continuation of ancient practices and problems; it can be seen as embedded in new frameworks of understanding, work procedures and social relations. It typified a depersonalized analytical paradigm. As such, it might be taken as illustrative of those distinctly modernist tendencies in medicine and society – surveillance and management. That some doctors resisted the military pressure to detect malingerers (as we shall see) can be read as underlining such tendencies.

An ahistorical regard of malingering and its detection is not the only reason why historians of war and medicine, and war and modernity, have largely avoided addressing the subject in any systematic way. As crucial to its neglect has been the historical preoccupation with war neurosis, and with shell-shock during the First World War especially. By virtue of invoking debates around sexuality, class, race and gender, the history of shell-shock is generally held to illuminate modernity, if not the First World War as the very 'birth of the modern'.[23] The literature on shell-shock has become such that the student of modernity, no less than the student of medicine and the First World War, might now be forgiven for thinking that there was no other subject. In the flood of recent literature on post-traumatic stress disorder, for example, the war of 1914–18 is frequently reckoned to be simply 'the war of shell-shock'.[24]

Although malingering features in the historical study of shell-shock, it commands no special attention. This is not because it is perceived as foreign to shell-shock, but rather, because it is presumed an unproblematic adjunct to it. As in the wartime literature on shell-shock, malingering is frequently referred to either as the phenomenon of shell-shock itself (that is, shell-shock dismissed as malingering), or as shell-shock's opposite – the conscious, not to say indulgent, practice of feigned neurosis. War-time and postwar texts on shell-shock sometimes regarded hysteria as predisposing to malingering,[25] but on the whole such texts were inclined to the contrary view, that malingering was a kind of manifestation of hysteria,[26] or at least was difficult to distinguish from certain forms of neuroses. According to the *Report of the Committee of Enquiry into 'Shell-Shock'* (1922), for example, 'the divergence of views over the detection of malingered shell-shock' was 'more apparent than real' since 'the dividing line between malingering and functional neurosis may be a very fine one'.[27] Shell-shock, some believed, was 'unconscious malingering', a manifestation of the basic desire to escape from an intolerable situation;[28] if nothing more, malingering might be symptomatic of shell-shock, a conception to which we will return.

But even if malingering could be regarded merely as shell-shock's unproblematic 'other', that is never all it was. A great many conditions besides shell-shock were feigned (or allegedly feigned) during the war. Certainly, the military command perceived malingering as a far more real and extensive problem than shell-shock; with or without reference to bacteriology, pre-war 'crowd theory', or notions of 'mental contagion', they appreciated that it could become epidemic.[29] So too, for the medical profession recruited to the military, malingering was perceived as troublesome, albeit often for very different reasons from those of the commanders.

MEDICALIZING MALINGERING

There can be no doubt that for many doctors during the First World War the experience of dealing with malingerers compounded an already existing tension in the performance of their duty. As hundreds of letters, diaries and autobiographical writings confirm, civilian doctors recruited into the military were sensitive to the tension between, on the one hand, the Hippocratic injunction to preserve health and life, and, on the other hand, the state's injunction to patch up the bodies of soldiers in order to re-equip them for killing and being killed. As Freud summed up their dilemma shortly after the war: 'The physicians had to play a role somewhat like that of a machine gun behind the front line, that of driving back those who fled. Certainly, this was the intent of the war administration. . . . The task was irreconcilable for the medical profession. . . . No compromise can be effected between compliance with humane values and compulsory military service.'[30]

The profession's involvement with malingering can be seen as having exacerbated these ethical tensions by serving to remind doctors of the distance from the usual peacetime clinical encounter with private patients. To suspect a soldier of malingering was to enter into a relationship which was essentially adversarial. It was founded not on the basis of a physician seeking (or sustaining) a patient's trust, but on mutual distrust and suspicion. It did not aim to promote health through the exposure of illness, but to elicit punishment through the exposure of deceit. Violated were the rules of confidentiality governing private practice; as in insurance work and industrial medicine, the secrets of patients were betrayed to a third party (the Army), the doctor's employer. The role was also adversarial in a more formal legal sense in that doctors found themselves compelled to give evidence at courts martial. Few doctors had either the skills or the inclination for such medical jurisprudential work which placed them in an awkward intermediary role between patients and the state.

Common soldiers and sailors were not of course private patients; nevertheless, civilian doctors carried over into the military norms of confidentiality and trust, sufficient for many of them to find the business of exposing malingerers deeply repellent. In Britain, the pre-war introduction of National Health Insurance had already led some practitioners to proffer expressions about 'the first duty of the doctor to his patient, without whose permission to open them the doctor's lips are absolutely closed concerning all he may come to know of his patient while in discharge of his professional duties to him'.[31] Only five months before the outbreak of the war, one doctor, in an address on medical ethics and politics published in the *British Medical Journal*, reminded his colleagues that it was 'no part of [their] duty to act as detectives' in the operation of the new National Health Insurance.[32] John Collie, as an insurance referee and medical officer to various large corporations and government departments, had of course no qualms about exhorting doctors to 'combine the methods of the detective with those of the physician and surgeon' in unmasking malingerers.[33] Nor was there much hesitation among some prison medical officers, who extolled the practice of soliciting information from malingerers through 'inferential interrogation'.[34] But the rest of the profession were unused to and hesitant about such practices. They may not have been completely 'at sea' with malingerers, or wholly lacking the 'mental alertness' and 'judgment' to detect them, as Collie maintained,[35] but their contentment with the task was not conspicuous. They may have appreciated the danger (well-worn in nineteenth-century writing on malingering) that by entering into the detective role in order to expose suspected malingerers, they themselves were acting deceitfully and hence rendering their own characters as bad or as worthless as those who tried to deceive them.[36] For this 'morally corrupting' reason, among others, 'the subject [of malingering] is not a pleasant one', opined the editor of the *Lancet* in 1913 in the course of remarking on the timely lectures of the (by then knighted) Sir John Collie.[37]

Such views were carried into wartime medical service, some doctors clearly being infuriated by the military's expectation that they act as policemen arresting malingerers.[38] Whether or not doctors were sympathetic to those who feigned illness or those who inflicted wounds on themselves in last-ditch defences against the terrors of the front – and many doctors were sympathetic, and were themselves not above malingering[39] – it is clear from their letters and diaries that they very much feared the wrongful exposure of the innocent, and the consequent inflicting of unnecessary punishment and pain, or even death. As Quain's *Dictionary of Medicine* had long warned them: 'Far better is it for us to be deceived twenty times, than for unjust suspicion to be directed to the victim of some painful and depressing disease.'[40] '[T]here is no greater danger [than] our mistaking a man who is really ill for one who is not,' warned a military psychiatrist,[41] not least because a medical officer could risk losing face among the troops and among fellow officers in the event of an accusation of malingering not being upheld at a court martial.[42] As medical reputations could be destroyed by clever malingerers, so they could be ruined by the decisions of non-medical military commanders. Medical officers were also aware that 'he who lets many malingerers slip through his fingers . . . commends himself for his kindliness and incurs no dislike among fellow-officers or men; while the medical officer who has constantly before his eye the hard necessity of keeping the men in the ranks, is often harassed by doubts as to the equity of some decision, and he is likely to be regarded by those around him as cruel and unjust towards those for whose ills he is supposed to bring succor.'[43]

The military, for their part, were not above making scapegoats of doctors who were soft on malingerers. To them, dissimulators were simply cowards, and medical officers who tolerated them were dangerous perpetrators of bad morale. When, on the eve of what turned out to be an abortive late-night assault on enemy trenches on 9 July 1916, medical officer Lt Kirkwood (RAMC) accepted the self-assessment of the two dozen exhausted troops who reported to him as suffering from shell-shock, he was not only quickly relieved of his post, but was blamed for the mission's failure.[44]

It is not, therefore, difficult to understand why some doctors might have been only too happy to turn the encounter with malingerers into something less confrontational and less ensnared in the politics of military authority. If malingering were cast as a psychological condition it could serve as a means both of asserting medical authority and of gaining professional autonomy in the face of the military's employment of doctors as mere medical police. Doctors might thereby extricate themselves from positions which, vis-à-vis the military, were parallel to those of malingerers in their relation to medical officers. In effect, through psychologization, the malingerer's use of his body in the struggle against military power, as well as the medical profession's relations with the military, could be depoliticized, or at least removed from the space of medical jurisprudence.

The resources for such a move were available long before the war. From around the 1890s psychodynamic ideas began to gain ascendancy within what was to become known as the 'new psychiatry'. As early as 1911 some military doctors were arguing that 'a malingerer is almost invariably either insane or a psychopath' (and hence not responsible for his deceitfulness).[45] In medical textbooks, malingering was frequently spoken of in the same breath as hysteria and neurasthenia. In part, this was because the meaning of 'feigned disease' had changed since the early nineteenth century; from being more or less the same as malingering, it had been transformed into its opposite, 'disease simulated *involuntarily*'.[46] In the pan-European discussions of malingering in relation to workmen's compensation, and in the more intensive debates in Britain in 1913 in the wake of National Health Insurance, it was not uncommon for doctors to invoke concepts of unconscious or non-deliberate action in explaining or accounting for the phenomenon.[47] As a result, the exact meaning of the word malingering became unclear; in Paris a special meeting of the Neurological Society was held in 1915 precisely in order to arrive at a clearer definition.[48]

In the course of the debate over shell-shock during the war, it became even easier to embrace psychopathological perspectives on malingering and, in particular, to tie it to notions of involuntary behaviour. A contributor to the *Lancet* in 1916, for example, contended that malingering was 'a disease of the highest conscious cerebral centres in the frontal lobes', 'a moral cell disease' which was not easily distinguished from hysteria, neurasthenia and shock.[49] Doctors did not entirely abandon the idea that there were persons 'with full knowledge, intent and responsibility' who endeavoured to 'counterfeit, exaggerate, create or conceal disease' – the 'rascals' whom Collie in 1910 referred to as 'true malingerers'. But it was increasingly the view that such persons were 'extremely rare'.[50] Asserted instead was the prevalence of 'a second group of which the members are hypochondriacs or constitutionally inferior individuals who, throughout their lives, have never been able to meet disagreeable situations without complaint and ruse, deceit and evasion'.[51] In line with this view, the authors of what became the standard British textbook on malingering, published in 1917, were inclined to regard malingering as 'due to a depravation of the primitive Imitative impulse', 'an hypothesis suggested on biological grounds, [and] one, moreover, which derives colour from the particular types of individual most prone to malinger – the hysterical, weak–minded, or those of neuropathic heritage'.[52] 'Heritage', or eugenic and racial concepts, were frequently invoked in such discussions.[53]

It is not hard to understand how such elaborations of malingering might also have served militarists, if not the military: the implication could be that war is not so bad after all, and that those who malingered their way out of it were, in effect, mentally subnormal. 'The simulation of neurasthenia and insanity', contended one neurological consultant, 'approaches more closely to the actual affections . . . the nearer [the malingerer's] mental condition borders on insanity or degeneration. Thus it happens that feigning is best seen in those actually suffering from insanity.'[54] One wartime American surgeon was convinced that 'whether the malingering took the form of mental or nervous or physical defects it was based in almost every instance, on an actual unstable or defective mental state'.[55] '[F]raud in disease', maintained another, 'is usually one more indication of the presence of the mental soil that gave rise to the criminal tendency.'[56] For Dr Auckland Geddes, the British wartime Director of Recruiting, it was the 'men of the lower categories' who presented the biggest problem and against whom recruiting officers had to be continually on guard.[57]

There is little evidence that medical writers on malingering deliberately pruned their prose to please militarists. Much of what they wrote, however, bears the stamp of a self-serving professionalizing rhetoric. The allegedly incompetent doctor who either sees malingerers everywhere or is forever fooled by them was repeatedly castigated. 'Here, just as in cases under the Workmen's Compensation Act', it was claimed by a couple of French doctors in a work of 1918 on the psychoneuroses of war, 'it is the least experienced [medical] observers who diagnose the most cases as malingerers.'[58] This was not unlike the professionalizing argument of Collie in 1910, except that it was now couched almost entirely in psychological terms (to which Collie remained resistant, even after becoming one of the key figures in the development of shell-shock treatment and pensions policy after the war). A writer on malingering in the *Military Surgeon* in 1919, for example, provided a long list of psychiatric luminaries from Charcot onwards who were all of the opinion that 'malingering is too often based on the ignorance of the doctor', or is perceived as prevalent because of a 'common lack [of] thorough knowledge of mental disease, especially hysteria'.[59] 'It ought to be recognized that it is chiefly physicians who have not made a special study of neurology' who misdiagnose and misunderstand malingering, complained the above-mentioned French authors in the section of their text on malingering (the object of which was to render the subject more logical and scientific and therefore less bound to the legal profession).

By the end of the war it had become almost impossible to conceive of malingering outside a psychological or psychopathological framework. In the 1920s, spokesmen for employers and insurance companies, no less than those for labour, could be quoted for their views on malingering as a 'neurasthenic condition'.[60] There was no real going back on this inclination, although in relation to National Health Insurance and workmen's compensation the tendency towards it was often less conspicuous, especially among legally-minded medical men in the employ of government and industry. Donald Norris, for instance, a barrister who was also a Fellow of the Royal College of Surgeons as well as chief medical officer to the Metropolitan Water Board and the Bank of England, was insistent in his article on malingering in the *British Encyclopedia of Medical Practice* in 1938 that 'Malingering is not a disease but a species of fraud, and it might well be considered that a medical man as such has no special qualifications to decide whether his patient is guilty of fraud'.[61] Yet even Norris had to admit that the problem 'may be exceedingly difficult, and an approach to its solution may call for a profound knowledge of psychology, both normal and abnormal'.[62] There were also those, even in military psychiatry in the 1920s, who refused to submit to the 'opinion . . . that every simulator is proved by that very fact to be abnormal mentally . . . To call all such cases unsound of mind would be a travesty of psychiatry and a forensic stupidity which would quickly demoralize any army, or for that matter any society.' But the passion with which this author had to contend against what he called the befogging 'plausibilities of a mass of nebulous psychopathological theories in which vastness assumes the guise of profundity', may be read as testimony to the force of countervailing rhetoric.[63]

Certainly by the 1930s the link between malingering and psychoneurosis was well fastened. The bond was so secure in fact that malingering was in danger of being wholly psychologized. Malingerers were 'almost invariably cases of frank psychoneurosis or of organic disease or trauma which has passed into a psychoneurotic phase', explained the medical officer to the Boots Pure Drug Company in an article in the *Lancet* in 1934, adding that 'It is not correct, however, to call these people malingerers'.[64] As the medical officer to the Trades Union Congress put it in a private letter in 1936, 'the new psychology killed the idea of malingering.'[65] A year later, labour leader and politician Ernest Bevin, writing in the *British Medical Journal*, expressed a similar view:

> For a long time it was assumed that the main thing to be decided in the case of a worker who was ill was whether or not he was a malingerer. Practically the whole of the Workmen's Compensation Laws and restrictions associated with certain health services have been based upon the assumption that protection had to be secured against exploitation on the part of the worker, and to that extent the service has been handicapped in its outlook. I am not too sure that the attitude of the medical profession itself in the past has not been coloured by this conception. Happily, however, with the growth of the study of psychology and a deeper understanding of the health problem, this approach has to a large extent been changed.[66]

So successfully were psychopathological concepts and vocabularies drawn upon in the effort to reduce the 'differences between feigned and actual disability . . . to as accurate a science as the study of medicine can bring it',[67] that by the Second World War many Army psychiatrists seemed in little doubt that malingerers were mostly psychopaths.[68] Even those malingerers who had been defined out of the category could be psychologically reincorporated, at least linguistically. The man who 'swings the lead', according to the First World War-trained psychologist Millais Culpin, 'is not a pure malingerer', but the phrase 'when used by a soldier, signifies "to plumb the stream of consciousness of the medical officer"'.[69]

In the classic sociological sense of medicalization, then, 'badness' appears to have been transformed into 'sickness'.[70] The war helped render a problem of discipline (bounded by law and morality) into one of psychiatry (bounded by medicine). As noted in 1915 by an American asylum doctor (evidently on the professional make in psychiatry), malingering was formerly 'viewed primarily from the standpoint of the moralist', and this was a view which was unfortunately held by 'the average lawyer [who] still looks upon the ideas concerning crime and the criminal expressed by physicians of a forensic bent as totally unpractical and visionary'.[71] Now, however, so far as malingering was allowed clinically to exist, it was no longer to be understood in terms of an adversarial encounter between the soldier/worker and the employer (or state) with the doctor acting as arbiter; instead, it was to be regarded as a clinical encounter, governed by medical discourse in general, and by modern psychiatric and psychological experts in particular. Thus, so far as professionalization, medicalization and psychologization can be read as characteristics of modernity, malingering had been embraced by it.

BEYOND MEDICALIZATION – PRACTICE AND POLITICS

Or so it might seem. However, if we look beyond the wartime and postwar psychological literature on malingering, and look beneath the surface of some of the above statements, a rather different impression is gained. It is one in which malingering is situated in a far denser web of social relations and politics than reference to writing on psychology alone. But before we turn to this, it should be noted that the practical effect of modernity's embrace of malingering is not widely apparent. For all the rhetoric, there is little evidence that those who scripted malingering psychologically were able successfully to sell their wares to the state. The court-martialling of malingerers continued apace during the war.[72] From the military's point of view, the medicalization of malingering could only serve to encourage it and run up demands on war pensions. In any case, there was never any suggestion in the psychological writing of rehabilitation procedures for malingerers. And even if in the course of the war there were changes of attitude towards malingerers by military medical personnel, there are, as we shall see, more credible reasons for this than the writings of psychologists. Nor, finally, is it noticeable during the Second World War that the Army consequently regarded malingering in any different light than during the First World War. To a degree, the great concern in 1939 not to acknowledge shell-shock, and hence to deny it pensionable status, closed a space for psychological discourse on malingering.

But the main reason why it is difficult to fit the medical detection of malingering into a modernist psychological script is that not all medical officers adopted, or wanted to adopt, psychological understandings of malingering. Here, we need to be cognizant of the heterogeneity of the profession at the time, and its deep political divisions. In Britain, National Health Insurance, the debate over the reform of Poor Law medical services, plans for a Ministry of Health, changes in the Local Government Board maternity and child health services, and a variety of other far-reaching proposals served both to politicize the profession and to confound it. To many doctors, the bureaucratic red tape of medical practice under the military seemed a foretaste of 'socialized medicine'. Others, however, perceived salvation in a nationalized or municipalized medical service with efficient rationalized functions and a salaried profession. Still others – a reform-minded consultant elite empowered by the war – imagined the future in terms of health centres within a new hierarchy of power with general practitioners and outreach services firmly under their command.[73]

The political divisions in British medicine were sufficient to threaten the British Medical Association (BMA) itself. Manifestations of its inability to coordinate the profession are clear in the range of alternative bodies set up (or attempted) at this time. In 1912 the socialist State Medical Services Association was created; in 1914 a Medical Federation was proposed to exploit the distrust of many doctors of the Insurance Acts; a few years later the National Medical Union was established, followed by the Medico-Political Union (a trade union), and subsequently an Association of Panel Committees. A new formation immediately after the war, the British Federation of Medical and Allied Societies, sought to bring together some forty-seven different societies interested in national health, *excluding* the BMA. The federation was evidence, according to one physician,

> of the profound distrust, suspicion, disappointment, or disgust which at present exists in the minds of many with regard to the British Medical Association as an efficient, reliable, virile, up-to-date organization capable of dealing with medico-political and sociological problems with vision, imagination, grit, and some of the enthusiasm of youth; and to be relied on to lead the profession and the public on questions affecting health safely through the many difficulties and dangers of the transitional and reconstruction periods of the new age now upon us.[74]

Structural divisions between general practitioners and hospital consultants sometimes mapped on to these political divisions,[75] but there were also hierarchical divisions between types of surgical and medical consultants (e.g., between psychologists and pathology-based specialisms), as well as between civilian and military doctors (at all levels). Additionally, between psychologists, psychiatrists and neurologists – the boundaries of whose disciplines remained fluid – there were profound differences in orientation, most notably around whether shell-shock was an organic or a psychical condition. The psychologist William McDougall recalled hearing fellow medical officers declare that if no organic damage could be identified in a particular case, then it was clearly a question of malingering and the individual concerned should be shot.[76] Among the consultants in this area who came to regard shell-shock as 'hysterical malingering', there were further divergences as to whether it could be considered unconsciously or willfully motivated. Some, such as the neurologist and psychiatrist Frederick Mott, took an exceedingly unpsychological view of malingering, regarding it as straightforward criminal activity.[77]

It is also important to realize that a consultant, or putative consultant, at this time might have two or three areas of special interest or specialist professional attachments, and he (rarely she) might or might not aspire to specialist practice. Thomas Lumsden, for example, the author of the above-cited article on malingering in the *Lancet* in 1916, was primarily a nose and throat specialist, but he was also a Fellow of the Psychological Medical Association and a civil member of the Special Medical Board for Functional Nervous Disease. As well as serving as the medical officer to the London Fire Brigade, the Water Board and the London County Council Tramways, he ran a private practice in fashionable Belgrave Square.[78] Such practitioners were not uncommon – a fact that renders it difficult to match those with tendencies to psychologize malingering to specific professional locations and identities. Although more research needs undertaking to determine the precise background and professional status of those who argued for the psychologization of malingering during the First World War, it is not certain that such research would produce identikit answers.

What can be said is that most of those in medicine who published on malingering during and after the war were not those who experienced its practice at the front or in the regimental camps. Those who sought to make a name for themselves by publishing on the subject tended to be employed as neurologists, psychologists or psychiatrists at the base hospitals, or were armchair authors in civilian practice or in schools of military medicine. By contrast, those at the front, or those involved with routine medical work at the base camps – much of it concerned with matters of sanitation, stretcher drill, foot drill, lectures on first aid etc. – tended to be recruits from general practice and from public health (Medical Officers of Health). Their views on, and attitudes towards, malingering could be very different from those involved in its medicalization. According to contemporary observers, many rank-and-file medical officers were obsessed with the idea that all soldiers who reported sick were malingerers.[79] Some of the 'obsessed' may have been overcompensating for their lack of military experience by bending over backwards to kiss the boots of the military high command. (As Freud said of these doctors, 'They allowed the sense of their power to make an appearance in a brutal fashion.')[80] Soldiers took note; one recollected that upon his arrival in France, the medical officer quickly inspected the ranks 'with his face fixed in a supercilious state . . . If he wanted to create an impression of inhumanity he could hardly have done it more effectively'.[81]

But we need not typecast rank-and-file medical officers in this way to understand their views on malingering. It needs bearing in mind that much malingering was of a sufficiently low order as to hardly merit the label. Of one set of war-devised categories of malingering – 'assumed', 'invented', 'exaggerated' and 'prolonged' – the latter two forms of 'sodgering' were by far the more common, and rarely tested the diagnostic metal of medical officers.[82] Dr W.M. Child, for example, previously the Lindfield District Medical Officer, wrote to his wife on 23 September 1916: 'I had a large sick parade of malingerers today: they were inoculated the day before yesterday and given a very light day yesterday, and this morning they refused to get up and go to work and all went sick. So of course I did not treat them but just sent them back for extra duty.'[83]

In such routine encounters with 'malingerers', sophisticated psychological theorizing or pathologization was neither required nor offered. Mild discipline, not medicalization, was the order of the day, and it was readily dispensed. As historian Marya Arfer has found in her study of rank-and-file doctors at the front, they tended to respond to malingering not as a treatable pathology, but in terms of personal cowardice – a flaw of character, or a failure of manhood, patriotism or class which might even be momentarily empathized with.[84] By and large this was also how the non-psychologically-inclined Sir John Collie dealt with malingerers: 'a serious appeal to the sense of honour, or friendly encouragement to "play the man", or even judicious neglect, have a most stimulating effect.'[85]

Thus among rank-and-file medical officers, as opposed to the elite psychologically-inclined ones, the encounter with malingerers might be *demedicalized*. And in this way, as effectively as through psychologization, malingering could be demilitarized, in the sense of being withdrawn from the military's disciplinary regime for malingerers. As one medical officer put it, front-line doctors could deal effectively with malingerers 'without coaching from the rear'.[86]

It is a moot point whether this also constituted the depoliticization of malingering; in many ways the rank-and-file doctors' demedicalizing and demilitarizing of malingering was no less inherently political than the act of malingering itself or, for that matter, its psychologization. We can be certain, however, that the political implications of the demilitarization of malingering mattered more to rank-and-file medical officers than to the psychologizers of malingering, or to the many doctors specializing in such areas as ophthalmology and cardiology who also had professionalizing stakes in the detection of malingerers. After all, the rank and file were at the sharp end of the state's use of doctors as salaried servants and third-party medical detectives. It was this relationship with the state that mattered most to general practitioners (GPs), rather than that with individual malingerers. It mattered especially to those who were strongly under the impression that outside the military, in civil practice, 'the system of individual employment is on trial', or that a salaried medical service was in the offing.[87] GPs were under threat of becoming merely intermediaries between patients and the state, their market-sovereign autonomy jeopardized. This was the feared new role of which the enforced detection and court-martialling of malingering in the military was symbolic.

Most important to us here is that in the course of their struggle against that threatened loss of autonomy, GPs took up what might well be described as an anti-modernist position, at the heart of which was the trope of the sacred voluntary relationship between doctors and patients. This relationship they now propelled into its 'modern' rhetorical form. In article after article in the medical press, GPs celebrated the neo-Hippocratic beneficent relationship between doctors and patients – the antithesis of the state-mediated relationship between the malingerer and the military or industrial doctor. 'I personally should not care, and I am confident that my patients would not care, for the tie between them and myself to be [broken, or replaced by] a record card,' asserted Peter MacDonald, a wayward socialist GP of York, in an article in the *British Medical Journal* in 1918. 'These are not the present day relations of doctors and patient, except in the army. *At risk of being considered old-fashioned and conservative*, I profess my preference for the present personal relations' (my italics).[88] Medical ethics were wheeled out in defence of these relations, which were now upheld as 'the primary reason for the doctor's being'.[89] In America in the 1920s, a new edition of Thomas Percival's *Medical Ethics* was justified on the grounds that the 'close personal relations which formerly existed between physician and patient' were breaking down as a result of 'group practice, health insurance, and state medicine'.[90] British GPs in their 'Panel' practices for National Health Insurance (NHI) therefore came to support the principle of independent referees to whom suspected malingerers could be delegated.[91] In this way they could hope to preserve good relations with their panel patients and, as important, with the families of those patients from whom most of them earned their keep in private practice.

In the case of GPs, then, the wartime encounter with malingerers engendered responses which were the very opposite of those associated with modernity, either in its psychologistic sense or in terms of an administrative way of knowing and proceeding. Psychological modernism was not embraced, and neither were any standardizing routines. For the most part, malingering was managed paternalistically on an individual informal basis, essentially in reaction to the managerial forces of modernity, and in disdain of psychological expertise. If malingering in modernity signifies rebellion against industrial disciplines and routines, then GPs and malingerers had much in common.

The argument for the medical detection of malingering 'in modernity' also needs to take cognizance of the fact that, postwar, malingering was largely de-problematized. Malingering in industry emerged as nothing like the spectre that Collie and some others had represented it before the war. Between 1906 (when the Workmen's Compensation Consolidated Act was passed) and 1912, there was a 44 per cent increase in workmen's compensation claims,[92] but there were no comparable increases after the war; 'scrimshanking employees' did not appear 'in want of restraint', as it seemed to some during the first decade of the century.[93] Even in 1914 Collie was accused of exaggerating the problem. In one doctor's opinion, 'working men were on the whole less disposed to malingering than any other class. What was wanted was a proper relationship between doctor and doctor and a better understanding between the [approved societies under NHI] and the medical profession.'[94] As under the Poor Law, where the extent of chronic sickness rendered malingering virtually a non-issue by the 1900s,[95] so in medicine generally, and under NHI and Workmen's Compensation in particular, malingering gradually ceased to be perceived as a serious issue. As with similar legislation in other countries, it was found that after an initial flood of sick claimants (of whom many were presumed frauds), the numbers levelled off, and the 'malingerers' proportionately.[96] To the extent that malingering persisted, its costs appear to have been absorbed into the general cost of sickness benefit. On occasions during the interwar period when unemployment was high, the state sought to clamp down on alleged malingering, but its target was not the malingerers so much as the GPs, who were accused of 'lax certification' in processing sickness benefit claims.[97] In the open medical market, GPs were at the commercial mercy of unemployed workers and their families. Although state medicine was ultimately to save general practice by rendering it economically viable, a new role for GPs as 'gatekeepers' protecting society from malingerers was not one that flowed easily or instantly from the experience of the First World War.[98]

In industry some attempts were made to police malingerers after the war, and some medical officers who had specialized in detection during the war offered their skills to employers. However, as Joanna Bourke has pointed out, unlike the military there were few punitive measures that employers could take, short of not employing the worker and other family members.[99] Bourke has argued that attention therefore turned from the punishment to the prevention of malingering in industry and that it was here that psychology came into its own. That Ernest Bevin and others could refer to the 'new psychology' in 1937 may reflect that fact. But it should also be borne in mind that it was very much in the interest of Labour Party politicians and trade union medical officers to maintain that malingering had been 'done in' by the new psychology. Upheld thereby was not only the moral integrity of the working class, but also the political pitch for state medicine (against those alleging that such a system would be inundated with malingerers). Thus, here too it might be argued that the psychologization of malingering was less significant than the ideological context within which it was located, embraced, resisted or evaded.

CONCLUSION

No less than labour leaders or the GPs discussed above, historians of medicine and the First World War can be accused of shying away from the subject of malingering. It would be wrong, however, to claim that they have acted like malingerers with pens, artfully dodging the subject. Least of all can they be accused of having done so by focusing attention on shell-shock and the psychological rethinkings occasioned by the war. As we have seen, much of the wartime discussion of malingering was cast within and reflective upon such rethinking. To focus on shell-shock rather than malingering is therefore to engage directly with the wartime history of psychology, and to acknowledge the dominant idiom within which much debate over the problems of military work-time discipline was articulated. But as we have also seen, the medical experiencing of malingering during the war cannot be wholly comprehended within that framework. The medical engagement was at once broader and more historically complicated, involving conflicts of political interest as much as psycho-therapeutic and physical techniques for the unmasking of certain behaviours. Adversarial encounters with malingerers were based on more than merely doctor–patient relations or on narrow professionalizing concerns; they hinged on fundamental transformations in the structure and funding of medical care which predated the war. Hence, to ask what the war did for the detection of malingering may be to ask the wrong question; more pertinent is what the wartime experience with malingerers did for the medical profession. The answer, as in so many other domains of medicine, is that the war compounded pre-existing aspirations as well as anxieties. It provided a few doctors with better claims to expertise in cases of purported fraud, and others with further resources for the psychologicalization of patients. For most in the profession, however, the encounter epitomized and symbolized a largely loathsome 'militarized' or state-bureaucratized type of medical practice that was seen to greatly diminish professional autonomy.

Nevertheless, even in the light of this relatively negative encounter, the wartime medical experience with malingering cannot be reckoned outside the processes of modernity. However we estimate the responses to it, malingering and its detection was in and of modernity. The reactions of the GPs, like those of all others in medicine, were prompted and underwritten by the same forces that led workers and soldiers to malinger: the routinized, disciplining demands of the modern industrial world and its warfare. Thus the history of the medical encounter with malingering during the war, whether perceived in terms of medicalization or anti-medicalization, cannot be other than a window on the politics of modernity's experience.

ACKNOWLEDGEMENTS

Different versions of this chapter were aired in 1995 and 1996, firstly, in London, at the Wellcome Institute for the History of Medicine, and at Imperial College, and then in Manchester at the Centre for the History of Science, Technology and Medicine. I am grateful to the participants for their many helpful insights. For forcing me along, I am especially grateful to Marya Arfer, Peter Barham, Joanna Bourke, Matthew Ramsey, Steve Sturdy and Bob Joy (who also generously supplied me with many American sources). As ever, I am grateful to the Wellcome Trust for their funding.

Notes

1 See Roger Cooter, *Surgery and Society in Peace and War: Orthopaedics and the Organization of Modern Medicine, 1880–1948* (London, Macmillan, 1993); Paul Lerner, 'Rationalizing the Therapeutic

Arsenal: German Neuropsychiatry in World War I' in Manfred Berg and Geoffrey Cocks (eds), *Medicine and Modernity: Public Health and Medical Care in Nineteenth- and Twentieth-Century Germany* (Cambridge University Press, 1997), pp. 121–48; and the chapters in this volume by Sturdy and Howell. On dentistry's wartime rationalization, see W.G. Macpherson, *History of the Great War Based on Official Documents. Medical Services, General History*, vol. 1 (London, HMSO, 1921), pp. 134–6.

2 The resulting report, compiled by Maj Pearce Bailey, was unique in addressing the question of the management of malingering. Office of the Surgeon-General, 'Malingering in U.S. Troops, Home Forces, 1917', *Military Surgeon*, 42 (1918), 261–75, 427–49.

3 The sole exception is the chapter on malingering in Joanne Bourke's *Dismembering the Male: Men's Bodies, Britain, and the Great War* (Chicago University Press, 1996). Focused primarily on the malingerers, Bourke's chapter complements the focus here on the medical profession.

4 Frederick Winslow Taylor, *Scientific Management* (New York, Harper, 1911), p. 30.

5 R.J. Collie, 'The Malingerer' in Douglas Knocker (ed.), *Accidents in their Medico-Legal Aspect by Leading Medical and Surgical Authorities* (London, Bailliere, Tindall & Cox, 1910), p. 545.

6 Ilza Veith, 'On Malingering', *Bulletin of the Cleveland Medical Library*, 2 (1955), 67–73.

7 'Recent Works on Malingering', *Dublin Journal of Medical Science*, 144 (1917), 119.

8 Galen, 'How to Detect Malingerers' in *Greek Medicine*, tr. and annot. Arthur J. Brock (London, Dent, 1929), pp. 225ff. Brock was among those who worked with W.H.R. Rivers at the Craiglockhart hospital for shell-shocked officers during the First World War. The word 'malingeror' appears in British military slang in the eighteenth century; Capt Frances Grose's *Classical Dictionary of the Vulgar Tongue* (1785) defines it as a 'military term for one who, under pretence of sickness, evades his duty'. The word appears to have derived either from French *malingre*, 'sickly', or Latin *malus aeger*, 'evil disposition'.

9 Matthew Ramsey, 'Conscription, Malingering, and Popular Medicine in Napoleonic France' in Robert Holtman (ed.), *The Consortium on Revolutionary Europe, 1750–1850: Proceedings, 1978* (Athens, Georgia, 1978), 188–99.

10 The transmission of the knowledge was not all by word of mouth. Although the military doctor John Cheyne writing on malingering in the 1820s spoke of 'a kind of free masonry among soldiers', he also refers to a printed report of 1807 on malingering which was circulated among the troops. Cheyne, 'Medical Report on the Feigned Diseases of Soldiers, in a letter addressed to George Renny, Director General of Military Hospitals in Ireland', *Dublin Hospital Reports and Communications in Medicine and Surgery*, 4 (1827), 127–8. See also John Hennen, 'On Feigned Diseases' in his *Observations On Some Important Points in the Practice of Military Surgery* (Edinburgh, 1818), p. 476, where he refers to 'a paper of corrosive sublimate . . . found in [a soldier's] possession, with some manuscript directions for its use'. The recipe was for a 'decoction of parsnips and clover, with which the eye was to be fomented'. In the USA in the nineteenth century many of the tricks known among conscripts in Europe were directly transplanted by the emigres who left their homelands during the 1840s and 1850s in order to avoid compulsory military service. As previously in France, a lively trade sprang up in medico-legal bribery in the USA during the American Civil War, with certain doctors performing operations on draft-dodgers, such as inflation of the scrotum. See James C. Mohr, *Doctors and the Law* (New York, Oxford University Press, 1993), p. 157. See also 'A Civil War Medical Examiner: The

Report of Dr. Horace O. Crane' in Peter T. Harstad (ed.), *Wisconsin Magazine of History*, 48 (1965), 222–31; Grace Palladino, 'Opposition to Conscription in the Coal Regions, 1862–63' in her *Another Civil War* (Urbana/Chicago, University of Illinois Press, 1990).

11 On these and other tests, see Donald Norris, 'Malingering' in *British Encyclopedia of Medical Practice*, ed. Sir Humphry Rolleston (London, Butterworth, 1938), p. 363.

12 See R. Cranston Low, 'Some Queer Patients – Some Notes on Artifacts', *Edinburgh Medical Journal*, 45 (1938), 88–100, at p. 90; see also Ilana Lowy, 'Testing for a Sexually–Transmitted Disease 1907–1970: The History of the Wassermann Reaction' in Virginia Berridge and Phil Strong (eds), *AIDS and Contemporary History* (Cambridge University Press, 1993), pp. 74–92.

13 See 'Tests for the Detection of Malingering Among Soldiers', *Lancet*, 8 July 1916, 80–1.

14 See, for example, William Wallace, 'Methods of Examining the Vision of Recruits and Soldiers with Special Reference to Assumed and Real Defects', *Journal of the Royal Army Medical Corps (JRAMC)*, 27 (1916), 471–80; Alan W. Sichel, 'A New Test Type for the Detection of Malingerers in the Army', ibid., 30 (1918), 326–31.

15 See Roy Porter, 'The Rise of Physical Examination' in W.F. Bynum and Roy Porter (eds), *Medicine and the Five Senses* (Cambridge University Press, 1993), pp. 179–97; on the reluctance of some nineteenth-century surgeons to accept the patient's testimony, see Alison Winter, 'Ethereal Epidemic: Mesmerism and the Introduction of Inhalation Anaesthesia to Early Victorian London', *Social History of Medicine*, 4 (1991), 1–28.

16 John V. Pickstone, 'Ways of Knowing: Towards a Historical Sociology of Science, Technology and Medicine', *British Journal for the History of Science*, 36 (1993), 433–58.

17 William Wallace, 'The Vision of the Soldier with Special Reference to Malingering', *JRAMC*, 37 (1921), 40. For similar, see Lewis Yealland, 'Malingering' in his *Hysterical Disorders of Warfare* (London, Macmillan, 1918), pp. 237–48 at pp. 238–9.

18 For the use of the sporting metaphor, see also Maj C.E. Pollock, 'Malingering', *JRAMC*, 16 (1911), 50.

19 See Judith Leavitt, '"Typhoid Mary" Strikes Back: Bacteriological Theory and Practice in Early Twentieth Century Public Health', *Isis*, 83 (1992), 608–28.

20 Wallace, 'The Vision of the Soldier', p. 478; *idem*, 'Methods of Examining the Vision of Recruits and Soldiers', pp. 41, 44.

21 I am grateful to Janice Wilcox for information on notification from her 'The Notification of Infectious Diseases: Bolton and Huddersfield, 1877–1920' (Ph.D. thesis, University of Huddersfield, forthcoming).

22 Pollock, 'Malingering', p. 50.

23 Best known, perhaps, is the work of the literary historian, Elaine Showalter: 'Male Hysteria: W.H.R. Rivers and the Lessons of Shell Shock' in her *The Female Malady: Women, Madness, and English Culture, 1830–1980* (London, Virago, 1993), pp. 167–94; Showalter, *Sexual Anarchy: Gender and Culture at the Fin de Siècle* (London, Virago, 1992). More recent work adds a much needed comparative perspective: see Paul Lerner, 'Hysterical Men: War, Neurosis and German Mental Medicine, 1914–1921' (unpub. Ph.D. thesis, Columbia University, 1996), and Marc Oliver Roudebush, 'A Battle of Nerves: Hysteria and its Treatment in France During World War I' (unpub. Ph.D. thesis, University of California, Berkeley, 1995).

24 John Talbott, 'Combat Trauma in the American Civil War', *History Today* (March 1996), 41–7, at p. 47. See also Allan Young, *The Harmony of Illusions: Inventing Post-traumatic Stress Disorder* (Princeton University Press, 1995).

25 Yealland, *Hysterical Disorders*, p. 244.

26 Millais Culpin, *The Nervous Patient* (London, Lewis, 1924), p. 65.

27 *Report of the Committee of Enquiry into 'Shell-Shock'* (London, HMSO, 1922), pp. 140–4. Some witnesses of course continued to believe that shell-shock was malingering. See Ted Bogacz, 'War Neurosis and Cultural Change in England, 1914–22: The Work of the War Office Committee of Enquiry into "Shell-Shock"', *Journal of Contemporary History*, 24 (1989), 227–56 at p. 246.

28 Culpin, *Nervous Patient*, p. 64.

29 See Paul Crook, *Darwinism, War and History* (Cambridge University Press, 1994), pp. 146–52.

30 Quoted in K.R. Eissler, *Freud As An Expert Witness: The Discussion of War Neuroses Between Freud and Wagner-Jaugegg*, tr. C. Trollope (Madison, Conn., International Universities Press, Inc., 1986), pp. 60–1.

31 G.A. Heron, 'The Prevention of Malingering, Need For Protecting the Medical Profession', *Medical World*, 1 (30 October 1913), 492–3.

32 R.C. Buist, 'Medical Etiquette, Ethics, and Politics', *British Medical Journal (BMJ)* (21 March 1914), 642. See also F.S. Palmer, 'A General View of Malingering', *Lancet* (11 October 1913), 1064.

33 Collie, 'The Malingerer', pp. 554–5.

34 George Wilson, 'On Feigned Diseases, Their Detection and Management', *Edinburgh Medical Journal*, 17 (1871), 336.

35 Collie, 'The Malingerer', pp. 545–6.

36 Sir George Ballingall, 'Feigned and Factitious Diseases' in his *Outlines of Military Surgery* (Edinburgh, Adam Black, 1833), p. 575.

37 'The Case of the Malingerer', *Lancet* (1 February 1913), 330.

38 See for example, Philip Gosse, *Memoirs of a Camp Follower* (London, Longmans, Green & Co., 1934), p. 108.

39 Insiders often alleged that doctors in the RAMC were scrimshankers. See for example, the war diary of Dr James Henry Dible, 'First World War Account', cited in Bourke, *Dismembering the Male*, p. 93.

40 Robert Farquharson, 'Malingering' in Richard Quain (ed.), *A Dictionary of Medicine* (London, Longmans, 1882), vol. 2, pp. 919–20; for similar, see George Edward Male's *Epitomie of Juridical or Forensic Medicine* (London, 1816), p. 179.

41 Jean Lépine, 'Malingering and Unrecognized Lunatics' in his *Mental Disorders of War*, ed. Charles Mercier (University of London Press, 1919), p. 150.

42 See Pollock, 'Malingering', p. 50.

43 Harry R. McKellar, 'Malingering', *Military Surgeon*, 39 (1916), 294–5.

44 'Failure Of A Party Of An Infantry Battalion to Carry Out A Military Operation And Certificate By Medical Officer As To Unfitness Of The Men On Account Of Shell Shock', July 1915, RAMC/446/18, Contemporary Medical Archives Centre, Wellcome Institute for the History of Medicine. 'The conduct on the part of Lt. Kirkwood, R.A.M.C.,' the commander reported, 'shows him to be totally unfitted to hold a commission in the Army or to exercise any military responsibility . . . he had no conception of the duties and responsibilities of a regimental M.O. and so long as he is

allowed to remain in the service he will be a source of danger to it. There can be no doubt the conduct of the men and the failure of the operation are largely attributable to this officer's extraordinary ideas of duty.'

45 Heber Butts, 'A Psychopathic Malingerer', *Military Surgeon*, 28 (1911), 623–38, at p. 631.

46 E. Hyla Greves, 'On the Diagnosis between Real and Feigned Disease; With Cases', *Liverpool Medical and Chirurgical Journal*, 4 (1884), 38–50, at p. 38 (author's italics). Antecedents for such a view reach at least as far back as eighteenth-century writing on hypochondriasis. A commonplace pathologization of malingering was entertained in the nineteenth century in the medical regard of some patients 'in which diseases are feigned not by the direct action of the patient himself, but because he is unable to resist the vagaries of his weak and excitable nervous system'. Robert Farquharson, 'Feigned Diseases' in Richard Quain (ed.), *A Dictionary of Medicine* (London, Longmans, 1886), pp. 506–8. Collie and others held similar views. Collie fully acknowledged not only the 'gloomy hypochondriac, who worries only about himself', and the 'valetudinarians . . . easily upset by any little illness', but also 'auto-suggestion'. 'The Malingerer', pp. 548, 552.

47 See, for example, Palmer, 'General View of Malingering', p. 1064.

48 R. Roussy and J. Lhermitte, 'Malingering and Psychoneuroses' in introd. to their *Shell Shock or the Psychoneuroses of War*, tr. Wilfred B. Christopherson, and edited with prefatory note by William A. Turner (University of London Press, 1918), pp. xxx–xxxv, at pp. xxx–xxxi.

49 Thomas Lumsden, 'Malingering in Peace and War', *Lancet* (18 November 1916), 862.

50 Ernest B. Emerson, 'Mental States Responsible for Malingering', *Medical Press* (5 December 1917), 433–6, at p. 435.

51 Office of the Surgeon-General, 'Malingering in U.S. Troops', p. 261.

52 A. Bassett Jones and Llewellyn J. Llewellyn, *Malingering or the Simulation of Disease, With a Chapter on Malingering in Relation to the Eye by W.M. Beaumont* (London, Heinemann, 1917), p. vii.

53 On the 'foreign born' resorting to malingering, see 'Malingering in U.S. Troops', p. 263.

54 H.C. Marr, *Psychoses of the War* (London, Frowde, 1919), p. 41.

55 Quoted in 'Malingering in U.S. Troops', p. 261.

56 Joseph Catton, 'Malingering', *Military Surgeon*, 45 (1919), 708.

57 *Special Report and Report of the Select Committee on Military Service (Review of Exceptions) Act, 1917*, Parliamentary Papers, 1917–18, iii, 327, p. 351. See also W.G. Macpherson, 'The Medical Examination of Recruits' in his *History of the Great War: Medical Services*, vol. 1, pp. 118–37. Geddes (1879–1954), formerly a professor of anatomy, was then Minister of National Services. His brother, Eric C. Geddes, was the wielder of the postwar austerity 'axe'.

58 Roussy and Lhermitte, 'Malingering and Psychoneuroses', p. xxx.

59 Catton, 'Malingering', p. 707.

60 See Bourke, *Dismembering the Male*, p. 113, and F. Parkes Weber 'Possible Pitfalls in Life Assurance Examination and Remarks on Malingering' (presidential address before the Assurance Medical Society), *BMJ* (9 February 1918), p. 168.

61 Norris, 'Malingering', p. 358.

62 Ibid., p. 366.

63 Tom A. Williams, 'Malingering and Simulation of Disease in Warfare', *Military Surgeon*, 48 (1921), 520–33, at p. 521.

64 L.P. Lockhart, 'Industrialised Man and his Background', *Lancet* (2 April 1934), p. 827.

65 H.B.W. Morgan to Henry George Castellain (26 May 1936), TUC Archives, 292/140/1, Modern Record Office, University of Warwick.

66 Ernest Bevin, 'The Wider Issues of Health Legislation in Industry', *BMJ* (September 1937), 610–11.

67 F.O. Arnold, 'The Detection of Malingering', *Medico-Legal Review*, 8 (1940), 199.

68 Rankine Good (Capt RAMC, 'Graded Psychiatrist'), 'Malingering', *BMJ* (26 September 1942), 359–62.

69 Culpin, 'Mode of Onset of the Neuroses in War' in Emanuel Miller (ed.), *The Neuroses in War* (London, Macmillan, 1940), p. 46.

70 See Peter Conrad and Joseph W. Schneider, *Deviance and Medicalization: From Badness to Sickness*, rev. edn (Philadelphia, Temple University Press, 1992).

71 Bernard Glueck, 'The Malingerer: A Clinical Study', *International Clinics*, 3 (1915), 200–51, at pp. 200, 204.

72 Over 300,000 cases were brought before courts martial during the war, with a conviction rate of 90 per cent. War Office, *Statistics of the Military Effort of the British Empire during the Great War* (London, HMSO, 1922), p. 643.

73 See Steve Sturdy and Roger Cooter, 'Science, Scientific Management, and the Transformation of Medicine in Britain, *c.* 1870–1950', *History of Science*, 36 (1998), in press.

74 E. Rowland Fothergill, 'The Cult of Individualism', *BMJ* (13 September 1919), 358–9.

75 Frank Honigsbaum, *The Division in British Medicine: A History of the Separation of General Practice from Hospital Care, 1911–1968* (London, Kogan Page, 1979).

76 McDougall, *An Outline of Abnormal Psychology* (London, Methuen, 1926), p. 2, cited in Martin Stone, 'The Military and Industrial Roots of Clinical Psychology in Britain, 1900–1945, A Political and Socio-Economic Archaeology' (unpub. Ph.D. thesis, University of London, 1985), p. 154.

77 Mott, 'The Diagnosis of Malingering' in his *War Neuroses and Shell Shock* (London, Frowde, 1919), pp. 217–20.

78 *Medical Directory* (1916 and 1925).

79 Private Norman Gladden expressed a widely held view when he declared the 'MOs treated all sick as swingers'; Gladden, *The Somme 1916* (London, William Kimber, 1974), quoted in Anthony Babington, *For the Sake of Example, Capital Courts Martial, 1914–18* (London, Grafton, 1985), p. 76; for other examples, see Bourke, *Dismembering the Male*, p. 93 and *passim*.

80 *Freud As An Expert Witness*, pp. 60–1. Apposite here is Freud's further remark, 'In private practice one tries not to be disagreeable; otherwise one is replaced by a colleague who is less so. Naturally, this motive does not operate for physicians employed by the government.' Ibid., p. 66.

81 Gladden, *The Somme 1916*, quoted in Babington, *For the Sake of Example*, p. 76.

82 The categories are those of Roussy and Lhermitte, 'Malingering and Psychoneuroses', p. xxxi. Malingering in France during the First World War, recollected one psychologist, 'showed itself mainly as a tendency to perpetuate the existence of symptoms which would otherwise have passed away in due course, and to exaggerate the severity of those which were present'. Frederick Dillon, 'Simulated Mental Disorders Among Soldiers in the Late War', *Lancet* (23 September 1939), 706.

83 Capt W.M. Child, letters to his wife, Imperial War Museum, PP/MCR/386.

84 Marya Arfer, personal communication (11 October 1996). These views are elaborated in her 'Healing the Patient, Serving the State: Medical Ethics and the First World War in Great Britain and Germany' (Ph.D. thesis, University of California, Berkeley, forthcoming).

85 Collie, 'The Malingerer', p. 557; Collie, *Malingering and Feigned Sickness* (London, Edward Arnold, 1913), p. 378. This was also how some doctors dealt with the shell-shocked. A Second World War psychiatrist lampooned the therapy recommended during the First World War: '[the soldier] should be marched up and down to show him that his legs work still, then told to relax, pull himself together and go home. All he really needs is sleep and encouragement'. Felix Brown, 'Civilian Psychiatric Air-Raid Casualties', *Lancet* (31 May 1941), 686–91. Quoted in Ben Shephard, '"Pitiless Psychology": The Role of Deterrence in British Military Psychiatry in the Second World War', *History of Psychiatry* (forthcoming).

86 Lawrence Gameson, typescript memoir, Imperial War Museum, con shelf, p. 85.

87 Buist, 'Medical Etiquette, Ethics, and Politics', p. 642. In relation to having to act as 'civil servants' for local authority health services, see 'Report to the BMA Medico-Political Committee on the Local Government Board circular concerning maternity and child welfare of July 30, 1914', British Medical Association, *Maternity and Child Welfare Minutes I, 1914–34*, SA/BMA/J, pp. 61–2, Contemporary Medical Archives Collection, Wellcome Institute for the History of Medicine.

88 Peter MacDonald, 'The Future of the Medical Profession', *BMJ* (23 November 1918), 588. On MacDonald, see Honigsbaum, *Division in British Medicine,* pp. 333–4, according to whom MacDonald's article had considerable influence in the shaping of Labour health policy.

89 Buist, 'Medical Etiquette, Ethics, and Politics', p. 641.

90 Chauncey D. Leake, *Percival's Medical Ethics*, ed. (Baltimore, Williams & Wilkins, 1927), pp. viii–ix.

91 See, for example, Buist, 'Medical Etiquette, Ethics, and Politics'; Palmer, 'A General View of Malingering'; and Heron, 'The Prevention of Malingering'.

92 Cited in Stone, 'The Military and Industrial Roots of Clinical Psychology in Britain', p. 40.

93 'Workmen's Compensation and Medical Evidence', *BMJ* (16 April 1910), 958.

94 Dr A. Drury in response to an address by Collie at a BMA meeting, *Lancet* (15 August 1914), 452.

95 Of far more rhetorical concern was mendicity in relation to medical charity. See 'Malingery', *Lancet* (7 January 1905), 45–7; 'Clever Malingering', *Medical Press* (16 November 1904), 526; and 'Charlatans and "Miracles"', *Guy's Hospital Reports*, 28 (1915), 37–54.

96 Catton, 'Malingering', pp. 708–9.

97 See Norris, 'Malingering', p. 357, and Brenda White, 'Lax-certification and Morbidity Statistics in Scotland, 1926–1937', paper delivered to the Conference on 'Work in Progress', Aberdeen, 1994.

98 Cf. Anne Digby, *Making a Medical Living: Doctors and Patients in the Market for Medicine, 1720–1994* (Cambridge University Press, 1994), and Deborah Stone, *The Disabled State* (London, Macmillan, 1984).

99 Bourke, *Dismembering the Male*, pp. 102–3.

8

STATUS, MANPOWER AND MENTAL FITNESS: MENTAL DEFICIENCY IN THE FIRST WORLD WAR

Mathew Thomson

Under modernity, the concepts of war and mental disorder have been intimately bound up.[1] The First World War is given a seminal position in the development of this relationship: anxieties over mental deterioration of the population, crowd psychology and inherent aggressive instincts are seen as creating an environment which made war possible;[2] and the trauma of trench warfare is seen as precipitating mass nervous breakdown of 'shell-shocked' troops. The handling of this crisis has been interpreted as a watershed between an era of hereditarian, somatic and often inhumane approaches to care of the mentally disordered, and a postwar era of environmental, psychological and more humane attitudes.[3] Such an interpretation is deeply bound up with the mythology of the First World War. In this respect, the roles of such myths as the 'great sacrifice', 'the lost generation' and the 'birth of the modern' in shaping a problem such as shell-shock need to be made more explicit.[4] In other respects, our understanding of the relationship between mental disorder and war will only be furthered by stepping outside the myth; for example, concentration on shell-shock has resulted in at least three serious interpretative limitations: firstly, the analysis of the troops is rarely balanced by consideration of the home front; secondly, the 'watershed' thesis is rarely verified by parallel studies of pre- and postwar psychiatry and mental health care; and thirdly, interest has tended to be limited to those suffering from the trauma of war, rather than those with serious mental illness or those described as mentally defective.[5] This paper will attempt to redress the balance by incorporating an analysis of the problem of mental deficiency during the war.[6]

In 1912, Tory MP Gershom Stewart had adopted a series of military metaphors in support of legislation to provide a special system of segregative care for mental defectives (people who might now be considered to have conditions ranging from disabling mental handicap (low-grade defectives) to learning and behavioural difficulties (high-grade defectives or the feeble-minded)). In Stewart's words, and in the context of the increasingly tense international situation, the nation was an 'army on the march' which could not afford to be 'escorted by a helpless army of camp followers who can never be efficient people'.[7] A year later,

parliament passed the Mental Deficiency Act. The link between the 1913 Act
and Stewart's anxieties over national, military and racial efficiency, epitomized by
Britain's failures in the Anglo-Boer War, seems obvious, and has been
emphasized in historical accounts of the subject. Considering this, it is somewhat
surprising that so little attention has been paid to the development of attitudes
and policies during the war of 1914–18 which followed the Act. Study of this
period in fact casts real doubt on Stewart's assumption that mental defectives
were a 'helpless army of camp followers'; it demonstrates that social inefficiency
was a relative concept, very different under circumstances of wartime manpower
demand. In doing so, it also suggests that historians may have exaggerated the
importance of national efficiency arguments, like those of Stewart, as a cause of
the early twentieth-century mental deficiency alarm. In drawing attention to the
way that the problem of mental deficiency was shaped by 'manpower' demands,
the essay also suggests that, although historians of mental deficiency have been
very alert to the Act's function as a tool of moral and sexual regulation of female
behaviour, they have paid too little attention to its relationship to masculinity.
Through concepts such as manpower, work, efficiency and fitness, the mental
deficiency system, quite clearly, was not simply a tool to control women, as is
sometimes suggested.[8] Finally, the essay aims to add to our understanding of war
and its relationship to social change. Through the case study of mental defectives,
it questions the idea that participation in the war effort necessarily led to longer-
term social benefits, and it highlights the way that status, here mental status,
mediated social rewards.[9] My main focus will be the position of mental defectives
in British armed forces; however, for comparative purposes I will also briefly
consider the situation on the home front and in the US army.

THE BRITISH ARMY

In reality, in the run-up to the 1913 Act, mental deficiency had not been
regarded as a serious problem within the military. In 1908, at the height of
concern over the publication of reports on physical deterioration and the feeble-
minded, the Army Medical Report had recorded that of 61,728 recruits
inspected only 58 were rejected for weakness of intellect.[10] Mental deficiency was,
in fact, scarcely discussed by the Interdepartmental Committee on Physical
Deterioration, set up because of alarm over the falling physical standard of
military recruits.[11] And the military were one of the few voices absent from the
host of witnesses who lobbied the Royal Commission on the Care and Control of
the Feeble-minded of 1904–8.

Despite the passage of the 1913 Act, and a consequently raised profile and
awareness about the issue, there was still virtually no attempt to detect mental
deficiency among British recruits when war broke out in 1914.[12] The peacetime
recruitment service, staffed by active and retired Royal Army Medical Corps

officers and civilian medical officers, had been capable of examining 50,000 recruits annually. It was therefore totally inadequate when inundated with volunteers in the first months of the war (500,000 coming for enlistment in September 1914 alone). As a result, the Army was forced to use inexperienced civilian examiners. Worse still, payment per recruit examined encouraged speedy and superficial screening. The flow of recruits was regulated in the following months, as examining officers were limited to thirty to forty recruits in a six- or eight-hour day. In early 1915, standing and visiting medical boards were established to monitor the system and rank troops, according to fitness, from grades A to D. In December 1915, civilian medical examiners were abolished and classification according to medical fitness was replaced by grades 1 to 5, based on manpower criteria, such as fitness for 'labour, such as road-making, entrenching and other work' and for 'sedentary work only'.[13] This transition continued as the 1916 Military Service Act introduced conscription for all men between the ages of eighteen and forty-one, with a new system of grades A to E integrating many of those previously defined as medically unfit and reclassifying them as fit for service behind the front lines, in labour units, or in home garrisons. By the end of 1917, about 300,000 British troops were in labour battalions, with the only qualification said to be an ability to march three miles, to perform three hours' hard labour, and to walk three miles back.[14] In 1917 the crisis in military manpower led to an attempt to widen definitions of fitness even further, with the Military Service (Review of Exceptions) Act calling for the re-examination of 100,000 men previously exempted on medical grounds. The Act caused an outcry in parliament and among the public, with condemnation of any attempt to enlist the unfit or to question the honour of those previously discharged on medical grounds. In response, a parliamentary committee was set up to investigate the exemption system, and in October 1917 the government and military caved in to public pressure and moved recruitment from military to civilian responsibility, placing it under the Ministry of National Service which reverted to a classification according to medical fitness.[15]

Recruitment examinations paid hardly any attention to mental ability. Time constraints and lack of preparation can account for this neglect at the start of the war. As standards of fitness were stretched to accommodate growing military needs for mass manpower and menial labour, there was little incentive to introduce the sort of tests which were being used to detect the feeble-minded within the nation's schools.[16] A small grant-aided committee was appointed by the Psychological Subsection of the British Association to consider what assistance psychologists could give in wartime. However, little was achieved, since there were few trained psychologists and their time was taken up in dealing with immediate practical problems.[17] Neither did mental defectives attract much attention in the parliamentary debates over wrongful recruitment, or in the investigation into the Exceptions Act.[18] What the latter did reveal was a general complacency about the absence of mental tests and the entry of high-grade mental defectives into the forces.[19]

By the end of the war the inadequacy of mental testing was beginning to be recognized. It was criticized in 1922 by the *Report of the War Office Enquiry into 'Shell-Shock'*. And as responsibility for recruitment shifted to the civilian Ministry of National Service, a very basic assessment of mental capacity was integrated into the grading system for troops.[20] The report of the Ministry of National Service for 1917–19, the first medical census of the male military-age population, found about 250,000, or 10 per cent, of the 2.5 million recruits examined to be unfit for any type of service, with mental defectives making up about 3 per cent of this class in sample areas.[21] However, this significant rejection rate was almost certainly not matched in earlier stages of the war: the political context of public outcry at enlistment of the medically unfit had raised standards; pressure to recruit was easing as domestic manpower demands to feed, fuel and arm the home and war fronts matched those of the military;[22] and the Ministry of National Service survey was drawing on a population with a high proportion of men already rejected on military grounds, and a deficit of those medically fit men who were either serving or had died in service. Even this 1918 rate of 0.3 per cent fell considerably short of the pre-war estimate that 0.46 per cent of the population were mentally defective (and even further behind postwar estimates).[23] As a cause of rejection from the Army, mental deficiency remained far less important than heart disease, weak limbs, general poor physical development, tuberculosis and varicose veins, and even epilepsy (though rarer than mental deficiency in the population as a whole).[24]

The low rejection rate could simply reflect that a very small number of mental defectives attempted to enlist. However, there is clear evidence that a significant number did enlist; as such, the low rate can also be attributed to the limitations of mental testing. After the war, psychiatrist Stanford Read would estimate that 13 per cent of the cases he had dealt with at Netley, a British clearing house for those evacuated from the front due to nervous disorder, were mentally defective rather than neurotic, and he supported this with figures of 18 per cent among 881 cases at Dykebar War Hospital, and 13.8 per cent of 2,429 cases at Derby War Hospital.[25] If Read's estimate of 13 per cent is extrapolated, then about 3,900 of the 30,000 shell-shocked troops sent to British hospitals may have been mental defectives;[26] assuming that at least some defectives were recognized before evacuation, there would have been even more among the 80,000 shell-shocked troops sent to Army hospitals behind front lines; and there would have been a significant proportion of mental defectives among the estimated 200,000 troops discharged because of their mental condition.[27] As C.S. Myers, head of psychiatric services in France 1916–17, reported, sometimes the only option available was to (mis)diagnose mental defectives as shell-shock cases: 'Cases were often sent down to the Base, labelled "mental", because they were intellectually too feeble or too deficient in self-control to stand the strain of life at the Front. These were not, in the legal or popular sense, insane, but from the military standpoint had to be so labelled in order to get rid of them or to save them from being shot for desertion.'[28]

In a series of case studies, Stanford Read exposed the disregard over admitting defectives to the Army: one case had been in the imbecile ward of an asylum for thirteen years, but was able to enlist; another was enlisted from an institution for mentally defective children, where he had been an inmate for eleven years.[29]

Read argued that it was a fallacy to think that defectives could be useful for menial work, let alone serve as efficient fighters.[30] Psychiatrist and Medical Superintendent of the Maudsley Hospital, Edward Mapother, speaking to the Committee on Shell-Shock after the war, was also critical on grounds of ability: 'the intellectually defective is incapable of endurable patriotism; in fact, of attachment to any ideal so abstract as his country'.[31] However, such concern was generally overridden by a desperate need for mass manpower. As the report of the Ministry of National Service argued: 'A modern Army is a collection of individuals not differing in kind from a large industrial community. Speaking broadly therefore every man who is fit to earn his living in civilian life is also fit to be employed in some capacity suited to his condition within the Army.'[32]

The deskilled nature of trench warfare made the quantity, rather than the quality of troops, the overriding military concern. The acceptance of defectives reflected a more general pessimism about the qualities and reliability of working-class recruits, and a 'cult of the offensive', which demanded mass manpower, troops who would follow and not question orders, and which accepted the need for heavy losses.[33] Medical men often accepted this. Dr George Shuttleworth, a leading specialist in mental deficiency, boasted that he knew of 170 ex-pupils of mental deficiency schools who were now serving in the war.[34] Having seen the work of defectives in the Anglo-Boer War, he refused to certify them as unfit to serve: 'There was something to be said in favour of institutional children, because they had a good deal of drill and were prompt in carrying out commands; moreover the Army discipline was likely to do much to keep them straight if they had sufficient nerve force to withstand the incidental shocks and strains.'[35]

There were also eugenic grounds for using defectives, as highlighted by the Consultant in Neurology to the French army, Professor G. Roussy: 'there would certainly be less emotional "shell shock" if they were excluded. But it would be an unfortunate thing for the nation if one kept behind all the mental defectives and sent all the men of higher mental capacity to the front.'[36]

Recognition of the problem of mental deficiency was also inhibited by the more pressing problem of mental breakdown among the mentally fit. The broadest estimates suggested that shell-shock was a factor in 1 in 7 disabled troops. In the first year of the war this was not a great problem, but in the trench campaigns of the following years loss of troops through shell-shock came to be seen as a serious manpower problem.[37] Once it had been accepted that this was a psychological rather than a physical condition, the diagnostic bind for the military authorities was that fear was cause and symptom of both shell-shock and cowardice: 'The psychological basis of the war neurosis (like that of neuroses in civil life) is an elaboration with endless variations, of one central theme: escape from an intolerable situation in real life to one made tolerable by neurosis.'[38] The high proportion of officers among the shell-shocked indicates that diagnosis was a sign of patient-power (a way to escape the horrors of the trenches) as much as medical control;[39] in contrast to an overall ratio of 1 officer to 30 troops, and 1 officer to 24 troops among all the wounded, there was 1 officer to only 6 troops among those admitted to special hospitals for war neuroses.[40] The rank and file were far more likely to be accused of malingering. In a 1918 sample of officers (who were sent to hotels rather than clearing centres to recuperate) only 6 per cent were sent back to duty, whereas 66 per cent were sent back to the base camp. By contrast, among lower ranks, 27 per cent were sent straight back to duty, and only 36 per cent were sent to the base camp. Similarly, only 13 per cent of the officers sent to base camp were eventually returned to the front and 25 per cent were sent home, whereas in the lower ranks, 48 per cent were sent back to the front and only 8 per cent were sent home.[41] Once evacuated to Britain, it was unlikely that these soldiers would be returned to the front. A high proportion went on to claim a war pension through the disabling mental trauma: some 49,000 by 1929.[42] What was emerging, therefore, was a gradation of therapeutic strategies, geographically ranked in terms of distance from the front line, from the worst option of immediate return to combat, to disciplinary therapy in a special clearing station, recuperation at a base camp hospital, to the best option of return home. Inevitably the place of an individual case within that gradation was heavily dependent on social status. Mental defectives with their low status, and limited power to argue their own case, were likely to fare very badly in such a system. As such, their relative wartime invisibility is unsurprising. The drain of manpower caused by shell-shock meant that medico-military concern over mental disorder centred on containment, rather than detection. Under such circumstances, there was little incentive to concentrate on exclusion of mental defectives from the Army.

Only under circumstances of peace, after 1918, was there an incentive to recognize the scale of service by mental defectives, and to acknowledge it as a problem. It was estimated that some 14 to 30 per cent of cases admitted to military mental hospitals were in fact mental defectives. And it was pointed out that the majority of conversion hysteria cases in the non-officer class were of below average intelligence. The dull, backward and high-grade mental and moral defectives, who had been passively accepted into the forces, were now blamed for the high rates of breakdown on the grounds that they had lacked the necessary quality of adaptability. On similar grounds, they could also be blamed for the high proportion of shell-shocked troops who failed to recover, and who were now draining national resources through war pensions.[43]

THE BRITISH HOME FRONT

The concepts of status and manpower can also help to explain the the fortunes of mental defectives on the home front between 1914 and 1918. A high priority in 1913, mental deficiency was suddenly a far less important issue, placed alongside the demands of modern warfare. Support for research was cancelled, apart from schemes such as using institutionalized populations to research dysentery, which were seen as directly useful to the war effort.[44] Space in civilian mental hospitals was evacuated to accommodate wounded troops.[45] And in housing mentally disabled troops in separate accommodation to the civilian insane and defective so as to avoid the stigma and harsh conditions, the low status of the latter was confirmed.[46] Wartime asylum standards were so low in London's Metropolitan Asylums Board mental deficiency colonies that death rates rose from 11 per cent in 1914 to 16 per cent in 1916, 20 per cent in 1917, and reached 27 per cent in 1918.[47] These rates were partly due to tuberculosis and the influenza epidemic but were exacerbated by war-induced shortages of staff and food; only the patients on strenuous grave-digging duty were given the 'luxury' of three meals per day.[48] Provision of a national network of mental deficiency institutions and local authority agencies, which had been a high priority in 1913, was put on the back burner. Government circulars recommending economy and refusal to consider building plans until the end of the war encouraged local authorities to delay acting on the legislation of 1913.[49] Even voluntary care, in some ways provided with a wonderful opportunity to take advantage of state neglect, was hit by the demands of war. As the Central Association for the Care of Mental Defectives reported in 1918:

> The year has been one of the most difficult the Association has had to face. The months of strain and the concentration of the public mind on the vital issues of the War were naturally a serious hindrance to any effort to bring before the public problems of social importance. Added to this, the increasing shortness of staff of Local Authorities, the dearth of medical men, and the ever growing demands of the various Government departments on the time, services and energies of all public spirited men and women.[50]

The delay in acting upon the 1913 Act was also a result of the changing wartime parameters of 'social efficiency' – a key concept in defining mental deficiency under the 1913 legislation. With a high proportion of adult males absent in the Army or casualties of the war, and with increased demands for manpower within the domestic economy, opportunities were opened up in the civilian labour force for those normally on the margins, most notably women, but also groups such as adolescents and high-grade mental defectives. High-grade mental defectives were released from institutions to work in the community, to enlist, or were sent to other institutions to compensate for the loss of staff.[51] One specialist suggested that anyone who was forced into the workhouse in wartime circumstances should be suspected of mental deficiency.[52] In Birmingham, the percentage of ex-pupils of special schools in employment rose from 32 per cent in 1913 to 48 per cent in 1920. The rise in average wages was even more marked between these two dates, increasing from 9s 2d to 30s 10d. This partly reflected a 170–180 per cent increase in average manual labour rates between 1914 and 1920, though the increase for Birmingham defectives at over 200 per cent was substantially higher.[53] With the return to a peacetime economy, both indicators soon fell, the percentage in employment dropping to 32 per cent and wages to 21s 3d by 1922.[54]

The low profile of wartime mental deficiency was also a reflection of a more general calming of pre-war anxieties about the psychological status of the British people. There was a feeling that the war was healing social divisions and that the civilized social instincts of the British people would overcome the aggressive mentality of the Germans.[55] The falling number of mentally disordered in institutions was seen as a sign of British pluck under the strain of air raids, and the result of rising standards of living and a reduction in alcohol consumption, rather than related to the real causes of accommodation shortages, rising death rates and changing standards of defining who was in need of care.[56] Falling numbers suggested to the government that the construction of a system of mental deficiency institutions might not be necessary after all.[57]

The pre-war alarm over mental deficiency did subside, now that it was overshadowed by the war. A leader in the *British Medical Journal* in 1915 suggested that the pre-war pessimism about mental decline had proved to be largely unfounded under the challenge of war.[58] However, with the prospect of demobilization, anxieties revived, particularly when mental defectives were presented as a threat to the war effort. As Dr Alfred Tredgold, the country's leading expert in mental deficiency, put it:

> The military necessities of the county and the large number of casualties have already emphasised the importance of 'man-power' and directed attention towards the declining birth-rate and the conservation of child life. All this is quite right and proper; but it is an incontrovertible fact that the many medical rejections and the system of voluntary service have both led to these casualties being disproportionately incident upon the most fit. And there is a danger that an indiscriminate increase in the birth-rate, a demand for equality irrespective of quality, may still further contribute towards this result. Let us make no

mistake. The ending of the war will not end international competition; and if we are to maintain our national or economic supremacy, we shall need, not merely men and women, but the best men and women we can produce. If we are to do this, the problem of degeneracy must have a place in any scheme for increasing the birth-rate and building up the man-power of the Nation.[59]

The wartime environment had dangerously eased vigilance about this problem, leaving defectives 'full liberty not only to influence and corrupt others but also to reproduce'. Instead of defectives' earning role during the war being seen as evidence of their value as citizens, it was presented as a threat to the returning troops who expected to re-enter civil employment. It was predicted that defectives would lose their jobs and become a social nuisance, especially those who had developed a taste for money during the war. Of particular concern was the supposed threat of feeble-minded women acting as vectors for the spread of venereal disease among sex-starved returning troops: 'unemployed and in a time of turmoil and upheaval they will be exposed to continual temptation which they have no power to resist and will always be a source of danger to others'.[60]

Whereas the wartime deficit among the male population made male defectives, at least temporarily, more valuable in terms of manpower, the reverse may have been the case for women; the war made it even more important to mark out 'immoral' women – such as unmarried mothers, who threatened the current and future health of the nation – as being mentally defective and in the 'urgent status' category for segregation.[61] Evidently, even if the war did result in a popular swing towards social reform, and even if shell-shock did encourage greater sympathy for the mentally ill, the goodwill did not extend to the defective.[62] Thus, if the war was a watershed in attitudes and standards of care, it was a watershed which was differentiated according to status, benefiting the neurotic but leaving a ghetto of neglect for the defective and the chronic and incurable mentally ill.[63]

THE UNITED STATES

In the United States, at the outbreak of the 1914–18 war, there was nothing comparable to the British Act of 1913. In part, this was a reflection of the federal political structure which limited national legislation. Provision for defectives in colonies and schools was well developed in a number of north-eastern states, such as New York and Massachusetts, which served in certain respects as models for the British legislation of 1913, while elsewhere – in the majority of the country – provision was sparse or non-existent.[64] The United States did not enter the war until 1917. When it did so, its handling of the problem of mental disorder, including that of mental deficiency, was in marked contrast to that of Britain.

A central difference in mental deficiency policy was that an extensive programme of mental testing of recruits was attempted in the United States.

There were two main types of test: the 'alpha' test for the literate, and the 'beta' test for the illiterate. Both were group tests; it was hoped that individual supervision could be provided for a high proportion but this was obviously unrealizable on such a scale. The alpha and beta tests were adaptations of group tests which had been developed at Stanford by psychologist Lewis Terman. However, the wartime testing programme was headed by Terman's rival, Robert Yerkes. Though an advocate of individual rather than group tests, Yerkes accepted the latter, since his primary concern was to take advantage of the opportunity of the war to advance the status of psychology. His own interests lay in the application of psychology to biological questions. He was particularly interested in using apes to study the evolution of intelligence. The army provided a huge subject population to further this inquiry through research into racial dimensions of intelligence. This helps to account for questions on the tests regarding personal background, which the military authorities objected to as irrelevant but were later used, most notably by psychologist Carl Brigham, as evidence of variation of intelligence between races.[65]

This interest in race was probably one reason for the adoption of tests in the US army in contrast to Britain. A number of more technical explanations can also be posited. The Americans had time to observe the experiences of the continental adversaries and to take note of theories which linked the high rate of mental disablement to predisposition. The psychological lobby in favour of testing was stronger in the United States. As a discipline psychology was better developed in American universities, and during the war it became organized into a national association.[66] Yerkes argued that it was essential to match the German government's utilization of psychology, and apply this, not only to elimination of defectives, but also to vocational placement in the army; while Dr Stewart Paton of the National Research Council had a wider vision for psychology of 'mobilising the brains of the nation' in war and peace.[67]

The contrast between the high ambitions and the limited achievements of these US psychologists has been pointed out by historians. Their mental tests have been severely criticized: they were biased against those with limited schooling, non-native speakers, and those with a different cultural knowledge base to that presumed in the tests. The utility of the tests was questioned by military authorities at the time, so that they had only a limited impact as a tool of selection and distribution of ability.[68] Although the tests were used on about 1.7 million recruits, only 8,000 were recommended for discharge. The figure actually discharged may be smaller still, as the ultimate decision was not in the hands of the psychologist. In addition, about 19,000 defectives were recommended as fit only for service in labour battalions.[69]

When compared with the British figures, even from the more rigorous testing period under the Ministry of National Service, the American achievement seems less derisory: a rejection rate of about 0.5 per cent, compared to the British rate of 0.3 per cent (that a maximum and probably higher than earlier in the war). Moreover, the report of the Wartime Medical Services recorded the detection of a mental deficiency rate of 12.06 per 1,000, a much higher level than any of the official British sources.[70] The crucial failing of the wartime psychologists was, therefore, not a lack of ambition as in Britain, but their inability to convince the military authorities that rejection of defectives was a psychological, rather than a manpower, decision. This is unsurprising: the psychologists' tendency to equate educational inadequacy with mental deficiency was unlikely to be received enthusiastically by a military establishment whose primary interest was the physical ability of recruits to fight.

Although the American psychologists failed to establish an effective system of mental screening, their attempt was important in raising the profile of the issue and thereby establishing mental deficiency as an excuse for rejecting recruits or placing them in labour divisions.[71] Of the 5 million recruits examined in total – the majority without the psychological tests – 800,000 were rejected, 42,000 of these for mental or educational reasons, with a further 35,000 placed in separate divisions.[72] Accordingly, almost 1 per cent of all recruits were rejected for mental or educational reasons, and about 1.5 per cent were either rejected or specially allocated. Thus, despite the failure of mental tests per se, rejection on mental grounds was still far more common than in Britain.

Once again, the themes of manpower and status can help to explain this. The manpower problem in the United States was very different to that of Britain. There was a huge population to draw from via conscription, but a greater investment to make in order to send each troop across the Atlantic. It made sense to be more selective about troop selection, and consequently to consider more seriously the issue of mental ability. Thus, in contrast to Britain, 86 per cent of mentally defective troops were detected before the end of the training programme.[73] Rejection of troops for mental or educational reasons may have been influenced by the results of the earlier tests, or may simply have taken advantage of the category of mental deficiency to remove disruptive and untrainable troops.

The weeding out process reflected status divisions within the army. Whereas the British Army was most markedly divided by class, the American army was divided by race and ethnicity. In the British Army diagnosis as mentally disabled could be aided by higher status, with officers in greater proportion to troops among the shell-shocked, and the neurotic having a higher profile than the defective. In the US army, the opposite tended to be the case: an abundance of potential manpower at home and the cost of dispatch to Europe made the authorities more ready to reject the mentally weak.[74]

The American tests revealed higher rates of mental deficiency among lower status groups: among negro recruits, rather than whites; among southern and eastern European immigrants, rather than recruits of Anglo-Saxon stock; and among rural, rather than urban recruits. It was a problem of the 'less civilized'.[75] The diagnosis reflected and helped to legitimize exisiting status hierarchies; in practice, it also functioned as a tool for controlling behaviour. Troops became labelled as defectives, not simply through tests, but through being recognized as difficult individuals during the process of training. It was during this time of waiting to depart to Europe that disciplinary and character problems were most evident. Both in the training areas and at the front, mental defectives were said to account for 42.3 per cent of disciplinary problems.[76] In this filtering process, those of lowest status came off worst. For example, black troops diagnosed as defective were more likely than whites to be placed in labour brigades or convicted of offences, rather than be discharged.[77] Low status was also reflected in the poor treatment of discharged defectives: a low proportion were hospitalized, few were successful in obtaining pensions, and recovery rates were worst among disabled patients who were of lower intelligence.[78]

American psychologists maintained that the sieving out of the defective and 'predisposed' had been vital in contributing to the low overall rates of mental disablement from the front line. The 'mental alienation rate' of 160 per 100,000 contrasted to a rate of 300 per 100,000 in the fighting on the Mexican border in 1916, and there were also associated lower rates for ill discipline and suicide.[79] The US army was very conscious of the high rates of mental disablement in the British Army and deliberately set out to avoid the therapeutic strategy which had caused this. Undoubtedly, this preparedness, and also the greater presence of a testing culture, despite its weaknesses, were important in avoiding the scale of the shell-shock problem encountered by the British; however, it was also the fact that the manpower constraints facing the US army enabled them to screen out the mentally defective, the disaffected and the delinquent.

The US wartime civilian sphere was less disrupted than the British.[80] Nevertheless, in 1917 and 1918 large numbers of psychiatrists, psychologists, social workers and nurses joined the military services.[81] This exacerbated the already poor conditions of state hospitals for the defective. As in Britain, the war temporarily raised the employability of defectives either in colonies or in the community.[82] On the other hand, the attention drawn to mental deficiency in the army stimulated a flurry of postwar state legislation and colony construction which contrasts to Britain.[83] The raised profile of psychology continued to influence the problem of mental deficiency, as the Rockefeller General Education Board funded the development of a national intelligence test, and psychologists advised the government on the use of tests for immigration restriction.[84] Just as in Britain, however, the momentum of wartime psychology and psychiatry was soon directed towards a loose notion of mental hygiene which increasingly focused on promotion of mental health rather than care of the defective or mentally ill.[85]

CONCLUSION

When Gershom Stewart called for segregation of mental defectives on the grounds that Britain was a 'nation on the march', he was prescient; just two years later Britain would enter a war whose scale and demands were unprecedented. What Stewart did not realize was that such a war would demonstrate how relative the concept of mental deficiency really was. Under conditions of wartime manpower demand, mental deficiency was hardly recognized as a problem; indeed, many high-grade defectives contributed to the war effort in the forces or on the home front. By contrast in America, where manpower demands were less extreme, the problem of mental deficiency came to the fore. On the home front in Britain, mental deficiency was an increasingly neglected area, particularly as the shell-shock episode shifted public attention and resources to the mental health of higher-status citizens. In the long term, the wartime experience made little difference to the position of mental defectives within British society: their status was not raised by their wartime participation, and the boundaries of social efficiency shifted once more as troops returned to civilian employment, and economic depression and unemployment descended.[86] In Britain, the war marked a brief interlude and delay, but not a volte-face, to the plans for mass segregation; by the end of the interwar period some 40,000 were confined in institutions, and almost 100,000 were under some kind of supervision. As such, the shell-shock-dominated story of First World War psychiatry – of new knowledge and more sympathetic attitudes inaugurating an era of mental hygiene – is flawed: it focuses too exclusively on high-status individuals; the very different fortunes of the mentally defective may well be paralleled by other lower-status groups, such as troops suffering from more severe mental conditions. The central position of new psychological and medical theories in shaping the shell-shock experience is also questioned by the material presented in this chapter: manpower constraints, both practical and ideological, were just as important; and diagnosis was as much an issue of the relative power of the patients, as it was of medical enlightenment, or control.[87]

Notes

1 D. Pick, *War Machine: The Rationalisation of Slaughter in the Modern Age* (New Haven and London, Yale University Press, 1993).

2 G. Searle, *The Quest for National Efficiency: A Study in British Politics and Political Thought* (Oxford, Blackwell, 1971); R. Soffer, 'New Elitism: Social Psychology in Prewar England', *Journal of British Studies*, 8 (1969), 111–40.

3 M. Stone, 'Shell-shock and the Psychologists' in W. Bynum et al. (eds), *The Anatomy of Madness*, vol. II (London, Routledge, 1985), pp. 242–71.

4 See for instance, G. Mosse, *Fallen Soldiers: Reshaping the Memory of the World Wars* (Oxford University Press, 1989); J. Winter, 'Catastrophe and Culture: Recent Trends in the Historiography of

the First World War', *Journal of Modern History*, 62 (1992), 525–32; J. Winter, *Sites of Memory, Sites of Mourning: The Great War in European Cultural History* (Cambridge University Press, 1995).

5 The pioneering research of Peter Barham on the forgotten mentally ill service patients who entered asylums after the war, similarly challenges the shell-shock mythology.

6 For an overview see M. Thomson, *The Problem of Mental Deficiency: Eugenics, Democracy and Social Policy in Britain, 1870–1959* (Oxford University Press, 1998).

7 *House of Commons Debates*, 5th series, vol. 38, c. 1445–50.

8 Examples of accounts which portray the Act as a tool primarily if not exclusively directed at women include H. Simmons, 'Explaining Social Policy: The English Mental Deficiency Act of 1913', *Journal of Social History*, 11 (1978), 387–403; L. Zedner, *Women, Crime and Custody in Victorian England* (Oxford University Press, 1991). In fact, approximately equal numbers of men and women came under the Act, though the way in which their cases were handled was gendered; M. Thomson, *The Problem of Mental Deficiency*. For a general exploration of the war's impact on masculinity, J. Bourke, *Dismembering the Male: Men's Bodies, Britain and the Great War* (London, Reaktion Books, 1996).

9 The theory of the 'Military Participation Ratio' , in which wartime gains by the less privileged depended on the proportion of militarily utilized individuals in the total population was first propounded by the sociologist S. Andreski, and informed R. Titmuss's influential essay on Britain, 'War and Social Policy', *Essays on the Welfare State* (London, Allen & Unwin, 1955). Though his approach is broader and subtler, the idea also appears in the influential work of A. Marwick, for instance, *War and Social Change in the Twentieth Century* (London and Basingstoke, Macmillan, 1974). Recent work on the postwar backlash against women calls into the question a direct equation between participation and social or political rewards, and demonstrates the mediating effect of status; S. Kingsley Kent, 'The Politics of Sexual Difference: World War I and the Demise of British Feminism', *Journal of British Studies*, 27 (1988), 232–53.

10 A.G. Kay, 'Insanity in the Army During Peace and War and its Treatment', *Journal of the Royal Army Medical Corps*, 18 (1912), 146–58.

11 R. Solloway, 'Counting the Degenerates: The Statistics of Race Deterioration in Edwardian England', *Journal of Contemporary History*, 17 (1982), 137–64.

12 Lord Moran, *The Anatomy of Courage* (London, Constable, 1945), pp. 161–72.

13 The term 'manpower', originally 'man-power' emerged during the First World War, indicating an important shift in the state's attitude to managing labour as an industrial and military resource; K. Grieves, *The Politics of Manpower, 1914–18* (Manchester University Press, 1988), p. 2.

14 J. Ellis, *Eye-Deep in Hell* (London, Croom Helm, 1976), pp. 39–40.

15 A detailed account of examination of recruits is given in W.G. Macpherson, *History of the Great War Medical Services General History*, vol. I (London, HMSO, 1921), pp. 118–37. For the political context, Grieves, *Politics of Manpower*.

16 S. Sharp and G. Sutherland, 'The Fust Official Psychologist in the Wuurld: Aspects of the Professionalization of Psychology in Early Twentieth Century Britain', *History of Science*, 18 (1980), 181–206; G. Sutherland, *Ability, Merit and Measurement: Mental Testing and English Education, 1880–1940* (Oxford University Press, 1984).

17 'Psychology in War: The Military Work of American and German Psychologists', *Occupational*

Psychology, 16 (1942), 95. Burt considered the origins of military psychology to lie in the work performed by the American psychologists during the war.

18 *House of Commons* (29 March 1917), 5th series, vol. 92, c. 636–715; *House of Commons* (21 June 1917), 5th series, vol. 94, *c.* 1996–2114; *Special Report and Report from the Select Committee on Military Service (Review of Exceptions) Act, 1917* (London, HMSO, 1918), PP iii, (1917–18), p. 327.

19 *Select Committee on Military Service*, q. 2976–8, Judge Mellor, q. 4734; Surgeon-General W.G. Birrell, q. 2255; Surgeon-General Sir A. Keogh, q. 237–8; Col Tyrell, q. 2742–3; Dr A. Benthall, q. 4266–7, q. 850–935.

20 *Report of the War Office Committee of Enquiry into 'Shell–Shock'* (London, HMSO, 1922), pp. 27, 145, 166–8. For analysis of the report see T. Bogacz, 'War Neuroses and Cultural Change in England, 1914–22: The Work of the War Office Committee of Enquiry into "Shell-shock"', *Journal of Contemporary History*, 24 (1989), 227–56.

21 Ministry of National Service (1917–19), *Report Upon the Physical Examination of Men of Military Age by National Service Medical Boards, from November 1st, 1917 – October 31st, 1918* (London, HMSO, 1920), pp. 4, 136. Jay Winter has emphasized the extent of exculsion by the end of the war: 'Britain's Lost Generation of the First World War', *Population Studies*, 31 (1977), 449–66.

22 In four months of 1914 over a million troops enlisted, in 1915 and 1916 enlistment again rose above a million, but in 1917 it fell to 820,646, and in the eleven months of 1918 to only 493,462; Grieves, *Politics of Manpower*, p. 218.

23 *Report of the Royal Commission on the Care and Control of the Feeble-minded* (London, HMSO, 1908). The *Wood Report* of 1929 estimated that 1.049 per cent of the population were defective; *Report of the Inter-Departmental Committee on Mental Deficiency*, part iv, (London, HMSO, 1929), p. 175.

24 *Report Upon the Physical Examination of Men*, p. 136.

25 C. Stanford Read, *Military Psychiatry in Peace and War* (London, H.K. Lewis & Co., 1920), p. 102.

26 Due to the lack of systematic testing, there are no figures for defectives in the statistical analysis of the *History of the Great War*.

27 Stone, 'Shellshock and the Psychologists', p. 249 for problems in gauging the total of shell-shock casualties.

28 C.S. Myers, *Shell Shock in France, 1914–18* (Cambridge University Press, 1940), p. 82.

29 Read, *Military Psychiatry in Peace and War*, pp. 107–13.

30 Read, *Military Psychiatry in Peace and War*, pp. 103–4.

31 *Enquiry into 'Shell-Shock'*, p. 27.

32 *Report Upon the Physical Examination of Men*, p. 1.

33 T. Travers, *The Killing Ground: The British Army, the Western Front and the Emergence of Modern Warfare, 1900–1918* (London, Unwin Hyman, 1990).

34 *Lancet* (5 August 1916), 234.

35 *Lancet* (5 August 1916), 234.

36 *Enquiry into 'Shell-Shock'*, p. 21. It should be borne in mind that this, the most explicitly eugenic position among the committee's witnesses, comes from a French source. This sort of eugenic sentiment was surprisingly weak during the war itself, perhaps dimmed by the patriotic desire to see the fit fulfil their martial role and by the evidence that the 'unfit' were capable of serving. It later increased as recognition of the problem of differential class fertility highlighted the serious losses in

the war: F.W. Mott, 'The Neuroses and Psychoses in Relation to Conscription and Eugenics', *Eugenics Review* (April, 1922), 13–22.

37 Lt Col Sir John Collie, 'Neurasthenia: What it Costs the State', *Journal of the Royal Army Medical Corps*, 26 (1916), 525–44; Col H. Tooth, 'Neurasthenia and Psychasthenia', ibid., 28 (1917), 328–45.

38 T. Salmon, *The Care and Treatment of Mental Diseases and War Neuroses ('Shell-Shock') in the British Army* (New York, 1917), p. 30.

39 E. Leed, *No Man's Land: Combat and Identity in World War I* (Cambridge University Press, 1977), p. 168.

40 N. Fenton, *Shell Shock and its Aftermath* (London, Henry Kimpton, 1926), p. 37.

41 J. Ellis, *Eye-Deep in Hell*, p. 121.

42 *History of the Great War Medical Services*, vol. I, pp. 326–8.

43 E. Prideaux, 'The Relation of Psychoneuroses to Mental Deficiency', *Journal of Neurology and Psychopathology*, 2 (1921), 209–20. My thanks to Ben Shephard for this reference.

44 Public Records Office, Kew (PRO) Ministry of Health file (MH) 51/86, report by C.H. Bond of meeting with Dr Fletcher (22 September 1915); Thomson, *The Problem of Mental Deficiency*.

45 M. Cooke and H. Bond, *History of the Asylum War Hospitals in England and Wales* (London, 1920), Cmd. 899.

46 *History of the Asylum War Hospitals in England and Wales*, Cmd. 899, 1920, xxviii, 381–458.

47 G. Ayers, *England's First State Hospitals, 1867–1930* (London, Wellcome Institute for the History of Medicine, 1971), appendix III, table C.

48 Greater London Record Office, report of the Superintendent of Caterham (4–5 April, 8 February 1918); E.B. Sherlock, *Minds in Arrear* (London, Ballière & Co., 1932), p. 130.

49 PRO MH51/689.

50 *Annual Report of the CACMD*, (1918/19), p. 16.

51 See for instance, the *Metropolitan Asylums Board Annual Report for 1915*, p. 16: there were over 100 discharges in the year, with 23 mental defectives leaving institutions to join the Army.

52 Ibid., p. 13.

53 A.L. Bowley, *Wages and Income in the United Kingdon since 1860* (Cambridge University Press, 1937), pp. 104–6.

54 PRO MH 51/726, *Report of the Birmingham Special Schools After Care Committee* (1938), p. 9.

55 W. Trotter, *The Instincts of the Herd in Peace and War* (London, T. Fisher Unwin, 1916); W.C.D. Whetham, *War and the Nation: A Study in Constructive Politics* (London, John Murray, 1917).

56 On air raids, *Lancet* (14 July 1917), 55–6. On reduction of asylum population the reports of Dr George Robertson of Morningside Hospital, Edinburgh gained considerable attention; *British Medical Journal* (9 March 1918), 299–300. In 1916 a less optimistic view had been put forward; 'The Effect of War on Mental Health', *Lancet* (16 September 1916), 528–9.

57 PRO MH 51/689, Ministry of Reconstruction to Board of Control (3 May 1917).

58 'The Psychological Effect of War', *British Medical Journal* (13 March 1915), 475–6.

59 A.F. Tredgold, 'Degeneracy', *Quarterly Review* (July 1917), p. 50.

60 PRO MH 51/687; PRO MH 51/691, CACMD to Ministry of Reconstruction (24 October 1917).

61 This is not to argue that the war caused this situation. Such women had already been a major concern at the time of the passage of the Act; H. Simmons, 'Explaining English Social Policy: The English Mental Deficiency Act of 1913', *Journal of Social History*, 11 (1978), 387–403.

62 The extent to which popular fear and stigmatization of mental illness disappeared also needs questioning; E. Dean, 'War and psychiatry: Examining the diffusion theory in light of the insanity defence in post-World War I Britain', *History of Psychiatry*, iv (1993), 61–82.

63 E. Fox, 'Modern Developments in Work for Mental Defectives: A Historical Survey', *CAMW Annual Conference Report, 1934*, p. 45. For the spread of interest to the mental health of the whole population, N. Rose, *The Psychological Complex: Psychology, Politics, and Society in England, 1869–1939* (London, Routledge, 1985). By contrast, as might be expected, the neglect of the seriously mentally disordered is far more overlooked in the secondary literature.

64 James Trent Jr., *Inventing the Feeble Mind: A History of Mental Retardation in the United States* (Berkeley and London, University of California Press, 1994).

65 F. Samelson, 'World War I Intelligence Testing and the Development of Psychology', *Journal of the History of the Behavioural Sciences*, 13 (1977), 274–82; D. Kevles, 'Testing the Army's Intelligence: Psychology and the Military in World War I', *Journal of American History*, 55 (1968), 566; J. Reed, 'Robert M. Yerkes and the Mental Testing Movement' in M. Sokal (ed.), *Psychological Testing and American Society, 1890–1930* (New Brunswick, NJ and London, Rutgers University Press, 1987), pp. 75–94; J. Carson, 'Army Alpha, Army Brass, and the Search for Army Intelligence', *Isis*, 84 (1993), 278–309.

66 C. Brigham, *A Study of American Intelligence* (Princeton University Press, 1923), pp. 56–77.

67 R. Yerkes, 'The Relation of Psychology to Military Activities', *Mental Hygiene*, 1 (1917), 371–6; S. Paton, 'Mobilizing the Brains of the Nation', *Mental Hygiene*, 1 (1917), 334–44.

68 Kevles' focus on the 'false science' and bias of the tests tends to result in a somewhat ahistorical evaluation. It was not until the 1920s that the tests were heavily scientifically criticized. Nevertheless, their practical use was in question by the end of the war and they were not adopted by the peacetime army; Samelson, 'World War I intelligence testing', pp. 278–9. Significantly, witnesses to the British shell-shock inquiry shared the view that the tests had been a failure: 'Enquiry in "Shell-Shock"', pp. 182–5. For a sample of the tests see C. Yoakum and R. Yerkes, *Mental Tests in the American Army* (London, Sidgwick & Jackson, 1920). In the long term the major psychological development of the war was the application of vocational selection for the classification of US army personnel by Walter Dill Scott, R. Von Mayrhauser, 'The Manager, the Medic, and the Mediator: The Clash of Professional Styles and the Wartime Origins of Group Mental Testing' in Sokal, *Psychological Testing and American Society*, pp. 128–56.

69 Samelson, 'World War I Intelligence Testing', pp. 277, 282.

70 United States Surgeon-General's Office, *The Medical Department of the United States Army in the World War*, Volume X, *Neuropsychiatry* (Washington, US Government Printing Ofiice, 1929), p. 220.

71 As recent study of the programme suggests, psychologists compromised and negotiated with the army, and the tests and interpretation of 'intelligence' shifted as a consequence; however, in the process the tests did gain a new cultural authority; Carson, 'Army Alpha, Army Brass'.

72 Samelson, 'World War I and Intelligence Testing', n. 43.

73 US Surgeon-General, *Neuropsychiatry*, p. 222.

74 Compared to the British ratio of 1 to 6, the US forces had a ratio of 1 officer to 9 mental cases in other ranks (moreover this was starting from a 1 to 13 officer/rank ratio, compared to a British ratio of 1 to 30); Fenton, *Shell Shock and its Aftermath*, pp. 37–8.

75 US Surgeon-General, *Volume X. Neuropsychiatry*, pp. 219–31.

76 Ibid., p. 221.

77 Ibid., pp. 222–4.

78 N. Fenton, *Shell Shock and its Aftermath*.

79 Ibid., pp. 43–4.

80 Discussion of the impact of the war is virtually non-existent in Trent's account of care in the United States, *Inventing the Feeble Mind*.

81 W. White, 'The State Hospital and the War', *Mental Hygiene*, 1 (1917), 377–82; T. Salmon, 'The Use of Institutions for the Insane as Military Hospitals', *Mental Hygiene*, 1 (1917), 354–63.

82 C.S. Rossy, 'Feeblemindedness and Industrial Relations', *Mental Hygiene*, 2 (1918), 34–52.

83 This is evident from reports in *Mental Hygiene*. A contributory factor was concern over immigration; M. Clark, 'The Fourth Great Plague–Defectives', *Modern Medicine*, 1 (1919), 143–9.

84 Reed, 'Robert M. Yerkes and the Mental Testing Movement'.

85 W. Burnham, 'The Scope and Aim of Mental Hygiene', *Boston Medical and Surgical Journal*, 179 (1918), 749–55.

86 By contrast, it is generally believed that the Boer War and the First World War were together a real stimulus for development of domestic social policy and promotion of fitness. See for instance D. Dwork, *War is Good for Babies and other Young Children: The History of the Infant and Child Welfare Movement in England, 1898–1918* (London, Tavistock, 1987).

87 Literature on the combatants under greatest manpower pressure (France and Germany) suggests a harsher attitude towards the shellshock/malingering divide and would tend to confirm the model presented in this essay; G. Roussy and J. Lhermitte, *The Psychoneuroses of War* (University of London Press, 1918); P. Lerner, 'Rationalizing the Therapeutic Arsenal: German Neuropsychiatry in World War I' in G. Cocks and M. Berg (eds), *Medicine and Modernity: Public Health and Medical Care in Nineteenth- and Twentieth-Century Germany* (Cambridge University Press, 1997), pp. 121–48. The comparative generosity of pensions in the United States and Britain should also be noted.

9

SEX, MEDICINE AND MORALITY
DURING THE FIRST WORLD WAR[1]

Lutz D.H. Sauerteig

The First World War marked a crisis not only in public but also in private life. For many men, Joanna Bourke has argued, the war provoked a 'major crisis' in their lives.[2] Although at the beginning of the war mainly young unmarried men were enlisted, later on older and married men were included as well. During the war, nearly 50 per cent of the British and nearly 80 per cent of the French male population aged between fifteen and forty-nine, and nearly 50 per cent of the German male population aged between sixteen and fifty, served in the army. The dissolution of families and the separation of married (and unmarried) couples occurred on a unprecedented scale,[3] and many men and women suddenly had to suspend their usual sexual lives. The 'sexual problem' was even more difficult to cope with for Canadian, New Zealand and American soldiers because of the greater distance to their native countries, which made home leave nearly impossible and increased the period of separation from their loved ones. The problem of non-marital sexual relations, which had of course existed before, now acquired new dimensions.

Although it is impossible to estimate the degree to which soldiers really had non-marital sexual relations, a number of sources have pointed out that the war experience – a 'frontier' experience in the view of Modris Eksteins – and the permanent risk of being killed at the front changed moral scruples.[4] For an increasing number of men, morals and morale, which had been intertwined in the nineteenth century, now became two separate spheres.[5] In 1917 the German physician Isaak Spier-Irving claimed that the soldier's moral experience was broadened beyond that of normal bourgeois life.[6] The British officer Robert von Ranke Graves, who later taught poetry in Oxford in the 1960s, had a strong aversion to brothels in France and was in great fear of contracting venereal disease (VD). He was mocked by his comrades and finally thought himself to be an exception. But there were other servicemen besides Graves who abstained from sexuality, either because they were just too tired, compelled by circumstances, were afraid of VD, or simply because they wanted to be faithful to their wives. Nevertheless, Graves insisted that most of the soldiers knew 'that they had a good chance of being killed within a few weeks anyhow', and did not want to die virgins.[7]

The memoirs of John William Rowarth, a Cockney boy, gives us an idea of the problems involved in a visit to a brothel for a young British serviceman. Firstly, it

In Flanders, behind the lines, queuing at Madame Aline Plorimond. Madame Aline: 'The next gentleman please!' By Heinrich Zille (1917), from Heinrich Zille, *Für Alle. Ernstes und Heiteres* (Berlin, Neuer Deutscher Verlag, 1929). Reproduced with kind permission of the Heinrich Zille-Erbengemeinschaft, Bremervörde.

took him some time to collect enough money; then, because it was his first time, he had problems getting an erection and was thrown out of the brothel, losing his money. His second visit was more successful, although the prostitute had a queue of soldiers waiting and pressed him to finish: 'I ejaculated, I got the shock of my life, I was finished before I had started . . . I was hustled out the door and on the street.'[8] Graves remembered seeing long queues of soldiers waiting in front of brothels, as did the German soldier Erwin Blumenfeld, who later became a famous fashion photographer in the United States[9] (see illustration above).

SEX AND THE NATION

The sexual behaviour of both the military and the civilian populations became a matter of primary national concern during the war. In part, this needs to be seen in the context of longer-standing fears over the declining birth rate. Anxiety about population size existed in most western European countries from around the turn of the twentieth century. Now, in the light of the slaughter on the battlefields, population policy was thrust into the centre of public debate. For racial hygienists, the war was a nightmare. Even more than in the pre-war years, national strength was seen to be closely linked to the quantity and quality of human reproduction.[10] Germany and Britain both developed mother and child welfare programmes to counter infant mortality, while pronatalist policies acquired a new urgency and importance.[11]

This hardly made illegitimate births acceptable. In Britain, fears of a growth in illegitimacy were expressed from early in the war. But despite exhortations to chastity, the rate of illegitimacy began to increase from 1916 and by the end of the war was 30 per cent above the pre-war rates.[12] In Germany, in 1914, financial support for unmarried mothers (*Reichswochenhilfe*) was provided in cases where paternity could be confirmed; in 1915 even the illegitimate children of soldiers killed in service were entitled to pensions. These measures were deemed necessary to meet the desperate need for both economic production and human reproduction. Furthermore, important steps were taken towards equality before the law for illegitimate and legitimate children. But while some politicians accepted illegitimate children as a demographic good, conservatives and Catholics insisted that the legitimate family was the foundation of the state and society. The latter opposed pronatalist policies, and blocked further improvements in the legal status of illegitimate children.[13]

The sexual behaviour of soldiers' wives was also significant in another way, as it was seen to influence the morale of their husbands fighting in the trenches. In Britain two women's organizations, the Women Police Volunteers and the Women Police Service, monitored public morality during the war. By 1917, more than 2,200 women patrolled parks, railway stations and other public places in the cities in order to control female sexual activity. Public morality was also supervised by the state itself. The entertainment industry (cinemas, music halls, etc.), the arts and literature were more strictly controlled and censored than previously. Statutory separation allowances for soldiers' wives, which replaced the maintenance payments they might otherwise have expected from their husbands, could be withdrawn when a wife was found guilty of adultery.[14] Thus, the British state supervised not only public but also domestic morality. As Susan Pedersen suggests, it was 'women's bodies and not women's labor that were to be "bought" by the state and safeguarded until the husband's return'.[15] As I shall show below, the British government had a different attitude towards morality at the front.

In Germany, the Prussian War Ministry, which effectively functioned within Germany's federal structure as an imperial ministry, issued leaflets and brochures urging soldiers' wives to remain faithful to their husbands. The physician Spier-Irving warned his readers of the 'pirates of marriage', who tried to seduce soldiers' wives, and of their female counterpart, the 'unrestrained woman', who enticed men with 'a sex-impregnated glance'. As a remedy, Spier-Irving recommended that it should be made much easier for married soldiers to visit their wives at home, and that the age of marriage should be lowered. Both measures would contribute to 'stabilising the health of the nation and increasing the population'.[16] Night lodgers (*Schlafgänger*) – transient workers lodging in working-class homes – were perceived as another threat to morality. Even before the war, bourgeois social reformers considered night lodgers to be morally and hygienically suspect. During the war this form of lodging was much used by workers employed in the armaments or armaments-related industries, and provided a valuable source of additional income for lower-middle-class or working-class families. The state maintained strict surveillance over such arrangements, especially when the head of the household was away fighting for the nation. But statutory agencies realized there was little they could do to enforce chastity. Coercive measures were less Draconian than in Britain: most of the commissions that administered war allowances for soldiers' wives refused to withdraw the allowances in cases of adultery, for fear that women would then be forced into prostitution. Even in rural areas, where the self-policing of communities and the force of public disapproval was greater than in the relative anonymity of the city, and where adulteresses risked being denounced to the community or to their absent husbands, wives did not always remain faithful.[17]

Furthermore, both unmarried and married women had to face severe sanctions if they were found to have had sexual relations with prisoners of war. Although some journalists had to admit that their reports about such cases were completely fabricated, the German military used these articles to tighten controls on the sexual behaviour of women. Every woman whose contact with prisoners of war went beyond what was absolutely necessary in daily life could be legally prosecuted and publicly stigmatized, for instance by publishing the woman's name in the local newspaper. It is difficult to estimate how frequently sexual relations between the civilian population and prisoners of war actually occurred, however. For example, the Acting General Command in Leipzig – the authority responsible for law and order in the civilian population during the war – fined twenty-five women and sent them to prison in the first quarter of 1917. Benjamin Ziemann shows that in rural areas an increasing number of farm girls and farmers' daughters had affairs with prisoners of war which not infrequently came to light only when the girl became pregnant. The women's movement protested against this double standard of morality, which prosecuted unfaithful women but not soldiers who had committed adultery.[18]

SEX AND THE SOLDIER

The sexual behaviour of servicemen also became a matter of national importance. The concern was not primarily with the emotions of their wives at home or with general moral issues, however. Instead, the soldiers' sex lives were discussed in connection with health risks and fighting power. The German military greatly feared an increase in the VD rate.[19] Venereologists like Alfred

Blaschko, the secretary general of the German Society for Combating VD (*Deutsche Gesellschaft zur Bekämpfung der Geschlechtskrankheiten*: DGBG) argued that the VD rate always peaked during wars.[20] However, medical officers soon noted that, in this war at least, the VD rate among German soldiers was not increasing dramatically.[21] As the statistics published after the war showed, the incidence of VD in the field army fluctuated between 1.5 and 1.6 per cent during the first three years of the war and increased to 2 per cent in the last year. The occupying army had a much higher incidence of VD, namely 2.9 per cent in the first year, 2.8 in the second, 2.5 in the third and 2.7 per cent in the last year of war.[22]

In comparison to the VD rate in the German army, the Canadian Expeditionary Force was confronted with an alarmingly elevated VD rate. The first Canadian troops arrived in England in October 1914 and were placed under British command as part of the imperial Army. In 1915, as many as 28.7 per cent of the Canadian soldiers had contracted VD. Although the VD incidence among the Canadians declined significantly in the following two years, it was still at a high level of 15.8 per cent by the end of the war. The incidence among the Australians fluctuated between 13.0 and 14.5 per cent and was approximately 13 per cent among the New Zealanders. The British Army had to cope only with about 5 per cent of their soldiers suffering from VD; by the end of the war, this was halved.[23]

VD was not the only sexual matter to be dealt with by the military authorities. Since the mid-nineteenth century, physicians like the French army surgeon Auguste Debay, the British dermatologist John Laws Milton and the British neo-Malthusian George Drysdale argued that sexual abstinence caused serious health problems such as neuroses in women or spermatorrhoea in men, which could lead to early death. William Acton, on the other hand, considered sexuality such a dangerous urge that it had to be controlled and regulated at all costs to avoid moral and physical damage. In his view, sexual intercourse was harmless so long as it was practised moderately and within marriage.[24] By the end of the nineteenth century leading German physicians like the eminent venereologist Albert Neisser, the sexologists Albert Eulenburg and Albert Moll and the neurologists Paul Näcke, August Forel and Leopold Loewenfeld agreed that sexual continence outside marriage was physiologically practical and not unhealthy at all. Thus, an alliance of pedagogues and physicians advocated continence and a monogamous marriage as the safe route to preventing venereal infection.[25]

However, after the turn of the twentieth century, physicians like Alfred Blaschko came to regard the sex drive as a natural aspect of a healthy life. For Blaschko, abstinence was no longer a 'desirable aim' in itself, but at most a way of passing through puberty or avoiding venereal infection. Sexual abstinence could not be expected of everyone and was, therefore, an 'immoral' and 'unworldly' demand. Those who rejected abstinence should not be morally condemned.[26] A growing number of physicians endorsed the opinion of the

German sexologists Max Marcuse and Iwan Bloch and the Swedish physician Anton Nyström, that prolonged abstinence from sexual intercourse was fundamentally unhealthy and should never be recommended.[27] This medical view was popularized, for example, by the socialist August Bebel in his famous book *Die Frau und der Sozialismus*, first published in 1883 and continuously in print thereafter.[28] And it seems to have been accepted even by some British officers, for instance General Frank Percy Crozier, who claimed that 'a man – or a boy in 1918, could not fight well unless he could love well'.[29]

At the outbreak of the war, the military authorities in the combatant countries had to solve two difficult problems: if and how to meet the (hetero)sexual needs of their soldiers, and how to combat the spread of VD. Which was a greater threat to military strength, VD or immorality? For Spier-Irving, two supply problems had to be solved: supplying the sexual needs of women at home and those of men at the front.[30] In what follows, I shall analyse the strategic considerations adopted by the military in seeking to solve this conflict between moral standards, sexual needs and fighting power.

Neither in Germany, England nor the USA was a coherent policy adopted towards solving the problems of sexual morality and the preservation of health. Some officers fought for the preservation of sexual moral norms even under wartime conditions, whereas others actively made heterosexual contacts possible for soldiers or at least tacitly tolerated them. The Prussian War Ministry even made a distinction between younger single soldiers and older married men. Whereas the ministry considered sexual continence to be reasonable for the former, it did not believe that the latter, who were accustomed to intercourse, could stay chaste when separated from their wives.[31] Some British and American officers explicitly argued against prohibiting prostitution for fear that this would lead to even more serious violations of moral standards, such as masturbation or homosexuality. A poster of the Social Hygiene Division of the American Army Educational Commission, for example, warned soldiers not only of VD but also of 'enslaving habits' like masturbation (see illustration on p. 173). Not many sources reported on these sexual activities. Gustav Aschaffenburg, professor of psychiatry and medical adviser in Cologne during the war, stated that masturbation 'flourished' during the trench warfare in the German lines right behind the front.[32] Paul Fussell provides numerous references suggesting that masturbation and exhibitionism were linked with anxiety and excitement during battle. He argues that 'prolonged threat to the integrity of the body heighten physical self-consciousness and self-love'.[33] In the British Army homosexuality, its criminal and moral aspects apart, was considered a threat to hierarchical military order and to the nation's security, because it was assumed that German spies targeted British officers or other important persons in public life who were homosexuals.[34] In the German military, only a few homosexual relations were discovered and disciplined. Apparently, homosexual relations were not perceived as a serious

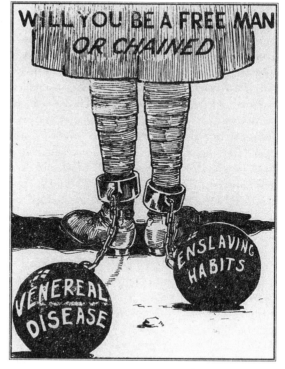

Poster produced by the Social Hygiene Division of the US Army Educational Commission, warning soldiers against venereal disease and masturbation, reproduced with kind permission of the Social Welfare History Archives Center, University of Minnesota, Minneapolis.

problem, although the number of homosexuals in the army was estimated to be quite high.[35] On the whole, it would seem that homosexuality was the exception in both the German and British military. More frequent might have been various expressions of sublimated homoerotic feelings within the male community at the front.[36]

ENCOURAGING CHASTITY

There were several possible answers to the sexual problems in the military. First of all, one could try to educate soldiers to stay chaste. However, this turned out to be a rather unsuccessful undertaking even in peacetime. Nevertheless, none of the belligerent countries abstained from moral appeals. In all armies, soldiers were warned of VD and informed about the horrible symptoms. The aim was to shock so that the soldiers voluntarily abstained from intercourse with prostitutes.[37] Health counselling leaflets strongly stressed that the best preventive against VD was continence. Soldiers were asked to control their sexual drive and erase sex from their minds.[38] When British troops left England in 1914 to fight on the Continent, they were admonished by Lord Kitchener, Secretary of State for War, to stay chaste.[39] Soldiers who disregarded Lord Kitchener's appeal – printed in each soldier's paybook – and who contracted VD were not paid during medical treatment; a similar regulation, though not strictly implemented, existed from 1912 for American soldiers.[40] In Germany, although some officers would have liked a similar regulation to be introduced, soldiers were paid during VD treatment lest they otherwise conceal an infection.

Army chaplains and especially Army doctors associated with the National Council for Combating Venereal Disease (NCCVD), an organization which emerged from the 1913 Royal Commission on Venereal Diseases, shaped the moral education of British soldiers and workers in the armaments and armaments-related industries.[41] The final report of the Royal Commission, published in 1916, recommended educating the civilian population on VD and its risks; young people in particular should be taught 'that to lead a chaste life is the only certain way to avoid infection'.[42] Meanwhile army doctors of the Canadian and the American Expeditionary Forces recommended abstinence as the best preventive against venereal infection, but at the same time informed their soldiers about prophylactics.[43]

German military doctors pursued a similar strategy, appealing to the soldiers' sense of honour and patriotism, and admonishing them to abstain from non-marital intercourse. The Prussian War Ministry distributed a seven-page brochure among soldiers with the telling title *Beware of Debauchery!*[44] During the war, VD education campaigns were intensified. From brochures, posters, lectures and special evening talks in barracks, soldiers learned about the horrible and disgusting symptoms of VD. The top-ranking Bavarian army physician, *Obergeneralarzt* Georg Reh, appealed to his soldiers' patriotism when he urged them to avoid sexual contacts with French women; soldiers must be able 'to fight and oppress their desires of lust with iron will', he declared.[45] It is clear, however, that reliance on the strategy of moral education depended on the prevailing circumstances. While self-control and abstinence might be promoted with a reasonable hope of success at the front, a more pragmatic approach was pursued in the rear area. At Brussels, for instance, which was known for being a centre of prostitution, soldiers arriving at the railway stations got a leaflet warning them of VD and prostitutes. Instead of suggesting chastity, these leaflets advocated the use of prophylactics.[46]

PROSTITUTION CONTROL

A second reaction to the sex problem was to control prostitution. But even before the war it proved increasingly difficult to define prostitution. In Germany, professional prostitutes were registered with the police vice squads and kept under surveillance. But there were more and more women who only occasionally worked as prostitutes in periods of economic crisis. Other women classified by the authorities as prostitutes considered themselves only as mistresses. From the turn of the twentieth century, all forms of non-marital sexuality came to be described as prostitution. Thus, every woman who had a non-marital relationship risked being called a prostitute and officially registered.[47] In Germany and England these women were classified as amateur prostitutes (the German expression was *heimliche Prostitutierte*) and regarded as a high-risk group for VD.[48]

To define prostitution was not the only problem. From the mid-nineteenth century, the whole system of state regulation of prostitution was heavily criticized by the women's movement, and later by physicians and public health administrators, for being medically ineffective. In countries such as Germany or France, which still clung to this system at the beginning of the twentieth century, intense debate raged over whether the old system of regulation by the police vice squads could be reformed or whether it should be closed down. Public health officials had to cope with an increasing number of amateur prostitutes, who could not be controlled by the vice squads.[49] The German military favoured stricter and more efficient control of prostitution, especially as it transpired that most of the soldiers who caught VD during the war did so at home and not at the front.[50] The Bavarian Ministry for the Interior doubted whether more rigid police control of prostitution would prove effective. But the Prussian military went ahead: bars with hostesses were closed in Berlin, for instance, and the regulations for prostitutes became more stringent.[51] Finally, even on the home front, the medical examination of prostitutes now became the responsibility of military physicians.

In Britain attempts were made in the 1860s to control the spread of VD in the military by introducing compulsory diagnosis, treatment and police registration of women suspected of being prostitutes.[52] But the vociferous protest of the women's movement, especially of Josephine Butler's Ladies' National Association, led to the repeal of the Contagious Diseases Acts in 1886. Since then, the British government had refrained from trying to reintroduce state regulation of prostitution, largely out of fear of the reaction of the women's movement. From mid-1915, however, the Home Office and the War Office came under pressure from the dominions, and especially the Canadians, to do something about controlling VD and to introduce legislation to protect their soldiers from prostitutes. Neither the Home Office nor the War Office could agree on a policy until February 1917, when the Home Secretary Sir George Cave introduced a Criminal Law Amendment Bill in Parliament which included measures to increase penalties for brothel keepers, to penalize soliciting and to make it a criminal offence for persons who knew they had VD to have sexual contacts. As this Bill gave rise to unexpected debates in the House of Commons and drew protest from the women's movement and social purity organizations, it was sent to a standing committee and thus delayed in Parliament.[53]

At the Imperial War Conference in April 1917, the Canadians finally threatened the British government that they would stop sending troops to the

European theatre of war. But it took another year before the War Cabinet, in March 1918, approved regulation 40d under the Defence of the Realm Act (DORA) making it a criminal offence for women infected with VD to solicit or have sexual relations with members of His Majesty's forces.[54] Whereas DORA 40d unleashed furious protest from the women's movement and social purity organizations, the dominions welcomed this regulation and the Americans even suggested having their soldiers placed under the 'protection' of 40d as well.[55] The War Office only half-heartedly implemented the regulation, however, which was repealed immediately after the Armistice was signed.

A similar problem occurred in the theatre of war itself. In France there were state-controlled brothels (*maisons de tolérance*) not only in nearly all major cities but also right behind the front line. Prostitution flourished wherever soldiers were accommodated. The French military intensified control over prostitution, and prostitutes in brothels were medically examined twice a week by French physicians, but not very thoroughly. The British commanders were not satisfied with these measures, but they could not stop their officers and soldiers from visiting brothels.[56] After the United States had entered the war in the summer of 1917, the VD rate in the American Expeditionary Forces took a rapid climb. One of the first reactions was for General John J. Pershing, commander-in-chief, to declare the *maisons de tolérance* off-limits to American soldiers.[57] The British public as well as the dominions now demanded a similar regulation. The British Army refused to take steps in this direction, however, considering it unrealistic to attempt to enforce such a regulation; soldiers would simply seek amateur prostitutes who were not medically examined at all. Moreover, the Army was afraid of snubbing the French military. And even in the British military there were advocates of medically controlled brothels. There was an outcry in Britain from the Church, the women's movement and social purity organizations, when rumours spread that the British Army was running its own brothels in Le Havre and Cayeux-sur-Mer.[58] Only in March 1918 did the War Office decide to declare French brothels out of bounds for all Crown troops. French authorities protested, since they were afraid of an increase in non-registered and hence medically uncontrolled prostitutes as well as an increase in sexual harassment and rape of French women.[59]

On the German side, control of prostitution in the occupied territories was being discussed as well. Early in 1915 Albert Neisser, at that time the president of the DGBG, advocated 'ruthlessly eliminating professional prostitution as well as the numerous women making themselves available for sexual intercourse in the occupied towns of the enemy'.[60] Despite vehement protest from the women's movement and social purity organizations,[61] the German military seemed to accept the fact that although soldiers were being taught to stay chaste, they must also be given opportunities for sexual contacts. This was never officially stated, of course, but behind the front there were numerous brothels, including separate institutions for soldiers and officers, which were partly controlled by army physicians and even run in part by the military.[62] In 1915, for example, *Oberstabsarzt* Wilhelm von Drigalski, who was stationed in Brussels, warned against condemning brothels in general. It was important to consider how a brothel was being run and controlled, he argued: 'If all men received a health check before and were forced to clean themselves afterwards, then most of the infections caught in brothels could be spared.'[63] *Generalmajor* von Sauberzweig, also stationed in Brussels, was in favour of combating street prostitution, but of tolerating brothels.[64]

Erwin Blumenfeld provides an impressive description of such a brothel. After having served as an orderly on the Western Front, he was posted as an accountant to 'field brothel 209' in the rue des Juifs in Valenciennes. The brothel opened at ten in the morning; eighteen prostitutes lived there, six of whom only served officers; the standard price for their service was four marks, of which the prostitute and the owner of the house each got one mark. Every morning the prostitutes had a medical check-up, though not a very thorough one; for this duty the Red Cross, which took 'medical-moral responsibility' for the brothel, received the remaining two marks. Each prostitute received about twenty-five to thirty customers a day, which gives an impression of how busy this brothel must have been.[65] Quite often, local commanders had to send guards to brothels to secure law and order.[66]

The health of the soldiers was the overriding priority. To reduce the risk of infection, military authorities at the front pursued a strategy of rigidly controlling and medically examining prostitutes, especially amateurs, and distributing prophylactics among soldiers and prostitutes. More and more brothels were placed under military control, and independent prostitutes had to show a special card which they got from the military authorities to prove that they regularly underwent medical examination. If VD was diagnosed, the prostitute was either deported or forced to undergo medical treatment in a locked military hospital.[67] Another strategy of the Germans to control prostitution was to remove the socio-economic reasons for prostitution. For example, a War Committee for Warm Underwear (*Kriegsausschuß für warme Unterkleidung*), founded by the Red Cross and the Empress Auguste Viktoria, financed job creation programmes for women in occupied Belgium.[68]

PROPHYLAXIS

A third reaction to the sex problem was to educate soldiers about prophylactic methods, such as relatively cheap chemical disinfectants (e.g., calomel ointment) and more expensive condoms. Prophylactics were being recommended and used in both the German army and the navy from the turn of the twentieth century.[69] Upon their return to the barracks after risky intercourse, soldiers could seek skilled disinfection by an orderly. Subsequently, the army installed vending machines in barracks to dispense packages containing all necessary items for disinfecting themselves – an arrangement which, because of its anonymity, proved particularly popular with the troops.[70] As a result, a marked decline in the VD rate was noted. The official position within the German military remained somewhat ambivalent, however. Neither the Prussian nor the Bavarian military intended to issue binding regulations for the distribution of prophylactics. But if prophylactics were made available for soldiers, this should be done without 'encouraging immorality'.[71]

The distribution of prophylactics, especially from vending machines, immediately unleashed protests from social purity organizations, who denounced the vending machines as 'a moral, religious and national threat'.[72] For Katharina Scheven, president of the German branch of the International Abolitionist Federation (an organization campaigning against state-regulated prostitution), the installation of vending machines was an 'official invitation to shamelessness'.[73] In January 1912, Emperor Wilhelm II prohibited the sale of prophylactics in barracks.[74] From then on, VD would have to be combated by morally educating soldiers and recommending chastity. However, the military did not intend to rely solely on the education strategy. Since only the sale of prophylactics was banned, troop commanders could have prophylactics distributed without charge by orderlies.[75] Controlled distribution of prophylactics was thus still possible. To obtain prophylactics, though, the soldier had to contact an orderly and was thus forced to admit to violating moral norms. It is not surprising, therefore, that soldiers did not seek skilled disinfection often.[76] To force soldiers to disinfect themselves after risky intercourse, the Prussian War Ministry gave troop commanders the power to punish those who caught VD because they had not been disinfected.[77]

After the outbreak of the war, the Prussian War Ministry issued new 'instructions for education about the risks of venereal infections'. The emphasis was still placed on moral education, but prophylaxis was at least mentioned at the end of these instructions.[78] In the navy, on the other hand, prophylaxis was still a major element in combating VD during the war. Ablution centres where soldiers could seek skilled disinfection were opened in major harbour towns, such as Kiel or Wilhelmshaven.[79] In the end, the army followed suit; Otto von Schjerning, the general physician at Prussian army headquarters, for example, recommended distributing prophylactics to prostitutes. The reason given to justify this change of policy was the increasing number of married soldiers who were accustomed to regular intercourse, and who therefore had to be protected against VD.[80] In 1917, the Prussian War Ministry had to take note of the fact that the vending machines had again been installed in barracks.[81]

Whereas in Germany prophylactics were widely used in the military even before the war, British medical officers had almost no experience in distributing prophylactics.[82] Prophylactics were used to combat VD only in the colonies, and even there without official permission.[83] Again, only under pressure from the dominions and the Americans, who were worried about the health of their troops, did the British government and Army command begin to consider prophylaxis. In some barracks in England ablution chambers, in which soldiers could seek skilled disinfection, were opened in 1916. The dominions objected that there were not enough of them. Soldiers were reluctant to use ablution chambers and medical officers were not very interested in organizing them. Consequently, in April 1918 this prophylaxis strategy was declared to have been a failure.[84] Another strategy for prophylaxis pursued in England was the distribution of prophylactic packages, called the packet system. For moral reasons the War Office wanted to have soldiers receive the prophylactic packages only on their return to the barracks and not when leaving, although disinfection was most effective when applied as early as possible after intercourse. The packet system, however, did not meet expectations. As in Germany, soldiers were reluctant to ask for packages, and those who did get one often waited too long before using it.[85]

Lawrence W. Harrison, who organized VD treatment in France during the war and became the War Office's adviser for VD in 1916, called for greater involvement of military physicians in educating soldiers about prophylaxis. But neither the military nor the British government really supported prophylaxis.[86] This is clear from the instructions issued by the War Office. On the one hand, the War Office made arrangements for ablution chambers in 1916; on the other, it warned against 'the adoption of any system of prophylaxis which might be said to afford opportunities for unrestrained vice'. Instead, moral education was to be intensified.[87] Only a few pragmatic Army physicians like Sir Archdall Reid in Portsmouth or army commanders like General Frank Percy Crozier ignored the War Office's decree and made prophylactics available.[88]

In contrast to British reluctance, New Zealand's military command and some Canadian officers made disinfectants and sometimes even condoms available to members of their Expeditionary Forces. The Canadians were sceptical about the effectiveness of the packet system. Thus, in the beginning of 1916 they began to establish their own ablution chambers, called Blue Light Depots because they displayed a blue light at night, in their training camps in the south of England. Later, they established further ablution chambers in their hospitals, even in London. However, the Canadians, too, had to learn that soldiers were reluctant to use ablution chambers, and although soldiers had regular medical check-ups, the VD rate continued to increase. The Canadians therefore reintroduced the packet system in December 1916, but they also opened new Blue Light Depots in nearly every city in England and in some French cities, including Paris and Le Havre.[89]

When the American Expeditionary Force arrived in France in the summer of 1917, they introduced prophylaxis after having realized that they would fail to control prostitution. Even before the war, American physicians had had experience with disinfection packages – the so-called Pro-Kits. Their use was morally controversial, however, and this controversy intensified during the war both within the military and among the American public. The American navy therefore prohibited prophylactics in 1915. But General Pershing gave the order to establish ablution chambers in every division of the army. Shortly before the end of the war, post-coital disinfection was made obligatory and non-compliance was penalized. Nevertheless, many soldiers still did not seek disinfection; sometimes ablution chambers were just too far away, soldiers did not know where they were, or the queues were too long.[90]

CONCLUSIONS

The public debate on questions of sexuality and sexual behaviour, which had begun around the turn of the twentieth century, expanded considerably during the First World War. Sexuality became a central subject of public discourses that were closely linked with nationalism. In journals and newspapers, theatres and cinemas, in parliament and at the front, in special lectures and leaflets, the civilian population and servicemen read and heard about illegitimate children, prostitution, VD and prophylactics, about sexuality and self-control. At the level of public discourse, then, tremendous changes occurred during the war.[91] Traditional sexual moral norms were questioned, perhaps in Germany more than in Britain.

Both in discourse and in practical action, however, the First World War seems to have exacerbated the double standard of morality for men and women.[92] Whereas sexual outlets for men were demanded and consequently created, women's sexual behaviour was morally monitored and controlled to ensure that they stayed chaste for the sake of the nation. While all combatant countries tried to preserve traditional, middle-class or bourgeois standards of morality at home, and sought in particular to prevent extramarital sex, the military pursued a more pragmatic approach to sexuality among their personnel. Their main aim was to diminish the health risks that sexual activity posed to the soldiers; VD especially was considered a great threat to fighting power. Therefore, the male population was taught how to use prophylactics, something which would have been impossible before the war. Moreover, although the prophylactic strategy was pursued with the main aim of protecting soldiers' health and the nations' military strength, the popularization of prophylactics seems to have removed or at least diminished the fear of VD and therefore, to a certain degree, the fear associated with sexuality in general. Indeed, military service may well have given many men a sexual education that they would not otherwise have received.

It is debatable to what degree the sexual behaviour of the population really changed during the war. Joanna Bourke doubts whether many British soldiers really had casual sex during their military service, because they seem only rarely to have had the chance to meet women behind the lines during their limited periods of training and occasional leave.[93] Nevertheless, this paper would suggest that, under the impression of war and faced by the daily threat of being killed at the front, many soldiers no longer felt obliged to adhere to traditional standards of morality. This fact, together with the loosening of social ties and relationships during the war – most notably the separation of families – probably led to a relaxation of sexual morality. An increasing number of women who were separated from their husbands, had suddenly to earn their own living, and had sexual relations with other men.

Those institutions that monitored the preservation of moral standards in Western societies, especially the churches, still had a strong influence on society, perhaps to a greater degree in England than in Germany, although their influence was generally waning. Thus the ambivalent reaction of the military is not surprising. On the one hand the military insisted on moral education, while on the other it stressed the use of prophylactics and controlled prostitution. Again, moral education seemed to have been more important in the British military than in Germany or the dominions, which were more sceptical about the power of moral education. Arguments about why soldiers should stay chaste also differed. While the German military claimed that soldiers should abstain from risky sexual relations out of responsibility towards their fatherland, the British military viewed chastity as being part of the soldiers' honour.

Overall, the debate on sexuality and sexual behaviour during the war became increasingly part of a medical discourse. This process had begun in about 1900 when physicians and racial hygienists began to argue that reproduction could be subjected to the controlling forces of science. Reproduction thus became a matter of intense public interest – a tendency that was greatly reinforced during the war, when reproductive capacity became a matter of national importance. Doctors were among the chief beneficiaries of this process. In Germany and the United States especially, they now came to be regarded and consulted as experts in the fields of sex education and sexuality more generally.[94] In effect, then, the social upheavals of the wars, and especially the concerns it raised about the management of industrial production, human reproduction and military efficiency, proved instrumental in hastening the medicalization of sexuality and, at least to an extent, in making possible new ways of rationalizing sexual activity.

ACKNOWLEDGEMENTS

I am indebted to the German Historical Institute, London, the German Academic Exchange Service, and the Fritz Thyssen Foundation, whose financial assistance made possible much of the research upon which this chapter is based. I would like to thank Margaret Andergassen, MA and the editors for their help with my English.

Notes

1 This is a considerable revision of Lutz Sauerteig, 'Militär, Medizin und Moral: Sexualität im Ersten Weltkrieg', *Die Medizin und der Erste Weltkrieg*, ed. Wolfgang U. Eckart and Christoph Gradmann (Pfaffenweiler, Centaurus, 1996), pp. 197–226.

2 Joanna Bourke, *Dismembering the Male. Men's Bodies, Britain and the Great War* (London, Reaktion Books, 1996), p. 13.

3 Susan Pedersen, *Family, Dependence, and the Origins of the Welfare State: Britain and France, 1914–1945* (Cambridge University Press, 1993), p. 79; Jay M. Winter, *The Great War and the British People* (Houndmills, Macmillan, 1985), p. 28; Christoph Sachße, *Mütterlichkeit als Beruf. Sozialarbeit, Sozialreform und Frauenbewegung, 1871–1929* (Frankfurt/M., Suhrkamp, 1986), p. 152; on the dissolution of the family see Elisabeth Domansky, 'Militarization and Reproduction in World War I Germany', *Society, Culture, and the State in Germany, 1870–1930*, ed. Geoff Eley (Ann Arbor, University of Michigan Press, 1996), pp. 427–63.

4 Modris Eksteins, *Rites of Spring: The Great War and the Birth of the Modern Age* (Boston, Houghton Mifflin, 1989), p. 155; see also Bourke, *Dismembering the Male*, p. 156.

5 Eksteins, *Rites of Spring*, pp. 223–4.

6 Isaak Spier-Irving, *Irrwege und Notstände des Geschlechtslebens im Kriege* (Munich, Universal Verlag, 1917), p. 14. (If not otherwise indicated, all translations are mine.) See also Paul Fussell, *The Great War and Modern Memory* (Oxford University Press, 1975), pp. 270–1.

7 Robert Ranke Graves, *Goodbye to All That: An Autobiography* (Oxford, Berghahn Books, 1995, orig. pub. 1929), p. 210. Fussel, *The Great War*, p. 274, attributes Graves's distaste of brothels to his homoerotic tendencies; cf. Adrian Caesar, *Taking it Like a Man: Suffering, Sexuality and the War Poets Brooke, Sassoon, Owen, Graves* (Manchester University Press, 1993), pp. 172–220. Also Bourke, *Dismembering the Male*, p. 161; and Benjamin Ziemann, *Front und Heimat: Ländliche Kriegserfahrungen im südlichen Bayern 1914–1923* (Essen, Klartext Verlag, 1997), p. 79–80, who both extensively used servicemen's correspondence, diaries and memoires.

8 John William Rowarth, 'The Misfit Soldier', Imperial War Museum, quoted in Bourke, *Dismembering the Male*, p. 160; for further examples see pp. 160–1.

9 Graves, *Goodbye*, p. 116; Erwin Blumenfeld, *Durch tausendjährige Zeit, Erinnerungen* (Berlin, Argon, 1988, orig. pub. 1976), p. 192. For further examples see Magnus Hirschfeld, *Sittengeschichte des Weltkrieges*, ed. Andreas Caspar (Leipzig and Vienna, Schneider & Co., 1930), vol. 1, pp. 311–16. See also Mark Harrison, 'The British Army and the Problem of Venereal Disease in France and Egypt During the First World War', *Medical History*, 39 (1995), 133–58, at pp. 141–2.

10 Stefan Kühl, *Die Internationale der Rassisten: Aufstieg und Niedergang der internationalen Bewegung für Eugenik und Rassenhygiene im 20. Jahrhundert* (Frankfurt/M. and New York, Campus, 1997), pp. 40–52; Domansky, *Militarization*, pp. 430–1; Richard A. Soloway, *Demography and Degeneration: Eugenics and the Declining Birthrate in Twentieth-Century Britain* (Chapel Hill and London, University of North Carolina Press, 2nd edn, 1995), pp. 138–46; Paul Weindling, *Health, Race and German Politics Between National Unification and Nazism, 1870–1945* (Cambridge University Press, 1989), pp. 291–304.

11 Edward Ross Dickinson, *The Politics of German Child Welfare from the Empire to the Federal Republic* (Cambridge, MA, Harvard University Press, 1996), pp. 113–38; Weindling, *Health*, pp. 286–8; Cornelie Usborne, '"Pregnancy Is the Woman's Active Service": Pronatalism in Germany During the

First World War', *The Upheaval of War: Family, Work and Welfare in Europe, 1914–1918*, eds Richard Wall and Jay M. Winter (Cambridge University Press, 1988), pp. 389–416; Soloway, *Demography*, pp. 146–62; Winter, *Great War*, pp. 189–204.

12 Cate Haste, *Rules of Desire: Sex in Britain: World War I to the Present* (London, Chatto & Windus, 1992), pp. 41–2; Arthur Marwick, *Women at War 1914–1918* (London, Fontana, 1977), pp. 118–19.

13 Dickinson, *Child Welfare*, p. 122–4; Sigrid Stöckel, *Säuglingsfürsorge zwischen sozialer Hygiene und Eugenik: Das Beispiel Berlins im Kaiserreich und in der Weimarer Republik* (Berlin and New York, de Gruyter, 1996), pp. 265–71; Christoph Sachße and Florian Tennstedt, *Geschichte der Armenfürsorge in Deutschland*, vol. 2 (Stuttgart, Kohlhammer, 1988), pp. 49–55.

14 Philippa Levine, "'Walking the Streets in a Way No Decent Women Should": Women Police in World War I', *Journal of Modern History*, 66 (1994), 34–78; Haste, *Rules*, pp. 33–8, 50–3; Susan Pedersen, 'Gender, Welfare, and Citizenship in Britain During the Great War', *The American Historical Review*, 95 (1990), 983–1006; Steve Humphries, *A Secret World of Sex: Forbidden Fruit: The British Experience 1900–1950* (London, Sidgwick & Jackson, 1988), pp. 150–2; Marwick, *Women at War*, p. 117.

15 Pedersen, *Gender*, p. 1000.

16 Spier-Irving, *Irrwege*, pp. 56, 63–4, 70, 78.

17 Ziemann, *Front*, pp. 303–6; Birthe Kundrus, *Kriegerfrauen: Familienpolitik und Geschlechterverhältnisse im Ersten und Zweiten Weltkrieg* (Hamburg, Christians, 1995), pp. 217–19.

18 Ziemann, *Front*, pp. 305–7; Kundrus, *Kriegerfrauen*, pp. 213–14; Ute Daniel, *Arbeiterfrauen in der Kriegsgesellschaft. Beruf, Familie und Politik im Ersten Weltkrieg* (Göttingen, Vandenhoek and Ruprecht, 1989), pp. 144–7; Barbara Guttmann, *Weibliche Heimarmee. Frauen in Deutschland 1914–1918* (Weinheim, Deutscher Studien Verlag, 1989), pp. 190–2.

19 *Generaloberarzt* Karl Pannwitz, memorandum on VD in Brussels (20 February 1915), Bundesarchiv Berlin (BAB), 15.01/11868, pp. 196–201.

20 Alfred Blaschko, 'Vorschläge zur Neuregelung des Prostitutionswesens', *Zeitschrift für Bekämpfung der Geschlechtskrankheiten (ZBG)*, 17 (1916–17), 183–92, at p. 183.

21 Cf., for example, Martin Kirchner's comments, 29 March 1915, BAB, 15.01/11868, pp. 173–80.

22 *Sanitätsbericht über das Deutsche Heer (Deutsches Feld- und Besatzungsheer) im Weltkriege 1914/1918 (Deutscher Kriegssanitätsbericht 1914/18)*, ed. Heeres-Sanitätsinspektion des Reichswehrministeriums, vol. 3 (Berlin, Mittler & Sohn, 1934), pp. 163–9, 66*-7* and table 17.

23 Jay Cassel, *The Secret Plague: Venereal Disease in Canada 1838–1939* (University of Toronto Press, 1987), pp. 122–3.

24 Debay's *Hygiène et physiologie du mariage*, first published in 1848, became a bestseller, totalling 125 editions by 1881; cf. Peter Gay, *The bourgeois experience: Victoria to Freud*, vol. 1 (Oxford University Press, 1984), p. 150. Drysdale's *Elements of Social Science or Physical, Sexual and Natural Religion*, first published anonymously in 1854, was translated into German and many other languages. It was largely read by a general public. See Roy Porter and Lesley A. Hall, *The Facts of Life: The Creation of Sexual Knowledge in Britain, 1650–1950* (New Haven and London, Yale University Press, 1995), pp. 144, 148–9; Michael Mason, *The Making of Victorian Sexual Attitudes* (Oxford University Press, 1994), pp. 189–213; J. Miriam Benn, *The Predicaments of Love* (London, Pluto Press, 1992); Lesley A. Hall, *Hidden Anxieties: Male Sexuality, 1900–1950* (Cambridge and Oxford, Polity Press, 1991), pp. 17–18.

25 Lutz Sauerteig, *Krankheit, Sexualität, Gesellschaft: Geschlechtskrankheiten und Gesundheitspolitik in Deutschland im 19. und frühen 20. Jahrhundert* (Stuttgart, Franz Steiner, forthcoming), ch. IV.2; Andreas Hill, '"May the Doctor Advise Extramarital Intercourse?" Medical Debates On Sexual Abstinence in Germany, *c.* 1900', *Sexual Knowledge, Sexual Science: The History of Attitudes to Sexuality*, eds Roy Porter and Mikuláš Teich (Cambridge University Press, 1994), pp. 284–302.

26 Alfred Blaschko, 'Hygiene der Geschlechtskrankheiten', *Weyls Handbuch der Hygiene*, ed. A. Gärtner (Leipzig, J.A. Barth, 2nd edn 1918–22), vol. 8, pp. 281–553, 424, 426; Alfred Blaschko, 'Zur Frage des Abolitionismus', *ZBG*, 16 (1915–16), 233–52, at p. 248.

27 Sauerteig, *Krankheit, Sexualität, Gesellschaft*, ch. IV.2.3.

28 August Bebel, *Die Frau und der Sozialismus* (new edn of the 1929 anniversary edn, Berlin and Bonn, J.H.W. Dietz Nachf., 1985), pp. 116–18. Cf. Robert Paul Neuman, 'The Sexual Question and Social Democracy in Imperial Germany', *Journal of Social History*, 7 (1973/4), 271–86.

29 Frank Percy Crozier, *A Brass Hat in No Man's Land* (London, Jonathan Cape, 1930), p. 58.

30 Spier-Irving, *Irrwege*, p. 29.

31 See report of the *Reichsamt des Innern* (30 July 1918), BAB, 15.01/11873, pp. 249–51.

32 Gustav Aschaffenburg, 'Die konstitutionellen Psychopathen', *Handbuch der Ärztlichen Erfahrungen im Weltkriege 1914/1918*, ed. Otto von Schjerning, vol. IV/1 (Leipzig, Johann Ambrosius Barth, 1922–34), pp. 122–53, at p. 151.

33 Fussell, *Great War*, p. 271.

34 Haste, *Rules*, pp. 54–6; Richard Davenport-Hines, *Sex, Death and Punishment: Attitudes to Sex and Sexuality in Britain Since the Renaissance* (London, Collins, 1990), pp. 147–9.

35 Aschaffenburg, 'Psychopathen', pp. 151–3.

36 Fussell, *Great War*, pp. 270–309; Bourke, *Dismembering the Male*, pp. 24–5. See also Aschaffenburg, 'Psychopathen', p. 151.

37 Regarding this strategy of moral education by means of deterrence, see Lutz Sauerteig, 'Lust und Abschreckung. Moulagen in der Geschlechtskrankheitenaufklärung', *Medizin, Gesellschaft und Geschichte*, 11 (1992) (Stuttgart, Franz Steiner, 1993), 89–105.

38 Sauerteig, *Krankheit, Sexualität, Gesellschaft*, ch. IV.2.1; Harrison, *British Army*, p. 138; Allan M. Brandt, *No Magic Bullet: A Social History of Venereal Disease in the United States Since 1880* (Oxford University Press, 1985), pp. 61–70.

39 G. Arthur, *Life of Lord Kitchener*, vol. 3 (London, Macmillan, 1920), p. 27.

40 Davenport-Hines, *Sex*, p. 180; Brandt, *No Magic Bullet*, pp. 65–6.

41 Lawrence W. Harrison, 'Venereal Diseases', *History of the Great War, Based on Official Documents. Medical Services: Diseases of the War*, ed. W.G. MacPherson, vol. 2 (London, HMSO, 1923), pp. 118–60, at p. 121.

42 Royal Commission on Venereal Diseases, *Final Report of the Commissioners*, 1916, Cd 8189, vol. XVI, p. 61.

43 Cassel, *Secret Plague*, pp. 131–2; Brandt, *No Magic Bullet*, p. 99.

44 Circular from the Prussian War Ministry (7 April 1913), Bayerisches Hauptstaatsarchiv, abt. IV (BHStA/IV/IV), MKr10103.

45 *Tafeln zum Unterricht der Mannschaften bezüglich der Gefahren des Geschlechtsverkehrs*, introd. by Georg Reh (Munich, 1916). A brochure entitled *Mahnruf* ('Word of Exhortation') and produced by the

Berlin Social Insurance Board argued along similar lines. This brochure was handed to nearly every soldier from mid-1915 onwards. Cf. Bundesarchiv Koblenz, R86,1063; BAB, 15.01/11869, pp. 115–22.

46 Memorandum by Professor Dr med. Pannwitz on VD in Brussels (20 February 1915), BAB, 15.01/11868, pp. 196–201; Hirschfeld, *Sittengeschichte*, vol. 1, p. 342; Daniel, *Arbeiterfrauen*, p. 140.

47 Karin Walser, 'Prostitutionsverdacht und Geschlechterforschung: Das Beispiel der Dienstmädchen um 1900', *Geschichte und Gesellschaft*, 11 (1985), 88–111.

48 Sauerteig, *Krankheit, Sexualität, Gesellschaft*, ch. IV.2.5; Hall, *Hidden Anxieties*, pp. 50–3; Lucy Bland, '"Cleansing the Portals of Life": The Venereal Disease Campaign in the Early Twentieth Century', *Crisis In the British State 1880–1930*, eds Mary Langan and Bill Schwarz (London, Hutchinson, 1985), pp. 192–208, at p. 202.

49 Lutz Sauerteig, 'Frauenemanzipation und Sittlichkeit: Die Rezeption des englischen Abolitionismus in Deutschland', *Aneignung und Abwehr: Interkultureller Transfer zwischen Deutschland und Großbritannien im 19. Jahrhundert*, eds Rudolf Muhs, Johannes Paulmann, and Willibald Steinmetz (Philo-Verlagsgesellschaft, 1998), pp. 159–97; Sauerteig, *Krankheit, Sexualität, Gesellschaft*, ch. IV.3.5; Alain Corbin, *Women For Hire: Prostitution and Sexuality in France After 1850* (Cambridge, MA, Harvard University Press, 1990).

50 *Obergeneralarzt* Georg Reh to the Bavarian War Ministry (29 October 1912), BHStA/IV, MKr10103; Oscar Gans, 'Venerische Infektionen im Kriege und im Frieden', *ZBG*, 19 (1919/20), 217–29; Wilhelm von Drigalski, 'Geschlechtskrankheiten', *Handbuch der Ärztlichen Erfahrungen im Weltkriege 1914/1918*, ed. Otto von Schjerning, vol. VII (Leipzig, Johann Ambrosius Barth, 1922), pp. 586–609, at pp. 586–8.

51 Minutes of a meeting on combating VD in the army (29 March 1915), BAB, 15.01/11868, pp. 173–80.

52 F.B. Smith, 'The Contagious Diseases Acts Reconsidered', *Social History of Medicine*, 3 (1990), 197–215; Judith R. Walkowitz, *Prostitution and Victorian Society: Women, Class, and the State* (Cambridge University Press, 1980); Paul McHugh, *Prostitution and Victorian Social Reform* (New York, St Martin's Press, 1980).

53 House of Commons Debates, 5th series, 90 (19 February 1917), cols 1098–1131; cf. *The Shield: A Review of Moral and Social Hygiene*, 1 (1916–17), 211–12, 217–23, 265–6, 274–8, 328–9. Cf. Cassel, *Secret Plague*, pp. 122–44; Suzanne Buckley, 'The Failure to Resolve the Problem of Venereal Disease Among the Troops in Britain During World War I', *War and Society: A Yearbook of Military History*, vol. 2, eds Brian Bond and Ian Roy (London, Croom Helm, 1977), pp. 65–85.

54 Public Record Office (PRO), CAB 23/5WC52(18)10, p. 122 (22 February 1918); 23/5WC365(18)14, p. 159 (13 March 1918).

55 The Association for Moral and Social Hygiene, for example, organized weekly public protest meetings: Fawcett Library, AMSH 311/2; *The Shield*, 2 (1918–20), 2–4; PRO, CAB 23/7/WC461(18)13, pp. 73–4 (20 August 1918). Cf. Haste, *Rules*, p. 54; Bland, *Cleansing the Portals of Life*, pp. 203–4; Edward H. Beardsley, 'Allied Against Sin: American and British Responses to Venereal Disease in World War I', *Medical History*, 20 (1976), 189–202, at pp. 198–201.

56 Harrison, *British Army*, p. 143; Haste, *Rules*, pp. 48–9; Corbin, *Women For Hire*, pp. 334–6; Peter Simkins, 'Soldiers and Civilians: Billeting in Britain and France', *A Nation in Arms: A Social Study of the*

British Army in the First World War, eds Ian F. Beckett and Keith Simpson (Manchester University Press, 1985), pp. 164–91, at pp. 184–5; Hirschfeld, *Sittengeschichte*, vol. 1, pp. 310–11.

57 Brandt, *No Magic Bullet*, pp. 103–4; Beardsley, 'Allied Against Sin', p. 197.

58 Memorandum of Lord Derby, Secretary of State for War, PRO, CAB 24/45/GT(18)3932, pp. 110–11 (15 March 1918); decision of the War Cabinet, PRO CAB 23/5/WC366(18)13, pp. 163–4 (18 March 1918); Harrison, *Venereal Diseases*, pp. 124–5. Cf. Harrison, *British Army*, pp. 144–5; Beardsley, 'Allied Against Sin', pp. 197–8.

59 PRO, CAB 23/5/WC366(18)13, pp. 163–4 (18 March 1918). Cf. Harrison, *British Army*, pp. 145–6; Brandt, *No Magic Bullet*, pp. 104–5; Beardsley, 'Allied Against Sin', pp. 198–9.

60 Albert Neisser, 'Die Gefahren des Geschlechtsverkehrs nach dem Kriege', *Berliner Tageblatt*, 120 (6 March 1915), BAB, 15.01/11868, p. 69.

61 Cf., for example, the petition of the *Bund deutscher Frauenvereine* and the *Katholischer Frauenbund*, urging the Prussian War Ministry to forbid soldiers to indulge in non-marital intercourse; Landesarchiv Berlin, Helene-Lange-Archiv 46–203.

62 Conference on combating VD in the army (29 March 1915), BAB, 15.01/11868, pp. 173–80; first report of the Population Committee (7 July 1917), pp. 1710–11, *Verhandlungen des Deutschen Reichstags*, vol. 321, No. 912; circular of the Prussian *Feldsanitätsdienst*, General Headquarters, 1916, BHStA/IV, MKr10104.

63 Drigalski, 'Bekämpfung der Geschlechtskrankheiten in Groß-Brüssel', paper given in a conference for combating VD in Brussels (8 October 1915), BAB, 15.01/11869, pp. 196–233. Cf. Drigalski, *Geschlechtskrankheiten*, p. 596.

64 Conference for combating VD in Brussels (8 October 1915), BAB, 15.01/11869, pp. 196–233.

65 Blumenfeld, *Durch tausendjährige Zeit*, pp. 192–8.

66 Hirschfeld, *Sittengeschichte*, vol. 1, pp. 312, 316. Cf. illus. 2.

67 Bundesarchiv Freiburg, Militärarchiv (BAF) RM31/970, pp. 75–6, 192–3; decree of the Prussian War Ministry (14 July 1915), BHStA/IV, MKr10103; Gans, *Venerische Infektionen*, pp. 219–20; Drigalski, *Geschlechtskrankheiten*, pp. 596–8.

68 BAB, 15.01/11868, pp. 191–5, 264; BAB, 15.01/11869, pp. 123–8, 196–233.

69 This is discussed in greater detail in Lutz Sauerteig, 'Moralismus versus Pragmatismus: Die Kontroverse um Schutzmittel gegen Geschlechtskrankheiten zu Beginn des 20. Jahrhunderts im deutsch–englischen Vergleich', *Neue Wege in der Seuchengeschichte*, eds Martin Dinges and Thomas Schlich (Stuttgart, Franz Steiner, 1995), pp. 207–47, at pp. 216–18.

70 The navy favoured the former strategy of skilled disinfection from early in the twentieth century, while the army inclined towards vending machines: BAF, RM31/970, pp. 25–59, 64–7; BHStA/IV, Mkr 10103; BAF, RM31/970, pp. 38, 51. The most commonly used disinfection package was called *Viro*.

71 Regulations of the Prussian War Ministry (18 May 1910), and note of the Bavarian War Ministry (8 October 1910), BHStA/IV, MKr10102.

72 *Deutscher Sittlichkeitsbund vom Weißen Kreuz* (German Morality Association of the White Cross, one of the several Protestant social purity organizations) to Josias von Heeringen, Prussian War Minister (8 November 1911), BAF, RM31/970, pp. 21–4.

73 Katharina Scheven, 'Gefahr der physischen und moralischen Verseuchung unseres Heeres', *Der Abolitionist*, 11 (1912), 4–5, at p. 5.

74 Decree of the Prussian War Minister (20 January 1912), BHStA/IV, MKr10103.

75 Report of *Obergeneralarzt* Georg Reh to the Bavarian War Ministry (29 October 1910), BHStA/IV, MKr10103; commentary to this by *Generalstabsarzt* in the War Ministry, Karl Ritter von Seydel (28 January 1913), BHStA/IV, MKr10103.

76 Reports of the corps physicians, BHStA/IV, MKr, Sanitätsinspektion, 62.

77 Decree of the Prussian War Ministry (20 January 1912), BHStA/IV, MKr10103; BAF, RM31/970, pp. 26, 76–7. Although a similar regulation existed in the navy as well, the Bavarian War Ministry refused to implement such measures. Bavarian War Ministry Medical Department (16 February 1912), BHStA/IV, MKr10103.

78 Condoms, however, were not at any rate to be recommended to soldiers. Decree of the Prussian War Ministry (14 July 1915), BHStA/IV, MKr10103; statement of *Generalarzt* Schultzen, Prussian War Ministry, at a conference on VD (29 March 1915), BAB, 15.01/11868, pp. 173–80.

79 *Marinestation Ostsee* to the *Reichsmarineamt* (21 July 1915), BAF, RM31/970, pp. 192–3; cf. BAF, RM31/974, pp. 146–56, 234–5.

80 Circular of the headquarters of the Prussian army (1916), BHStA/IV, MKr10104; report of the *Reichsamt des Innern* about the policy of the Prussian War Ministry (30 July 1918), BAB, 15.01/11873, pp. 249–51.

81 Circular of the Prussian War Ministry (9 March 1917), BHStA/IV, MKr10104.

82 For the following Sauerteig, 'Moralismus', pp. 222–3; Harrison, *British Army*, pp. 146–9; Sandra M. Tomkins, 'Palmitate or Permanganate: The Venereal Prophylaxis Debate in Britain, 1916–1926', *Medical History*, 37 (1993), 382–98; Bridget A. Towers, 'Health Education Policy 1916–1926: Venereal Disease and the Prophylaxis Dilemma', *Medical History*, 24 (1980), 70–87, at pp. 76–7; Buckley, *Failure*; Beardsley, 'Allied Against Sin'.

83 A.H. Safford, 'Venereal Disease Amongst British Troops in India', *Journal of the Royal Army Medical Corps*, 43 (1924), 252–63; Sir G. Archdall Reid, *Prevention of Venereal Disease* (London, William Heinemann, 1920), pp. 139–40; Lawrence W. Harrison, 'Those Were the Days! Or Random Notes On Then and Now in VD', reprinted from *Bulletin of the Institute of Technicians in Venereology*, n.d. (Wellcome Institute Library, London, Reprint Collection).

84 Decree of the War Office (18 March 1916), PRO, WO32/5597; *Report of the Interdepartmental Committee on Infectious Diseases in Connection With Demobilisation* [Astor-Committee], (1919), Cmd 322, vol. xxx, pp. 7–8, 24; conference in the War Office (10 May 1918), pp. 28–9, 39–40, PRO, WO32/11404.

85 Childs (War Office) to Sir Edward Troup (Home Office) (16 September 1917), PRO, HO45/10802/307990/33; conference in the War Office (10 May 1918), PRO, WO32/11404, pp. 12, 14–16, 22–3, 28–30, 35; conference in the War Office (11 July 1918), PRO, WO32/11404, pp. 2–3.

86 Lawrence W. Harrison, *A Sketch of Army Medical Experience of Venereal Disease During the European War, 1914–1918. Paper Read Before the British Medical Association Annual Meeting, 1919* (London, National Council for Combating Venereal Diseases, 2nd edn, 1922); Astor-Committee (1919), Cmd 322, vol. xxx, p. 20.

87 Decree of the War Office (18 March 1916), PRO, WO32/5597.

88 Reid, *Prevention*, pp. 127–49; Crozier, *Brass Hat*, pp. 50–1.

89 Cassel, *Secret Plague*, pp. 126–30, 140–1; Brandt, *No Magic Bullet*, p. 99; Harrison, *Venereal Diseases*, pp. 128–9.

90 Brandt, *No Magic Bullet*, pp. 98–121.

91 The same conclusion is drawn by Arthur Marwick, *War and Social Change in the Twentieth Century: A Comparative Study of Britain, France, Germany, Russia and the United States* (London and Basingstoke, Macmillan, 1974), pp. 93–4.

92 Kundrus, *Kriegerfrauen*, p. 215f.

93 Bourke, *Dismembering the Male*, p. 156.

94 Brandt, *No Magic Bullet*, p. 120.

10

FIGHTING MILITARISM? BRITISH NURSING DURING THE SECOND WORLD WAR

Penny Starns

It is generally agreed by historians, and even by some of the participants, that the Second World War was instrumental in advancing the nursing profession in Britain. Some scholars have viewed the impact of the war in a positive light simply because it resulted in the appointment of a chief nursing officer at the Ministry of Health.[1] Others have pointed to the introduction of national pay scales and the expansion of nursing practice. Among nurses themselves, faulty memory, or even collective amnesia, may have played a part in the shaping of this view. An older generation of British nurses identified with the military, proudly – too proudly – tracing their professional roots back to Florence Nightingale and the Crimea. Some nurses clearly had the time of their lives during the war, and some may have truly been empowered by it. In reality, however, for most of the nursing profession, the war was a colossal disaster. While civilian nurses experienced the erosion and dilution of their status, military nurses (faring somewhat better) were compelled to spend much of their time resolving the ambiguities of their position within the military.

This chapter explores how, as a means to improving the professional status of nurses during the Second World War, both branches of the profession adopted a militarist strategy. It looks to the different degrees of success they had in adopting this strategy, and to some of the implications for patients. First, though, it is necessary to look at the situation in which the profession found itself at the outbreak of the war.

STATUS UNDERMINED

Long before 1939, British nursing resembled a ship that was already half sunk. According to a report published in 1932, over 50 per cent of hospitals were experiencing problems in recruiting trained nurses and at least a third of all probationers failed to complete their training.[2] According to the *Interim Report* of 1939 of the committee under the Earl of Athlone, improved recruiting could only come about if the government afforded official recognition to assistant nurses and, at the same time, subsidized the voluntary hospitals to enable them to standardize training and improve salaries.[3] These recommendations were initially rejected by both the government and the nursing establishment. The government opposed the idea of funding voluntary hospitals, while the nurses believed that any recognition of assistants would downgrade professional status. Ultimately, however, as the war moved beyond its 'phoney' start, even the luxury of debate had to be surrendered. Addressing the immediate chaos took precedence.

Initial attempts to organize the medical services in preparation for war were ill-conceived, inefficient and heavily criticized by members of the medical profession. In a White Paper of 1939 the government had outlined an emergency hospital scheme and a system of first-aid posts to deal with the anticipated casualties of heavy air raids on London. It was intended that all such posts would be staffed by a qualified doctor with trained nurses in attendance. Many of London's voluntary hospitals were to act as casualty clearing stations and plans were unveiled to disperse a proportion of the population living in major cities to surrounding rural areas. To an extent, British emergency schemes for casualty clearance were based on medical experience gained during the Spanish Civil War. However, there were disputes between medical personnel and the government over the method of casualty clearance. In the event, these disputes were largely irrelevant since a severe shortage of medical personnel prevented the efficient implementation of any emergency scheme.

The hospital casualty clearing stations were staffed by untrained personnel almost as soon as war was declared, resulting in scenes of chaos.[4] The shortage of doctors forced medical schools to admit women for training; dentists were encouraged to acquire anaesthetic skills by means of intensive courses; staff were conscripted and subjected to the jurisdiction of the Ministry of Health; outpatients departments disappeared virtually overnight. By April 1940 Bartholomew's Hospital, one of the largest in London with a bed capacity of 780, had been virtually taken over for military cases, with only 145 beds left for civilian patients.[5] While the situation was less severe in rural areas, the ratio of bed allocation for civilians posed problems in several major cities. The subordination of civilian health care needs to those of military services also placed a substantial burden on the district nursing services.

The British Red Cross Society and the Order of St John provided Voluntary Aid Detachment nurses (VADs) to supplement both civilian and military nursing services.[6] Civilian services were also supplemented, in theory by nurses attached to the Civil Nursing Reserve (CNR). However, in practice, CNR nurses were initially restricted to working for the civilian emergency services and were therefore unable to alleviate severe staffing problems elsewhere. Moreover, the CNR was badly organized: the Emergency Committee responsible for the deployment of nurses was mismanaged, and before the end of 1939 was replaced by a Central Advisory Board for Nursing.[7] New policies were introduced to improve the allocation of nurses but, despite this overhaul, problems continued.

In their deliberations on the nursing required for the war, government and hospital administrators paid little attention to the various levels of nursing expertise. Prior to the war registered nurses had undergone a three-year training period leading to state registration, whereas assistant nurses had some nursing experience but were not registered. The auxiliaries were frequently women with no previous nursing experience. The Civil Nursing Reserve consisted mainly of the latter two groups; consequently, registered nurses who had volunteered for military service were usually replaced by assistants. The unrestricted flow of nurses into the armed forces before 1943 compounded this problem of dilution.

It is also clear that hospital administrators did not value registered nurses. Instead, they viewed the emergency conditions as an ideal opportunity to dispense with them in order to save money. By the end of November 1939 over 2,000 registered nurses were made redundant in London alone. Registered hospital nurses were paid on average £70 per annum whereas their CNR counterparts were paid £90 per annum. By the time hospital administrators had recognized the importance of retaining senior nurses, most administrators were unable to replace those who had volunteered for military service. Only later, in 1941, were steps taken by the War Office to return senior nurses to their respective hospitals on request if the institutions concerned were experiencing difficulties in filling senior positions. These steps, however, were ineffective. The delay between making a request to the War Office and receiving the released nurse tended to be at least six months. Nurses who had joined the military were often overseas and difficult to locate and recall.

Civilian hospitals, already suffering from the haemorrhage of senior nursing staff into the forces, were further hit by the high salaries offered by the Civil Nursing Reserve which drained off even more of their trained nurses. The salary discrepancies understandably caused chaos and belated government action in 1941 only narrowly averted a complete breakdown in civilian nursing services. In the same year, the role of the CNR was extended to include all institutions experiencing nursing shortages, and the Ministry of Health stated that regular hospital nurses should receive the same salary as reserve nurses. In doing so, the Ministry was forced to fund a percentage of the salary difference; therewith lay the foundations for the often-troubled postwar employer/employee relationship between the Ministry and the nursing profession.

For registered nurses, the salary differential between CNR and regular civilian nursing was a means to the erosion of their status. For one thing, most first aiders were paid more than registered nurses. For another, the government had already thwarted professional aims in 1939 by abolishing the minimum educational qualification for registered nurse training – a move that was designed to aid recruitment. High demand in certain specialities had also prompted the reduction of training periods in some fields of nursing. For instance, because of a demand for nurses to work in munitions factories it was possible to undertake a correspondence course in industrial nursing. Above all, however, it was the lack of distinction between registered and assistant nurses which polarized status issues in the civilian nursing field. Registered nurses described assistants as 'bath attendants' and asserted their own status by recalling tales of heroic military experience, whereas assistants replied by accusing their registered counterparts of élitism. As one assistant complained in the nursing press: 'I have no certificate to show for my hard work but I'll wager if I were to collect my testimonials they would carry me further than some of those people who are so fond of boasting of their registered status and medals.'[8]

Hostility between registered and assistant nurses increased when, in an attempt to attract more recruits, the government introduced a controversial Nurses Act in 1943, which gave official status to assistant nurses. To add insult to injury, a clause in the 1943 Act allowed Christian Science nurses to assume the official title of 'nurse' without possessing any relevant skills. The profession was appalled; for many registered nurses, the 1943 Act represented an outright betrayal of their professional ideals. The nursing press fulminated: 'It is almost incredible that after the profession of nursing has existed in England for a quarter of a century, that totally ignorant Ministers of the Crown should be permitted to smash up not only the status of an honourable profession but deprive the public of necessary safeguards to health and life.'[9]

Status issues were not the exclusive preserve of civilian nurses; military nurses experienced them too. A military divide had emerged between regular military nurses and those of the middle-class Voluntary Aid Detachments under the Red Cross and Order of St John. This divide was also fuelled by organizational difficulties: the VAD Council had received numerous complaints from VADs during the early stages of the war, mainly regarding accommodation standards and conditions of service. Several VADs refused to perform some of the more menial nursing tasks and many more objected to sub-standard living quarters. In an attempt to pacify the VAD Council, the Army Council limited the scope of VAD duties and afforded them official privileges.

But these concessions only served to increase the number of arguments relating to nurse status because the VADs were insufficiently skilled to assume officer workloads. Neither could the VADs replace male orderlies when they were transferred to front-line positions during the course of the war. The Army response to these problems was unprecedented: in 1943 comprehensive proposals were submitted to the War Office aimed at incorporating VADs into the Auxiliary Territorial Service (ATS). The latter service, which was established at the outbreak of the war, came under the jurisdiction of the Army Council and formed the official Army women's service. Its main purpose was to free up more men for the front line by training women in such male occupations as mechanics and so on. With a view to incorporating VADs into the ATS, the Army claimed that the existing structure for the organization of VADs was inefficient and did not fully utilize man and womanpower. Moreover, Army officials argued that a number of VADs were capable of undergoing training courses which would equip them for a nursing career in civil society once hostilities ceased. (Under the existing scheme, VADs were unable to take advantage of certain training opportunities, regardless of their individual abilities.)

It was suggested by the Army Council that the new VAD branch of the Auxiliary Territorial Service be organized through the office of the ATS and that the new branch 'would form an integral part of the ATS and not of the Royal Army Medical Corps or the Army Dental Corps'.[10] This statement reflected the Army Council's policy regarding female personnel, namely that there should only be one female corps within the Army. The Army Council's proposals, however, were not merely designed to encourage VAD training and resolve status issues; the proposals made provision for the Army to dispense with the services of the VAD Council. Army funds would therefore no longer be allotted to the VAD Council nor to VAD county controllers. Furthermore, the Army would acquire a substantial nursing force to direct at will.

There were, nevertheless, important flaws inherent in these Army takeover plans. Army officials had not, for example, considered the wider implications of a merger between VAD and ATS personnel. Aside from the potential ethical questions associated with a military takeover of voluntary services, the proposals, if accepted, would clearly compromise the British Red Cross within the international arena. If the military could take over Red Cross VADs, then why not their communications and administration? Red Cross principles were based on the concept of political neutrality: how could this political neutrality coexist with military compliance regarding voluntary nurses?

There was also the potential problem of loss of 'goodwill'. Voluntary bodies had made concerted efforts to train enough first aiders and nursing aids for wartime service. Given the overall shortage of medical personnel, it was not possible to administer adequate care to civilian and military casualties without continued voluntary assistance. A forced takeover bid of voluntary nurses was not likely to foster good relationships between the state and the voluntary bodies concerned. As the official historians of the Red Cross Society for the Second World War have noted, the suggested destruction of 'the oldest women's service met with the most violent resistance from the VADs and societies concerned'.[11] After much deliberation and ad hoc debate, the Army Council VAD Committee in June 1943 rejected the proposed merger and suggested that since the treatment of VADs in the armed forces had undermined registered nurse status, 'steps should be taken to avoid the use by VAD members of any articles of clothing which are generally identified with particular ranks of the nursing profession'.[12]

These concessions partially resolved the status concerns of military nurses, but those in the civilian field continued to be preoccupied with the erosion of their status. Senior nurses argued that if status could not be elevated or at least maintained it would be impossible to attract new recruits into the profession. The General Nursing Council (GNC), as the statutory body responsible for nurse training, appeared to be totally unable to protect nurse status from further erosion. The GNC did suggest that status could possibly be raised by lengthening the training period for registration, but this suggestion was economically driven rather than professionally motivated since a government appointed committee, chaired by Lord Rushcliffe, had in 1943 increased the pay differentials between probationer and registered nurses.[13] Nursing organizations were also powerless to protect registered status. The demands of war precluded the enhancement of prestige by usual professional means. Consequently registered nurses sought an alternative means.

MILITARIZATION

The nursing profession were no strangers to military service and had long exploited the association. As Anne Summers has demonstrated, nursing participation in the Boer War and the First World War gave considerable impetus to the movement for state registration of nurses.[14] During the Second World War recruitment propaganda concentrated on nursing's heroic and military past. A film which charted the life of First World War nurse heroine Edith Cavell raised £62,000 for the British Red Cross Society and gave impetus to the recruitment drive in the early stages of war.[15] Another film, *The Lamp Still Burns* (1943), highlighted the heroic military roots of nursing, while simultaneously drawing attention to the negative effects of military identification on nurse recruitment. The Ministry of Health was quick to capitalize on these heroic images for recruitment purposes. As one poster asserted: 'In every war in our history, Britain has looked to the women to care for the sick and wounded. It is women's work. The nurses never let us down. Florence Nightingale lit a candle in the Crimea 85 years ago. The women of today have kept it burning brightly not only in France, Egypt and Greece but in Poplar, Portsmouth, Liverpool, Hull and all other battlefields of the Home Front.'[16]

This militarization of recruitment was also apparent, for instance, in the proliferation of nurse cadet schemes. Indeed, militarization now became a distinct and deliberate feature of nursing policy. The leading protagonist of this policy was Dame Katherine Jones, a military nurse since 1916. Her policy began to take shape when she was mobilized on 11 September 1939 as Senior Principal Matron on the staff of the general headquarters of the British Expeditionary Force. As Matron-in-Chief of the Army, she argued explicitly that militarization provided an opportunity to resolve nurse status problems once and for all.

It is important, however, to identify the particular strategy of militarization that military nurses now adopted. An early strategy of militarization had failed to secure these nurses' interests. Army nurses were afforded nominal officer status and, since the Nightingale era, had been recruited primarily from the ranks of officers' wives, widows and daughters. They had also adopted the aristocratic military view that character was more important than intellect (military nurses were therefore born, not made). Recruitment practice, combined with royal patronage, ensured that military nursing occupied a prestigious position within the profession as a whole. Despite this prestige, however, the nursing position within the Army was always ambiguous. As Anne Summers has put it, nurses were 'in but not of the Army'.[17] Female military nursing units had existed since the Crimean War and were not disbanded along with other female military units in 1918.[18] Nevertheless, by the Second World War, the position of military nurses had declined both in terms of status and pay. In these respects, women in military nursing compared unfavourably with the women in the Auxiliary Territorial Service.

An alternative strategy was that pursued by the members of the ATS. They adopted a policy of military assimilation in order to secure their status – a policy that Dame Katherine believed could also benefit Army nurses. The ATS recognized that militarization provided the key which enabled women to gain commissioned officer status. As Dame Katherine observed: 'The ATS officer achieved that understanding from the start. It was reinforced by a multitude of detailed practices, it was emphasised by the cut and the colour of her uniform and there was no doubt at any point that she fitted into the army pattern. She was recognised everywhere by everyone as an army officer both on and off duty. It became my aim to profit from this experience and to achieve the same assimilation for the QAIMNS [Queen Alexandra's Imperial Military Nursing Service].'[19] More importantly, Dame Katherine argued that if registered nurses in the military sector obtained commissioned officer status, this would to some extent elevate and promote nurse status in the civilian sector. As she explained to the Association of Hospital Matrons (AHM): 'I want you to understand this as the imposition of the military rank pattern on the nursing profession. By superimposing this rank pattern on one particular section of the nursing profession, it seemed possible to not only confer status but to provide a framework to hold that status firmly in place.'[20]

With this goal in mind, the Matron-in-Chief initiated a full-blown militarization programme for Army nurses, which involved subjecting nurses to other types of military training from which they had hitherto been excluded. Army nurses' uniforms were changed from the traditional scarlet and grey to that of khaki and, for the first time, their uniform included a 'battledress'. These changes represented the tangible effects of militarization. One nurse described this transition: 'until this stage we sisters had never been drilled, suddenly we found ourselves forming fours and route marching three miles into the desert and back, all to get us fit for the Greek episode'.[21] At the same time, nurses were increasingly expected to administer care in front-line positions. One nurse, writing in 1942, described her feelings with regard to this policy: 'Waiting for the baptism of fire doesn't worry me much except for the usual empty feeling at the sound of planes and guns. One sister here has been through France, the Middle East and Greece with amazing experiences and I want to do likewise. At last my existence here seems justified and the year of fun and games preceding this will be something to be remembered with a tolerant smile.'[22]

Some nurses clearly viewed the introduction of route marches and drill procedures as 'fun and games'. Others, however, took the military procedures very seriously. In some cases nurses allocated beds to patients and examined them according to their rank. The lowest rank was always the last to receive medical attention, irrespective of the severity of illness and injury. But this overt enthusiasm for militarization was not shared by Commonwealth nurses, particularly the Australians, who claimed that British nurses were obsessed with status, rank and protocol.[23]

Militarization was successful in achieving the goals laid down by Dame Katherine Jones. Registered nurses were afforded commissioned officer status in the Army in 1941 and this status was extended outwards from the Army to include all nurses within the Royal Air Force, Royal Navy and Commonwealth nurses. Once hostilities had ceased, Army nurses were established as a distinct corps and even managed to negotiate a 'professional' salary lead over members of non-professional women's services. From being an ambiguous nursing unit they had established a firm place 'in and of the Army'. Dame Katherine's efforts were not of course appreciated by all nurses. Commonwealth nurses, for instance, resented the officer commissions and viewed them as an unwelcome military imposition on their 'civilian' vocation. And not all the military forces agreed that nurses should be militarized in this way. The Royal Air Force, for example, initially refused to give nurses military titles, and refused to align nurses with service pay, stating that pay should conform to the civilian Rushcliffe Committee.[24]

The front-line policy provided yet another focus for debate, this time between the British and Commonwealth forces. Military policy was inconsistent with regard to the deployment of women in operational areas. Confused evacuation procedures, which were initiated during a variety of campaigns, served to highlight this inconsistency. During the Greek campaign, for instance, British medical services decided that nurses should hold their position on the front line and risk capture, whereas Australian medical services insisted that nurses should be evacuated. Nurses themselves were eager to administer care on the front line where they believed their skills would be valued, and military officers generally supported this decision. Although there was some criticism of the masculine style khaki uniform, having a few 'pretty faces' around was considered to be good for the morale of the troops.[25] Dame Katherine justified this on the grounds that khaki was more suitable for administering care in jungles and deserts, and that it provided an important symbol of the front-line policy. 'Florence Nightingale, if she were alive now, would rejoice in the significance of this unfeminine apparel, for it means that we are getting ever closer to the front line.'[26] The nursing press concurred: 'The new khaki uniform which emphasises the military rank of members of QAIMNS is very impressive and becoming.'[27]

Numerous articles explained the significance of officer status for registered nurses and highlighted the advantages of adopting the Army pattern for the whole profession. But since the policy was imposed from the top down, it is difficult to assess the views of nurses working at ground level. Some clearly objected to military discipline and the extreme regimentation of nursing practice in the Army, while others supported these features, equating discipline with efficiency.

EXTENDING THE POLICY

To an extent, this model of militarization was also adopted by civilian nurses. For example, civilian nurse cadet schemes were set up which recruited fifteen-year-old girls. However, in contrast to military cadet schemes, these recruits were taken directly from school and were expected to perform skilled nursing tasks, often without supervision. The recruits were given no organized training or career planning. Nurse discipline also became more severe and stressed the importance of class distinction, duty and self-sacrifice.

Further aspects of the militarization of civilian nursing included the introduction of military style ward inspections and ceremonial functions such as the presentation of medals. In addition, civilian nurses' uniforms were increasingly militarized: stripes on sleeves were adopted to distinguish rank, and a mess dress was adopted. In their eagerness to identify with concepts of military efficiency, nurses became obsessed with punctuality in ward routines and a military attitude towards personal appearance. Nurses' shoes were expected to gleam, shoulder epaulettes had to be aligned with creases on sleeves, and aprons had to be stiffly starched. Daily inspections by the matron ensured that nurses were assessed much like soldiers on parade.

Ironically, the civilian nurses were emulating an ideal of the military that the military itself did not live up to. But there was a good deal of bluff in all this. Like their military counterparts, civilian nurses soon learned to cover up their bunglings. Indeed, this aspect of nursing acquired the look of policy as nurses lacking in competence were instructed to assume an air of confidence. This process of bluff was also used to reassure patients in times of medical crisis.

Although patients appeared to be blissfully unaware of nursing incompetence, they were none the less made painfully aware of the militarization of nursing practice. Nurse character traits associated with femininity, such as the expression of sympathy, tenderness and compassion, were systematically discouraged. Stressed instead was the image of efficient functionality which men already enjoyed. Priority was given to tidying lockers and straightening beds rather than the care of patients.[28] Thus the traditional image of the nurse was transformed from that of an 'angel of mercy' to that of an unfeeling 'battleaxe'. Much of this shift in identity reflected a wider trend, since women throughout the war had worked on the premise that anything associated with the military was afforded higher status and access to power than anything associated with femininity. Nevertheless, the shift in nursing image was accelerated by the profession's urgent desire to shed the image of motherhood and portray nursing skills in a more professional light. Identification with the military provided further prestige through their elevation to the status of military officers.

What the militarizers of nursing wanted, then, was to equate registered nurse status for civilian nurses with officer status in the military. This identification of registered civilian nurses with officer status became the keynote of efforts to enhance the status of nurses after the war. It was taken up by the Nursing Reconstruction Committee of the Royal College of Nursing, established in 1941 and chaired by Lord Horder. The Horder reports of 1942, 1943 and 1949[29] stressed that officer-class nurses – registered nurses – were essential in order to stimulate professional development. According to Horder, the main function of the officer-class nurse was to provide professional leadership – an explicit analogy with military officers. Official status was to confirm the elite standing of registered nurses and endorse their legitimate authority over less qualified nurses.

Status Reviewed

The identification of nurses with the symbolic trappings of military organization was designed to aid recruitment and elevate nurse status. To an extent this strategy was successful. Military-style cadet schemes, for instance, helped resolve staff shortages. Despite their lack of training, cadets quickly became adept at suturing wounds and performing other skilled nursing tasks. This situation posed a problem for registered nurses, however; how could a three-year registration period be justified if fifteen-year-old girls were able to acquire nursing skills with no training whatsoever? Improved recruitment through cadet schemes thus lowered nurse status, which ultimately did little for nurse recruitment.

Meanwhile, for the military nursing sector, applications flooded in. This can hardly be explained in terms of more attractive uniforms since, as noted above, the uniform was changed to a distinctive khaki during the war. In part the answer may lie in the opportunity that military nursing gave for the respectable expression among females of patriotic (male-like) military behaviour. The greater elitism of military nursing relative to the erosion of civilian nursing during the war is surely an important part of the explanation. But in the final analysis, the main explanation lies in the lure of the ready escape that military service provided from the routines of domestic life. As during the Anglo-Boer War and the First World War, military nursing was a means to foreign travel and excitement, 'It could bring a woman to the heart of the action on a world stage.'[30]

In terms of recruitment, civilian nursing could not hope to compete with a service which offered women an opportunity to participate in the international war experience. Against this, the trappings of the military introduced into civilian nursing also could not compete – indeed, they could only serve to deter. While a young woman might be prepared to put up with military authoritarianism in a hospital in Marachesh or Milan, it was quite another matter to have to endure 'the reign of the sergeant major' on wards in Manchester or Moorgate.[31]

It is hardly surprising, then, that the £166,000 of public funds spent on nursing publicity between February 1943 and September 1946[32] to attract civilian nurses was largely wasted. The civilian recruitment campaigns achieved very little. Senior medical men, like Sir Robert Hutchinson, a consultant at the Royal London Hospital, might claim that the nurses they relied on were 'like the Brigade of Guards, the pick of the Forces', but the rhetoric didn't go far with those expected to march to the recruitment stations – not least because, as Sir Robert reminded them, 'a nurse's character is far more important than [her] brains'.[33]

CONCLUSION

The civilian nursing profession emerged from the Second World War politically fragmented and weakened by a diminished ratio of trained to untrained staff. Military nurses were better off in terms of status, pay and the quality of recruits, and may therefore have been better prepared for the postwar competition from such newly established services as the Women's Royal Army Corps and the Women's Auxiliary Air Force, which offered a variety of training and career opportunities. Government policy with regard to civilian nurses continued to concentrate on improving recruitment levels since there was no doubt that civilian health care delivery had suffered as a result of wartime nursing shortages.

Throughout the war, status issues had dominated professional thinking and the militarization policy pursued by Dame Katherine Jones was indicative of this concern. As she herself proclaimed: 'If I survive at all in nursing history I shall doubtless survive as the militarising Matron in Chief. I am glad that it should be so. I have in fact done my best to militarise QAIMNS and the TANS [Territorial

Army Nursing Service] but I should like as many people as possible to know why I have done this and to realise that there is method in my madness.'[34] However, despite her 'method', it can be argued that militarization failed in the civilian sector as a result of a fundamental misunderstanding on Dame Katherine's part. Military nurses did better than civilian nurses during the war, not because of militarization, but because they secured a place within the service and, more importantly, secured a better salary scheme than their civilian counterparts.[35] The Ministry of Health acknowledged that higher salaries were justified for military nurses because of their position as officers in the armed forces. In addition to this monetary reward, officer status also gave military nurses a degree of political leverage within the services.

Within the civilian sector, however, nurses had no such political leverage, and they manifestly failed to achieve it. With the emergence of the National Health Service after the war, nurses were rapidly swamped by a growing number of other health care professionals. Although we might appreciate her motives, Dame Katherine's 'method' *was* 'madness'; the effects of the 'method' on nursing status, not to mention on patient care, were never evaluated by her or by the government during the war years. That civilian nursing practice needed to diverge from that of the military only became apparent in the postwar years.

However, the technological changes which had occurred within the military from 1939 onwards had exposed the weaknesses of 'aristocratic militarism'. The new technology demanded intellectual knowledge. Consequently, military training shifted in the direction of education and professionalism. But civilian nursing did not experience a similar shift in direction for many years after the war. The war had accelerated medical research, but technical advances in areas such as blood transfusions, radiography, physiotherapy and antibiotic therapy were slow to infiltrate civilian hospitals and communities. Although medical technology eventually revealed the inadequacies of nurse education, the profession chose to defend its practical system of nurse training. This resistance to reform had extensive ramifications for postwar nursing.

Nurses failed to fight militarism from 1939 onwards. Instead, they openly advocated military identification in the vain hope that once registered nurse status was linked to military officer-class status the overall position of the professional nurse would improve. This endorsement of militarism proved to be misguided since it acted as an immovable obstacle to change. Nurses were drawn to military ideology initially to secure state registration and they continued to endorse it in an effort to raise and protect this status. Subsequently, civilian nurses were encumbered by an anti-educational bias and an outmoded system of discipline, combined with a paramilitary organizational structure which precluded any flexibility of nursing practice.

The militarization process escalated during the postwar period and the military model of nursing became increasingly anachronistic within a rapidly changing society. The first real challenge to the military model arrived in the form of the Salmon administrative reforms in the late 1960s; however, the Salmon system eventually collapsed because it was poorly implemented. The system was designed to instil management techniques into senior nursing levels but the government failed to provide sufficient management courses for senior nurses and the 'corporate' challenge to the 'military model' failed. Nurses simply used the Salmon system to reinforce 'officer' status and to strengthen the professional hierarchy that the war had put firmly in place. The legacy remains; still today it is complained by some (in this case a male consultant) that 'a ward sister runs the place . . . like the sergeant major. . . . So if you clash with the sister, that's a problem, there's a complete obstruction in the middle, between the commander and the troops.'[36] Alas, continuing government concerns over nurse recruitment figures and the profession's preoccupation with status have meant that there has been 'no attempt to protect the patient and avoid placing him or her in the no-man's-land between the trenches'.[37]

Notes

1 R.B. and V.H. Splane, *Chief Nursing Officer Positions in National Ministries of Health* (The Regents, California University, 1994).

2 *Report of the Lancet Commission on Nursing* (London, HMSO, 1932), p. 3.

3 *The Athlone Interim Report conducted by the Ministry of Health in Co-operation with the Board of Education* (London, HMSO, 1939). The Athlone Committee was disbanded during the war but its findings were resurrected by the Rushcliffe Committee in 1943; see Lord Rushcliffe, *Reports of the Nurses Salaries Committee, conducted by the Ministry of Labour and National Service in co-operation with the Department of Health for Scotland* (London, HMSO, 1943).

4 The chaos is vividly described by contemporary newspaper articles; see, for example, *News Chronicle* and the *Daily Herald* for November 1939.

5 *Hansard House of Commons Parliamentary Debates*, 5th series (13 June 1940), debate between the Supply Committee and the Ministry of Health.

6 The VAD scheme was first introduced in 1909 as a result of an Army Council initiative; Imperial War Museum 536/172/K9584.

7 Public Record Office (PRO), MH/55; see also Royal College of Nursing files RCN/7/4.

8 *The Nursing Illustrated*, correspondence section (April 1939), p. 12.

9 *The British Journal of Nursing* (May 1945), editorial, p. 1.

10 *Report of the Committee on Voluntary Aid Detachments* (London, HMSO, 1943), p. 2.

11 P. Cambray and G. Briggs, *The Official History of the Humanitarian Services of the War Organisation of the British Red Cross Society and the Order of St. John of Jerusalem 1939–1947* (London, Official War Organization of the British Red Cross Society and Order of St John, 1947), p. 664.

12 Report of the Committee on Voluntary Aid Detachments, Imperial War Museum 536/172/K9584.

13 Lord Rushcliffe, *Reports of the Nurses Salaries Committee conducted by the Ministry of Labour and National Service in Co-operation with the Department of Health for Scotland* (London, HMSO, 1943).

14 Anne Summers, *Angels and Citizens* (London, Routledge, 1988), pp. 182–3.

15 Edith Cavell trained at the Royal London Hospital and nursed during the First World War; she was held captive by Germans in Belgium and later executed.

16 Imperial War Museum, London, 36/172/K9540, government recruitment poster.

17 Summers, *Angels and Citizens*, p. 98.

18 Female units other than nursing were disbanded in 1918 because the War Office subscribed to the 'ten year' rule, i.e., war unlikely for ten years and women not needed.

19 PRO, WO/222/178, address to the East Anglian Group of the Association of Hospital Matrons by Dame Katherine H. Jones (2 September 1944). The AHM was founded in 1907 and organized on a regional basis to keep abreast of nursing developments around the country. The AHM, however, was not a progressive body.

20 PRO, WO/222/178.

21 J. Bassett, *Guns and Brooches* (Oxford University Press, 1992), p. 121.

22 *Nurses League Review* [of the Royal London Hospital], 11 (1942).

23 Bassett, *Guns and Brooches*, p. 122.

24 This stance by the RAF formed part of an ongoing trend. As the youngest service the RAF was less entrenched in military tradition and often challenged War Office policy. RAF nurses did not fully align with the other services until 1953.

25 In particular, nurses received support for their front-line policy from Lord Mountbatten and Field Marshal Montgomery, according to Monica Baly (interview in November 1995).

26 PRO, WO/222/178, address to the East Anglian group of the AHM by Dame Katherine Jones (2 September 1944).

27 *The Journal of British Nursing* (January 1945), p. 3.

28 J. Cohen, *Minority Report on Recruitment of Nurses* (London, HMSO, 1948), pp. 73–4.

29 Details of the reports are discussed in Brian Abel-Smith, *A History of the Nursing Profession* (London, Heinemann, 1960), pp. 170–3.

30 Summers, *Angels and Citizens*, p. 2.

31 J. Cohen, *Minority Report*, p. iv.

32 PRO, MH/55/2074.

33 *Nurses League Review*, 15 (1946), p. 11.

34 PRO, WO/222/178. Dame Katherine Jones (2 September 1944).

35 Military nurses protected their status by refusing to take on 'regulars' for the duration of the war and were far outnumbered by reservists. By 1945 the Queen Alexandra's Imperial [Army] Nursing Service had expanded from 624 to 12,000 personnel, the Queen Alexandra's Royal Navy Nursing Service from 78 to 1,341 and the Princess Mary's Royal Air Force Nursing from 171 to 1,215.

36 S. Walby and J. Greenwell, *Medicine and the Nursing Professions in a Changing Health Service* (London, 1994), p. 67.

37 T. Clay, *Nurses: Power and Politics* (London, Heinemann, 1987), p. 2.

11

FIGHTING RESEARCH: ARMY PARTICIPATION IN THE CLINICAL TESTING AND MASS PRODUCTION OF PENICILLIN DURING THE SECOND WORLD WAR

Peter Neushul

On Saturday night of Thanksgiving weekend in November 1942, Dr Champ Lyons and his wife Naomi attended a dinner party at a colleague's house in Boston, Massachusetts. Lyons was a surgeon at Massachusetts General Hospital, where he specialized in treating bacterial infections. Late in the evening the dinner party was interrupted as Lyons and every other doctor in the Boston area received the horrifying news that a fire at the famous Cocoanut Grove Nightclub had caused serious injury to hundreds of patrons. The physicians rushed immediately to Massachusetts General, arriving to find the long brick hallways lined with dead partygoers. Much to Lyons's surprise, the victims' clothing exhibited little evidence of burning and in many instances the fuzz remained on the neckties of male victims. He began treating survivors immediately and did not return home for three days. Unbeknown to Lyons his presence at the hospital would change his career forever, taking him to army hospitals in Utah and Rhode Island and from there to the Mediterranean, where he was awarded the Legion of Merit for his service to the wounded. All of these travels resulted from his use of the revolutionary new antibiotic penicillin to treat victims of the Cocoanut Grove fire.[1]

Champ Lyons's role in the penicillin story provides insight into the process whereby penicillin went from a laboratory phenomenon in 1942 to mass production in 1946. This incredible 'scaling up' was facilitated by the swift transfer of science and technology across a series of boundaries that were seemingly insurmountable in peacetime. Major steps in the process included the discovery of clinical effectiveness, limited testing on human patients in Great Britain; transfer of science and technology to the United States, production of enough penicillin to conduct large-scale clinical tests on human beings, development of effective protocols, negotiations with pharmaceutical manufacturers, construction of manufacturing facilities, and mass production of the antibiotic. Technology transfer, a theme used by historians of technology, can also be applied to cases in the history of medicine.[2] In this paper transfer will be broadened to include disciplinary as well as geographic boundaries. With the help of US and British military establishments, the War Production Board (WPB), and government laboratories, penicillin was tested and given to corporations for production. When pharmaceutical houses balked at the idea of building new factories the government provided financing, access to the necessary materials, and an efficient process for mass production. Military and government officials played a key role in practically every stage of penicillin's astonishing evolution from mould to life-saving antibiotic. In fact, there is no doubt that without the international crisis of the Second World War and the ensuing military interest in treatment for infectious diseases, adequate testing and production of penicillin would have been delayed for years.

Penicillin is perhaps the most significant achievement of the Second World War science and technology, saving thousands of soldiers from the horrors of gas gangrene and the other bacterial diseases that were rampant during previous conflicts. Unlike the First World War, where 12 to 15 per cent of the wounded treated in front-line hospitals died of infections, only 3 per cent of Second World War wounded died, due largely to advances in medical care.[3] Penicillin was particularly effective in preventing deaths from infected wounds. From D-Day, when penicillin was first available in large quantities, until the collapse of Germany, deaths resulting from infection were reduced almost to zero. In the postwar era, millions of civilians benefited from wartime development of the new antibiotics industry. In the 1990s, over fifty years since its discovery, penicillins are still among the most effective broad-spectrum antibiotics.

The penicillin programme was one of the largest wartime initiatives and is undoubtedly among the most successful research and development ventures ever. Most important, the project demonstrates the positive impact of government-sponsored research on industrial development. It is also an outstanding example of how to decisively expedite transition of a product from the laboratory to mass production. In the US, the military played a key role in this process, both by conducting large-scale clinical tests and aiding efforts to scale-up production. A special agency known as the Office of Scientific Research and Development (OSRD) was formed to harness the military potential of American science and technology. The Committee on Medical Research (CMR), a division of OSRD, focused specifically on military medicine and was responsible for organizing development of the new antibiotic. This was no small task considering the fact that penicillin was hardly a household name despite being discovered fourteen years earlier.

DISCOVERY OF PENICILLIN

The penicillin story began in 1928, when a stray spore of greenish mould, later identified as *Penicillium notatum*, found its way onto a Petri dish that Alexander Fleming had seeded with a culture of *Staphylococcus*, a pathogenic bacterium. Fleming was a bacteriologist working at St Mary's Hospital in London. In a moist environment, the common blue-green mould grows on anything from strawberry jam to shoe leather.[4] Later, while examining his plates prior to discarding them, Fleming noticed that bacteria adjacent to the mould were dead. He published several papers describing the antibiotic effect of penicillin *in vitro* using chemically undefined mould filtrate. Fleming never produced any extracted penicillin and made no extensive clinical tests.[5]

Twelve years later, in 1940, Howard W. Florey, Ernst Chain and Norman G. Heatley performed the first successful clinical tests of penicillin, after producing small quantities of the antibiotic from surface cultures and developing a method for measuring the amount extracted.[6] Florey's group began work on antibiotic substances in 1936, when he received a Rockefeller Foundation grant of £250 for the purchase of equipment.[7] Spectacular results were obtained when penicillin was used to treat mice infected with a virulent strain of streptococci. In 1941, the Oxford Group's first clinical tests with human patients were also successful although hampered by a continual shortage of the antibiotic.[8]

After unsuccessfully attempting to interest a beleaguered British pharmaceutical industry in penicillin production, Florey and Heatley travelled to the USA, where they hoped to persuade American pharmaceutical companies to produce enough penicillin for continuation of their clinical tests.[9] The scientists began their quest in Washington, DC, where they met with Ross G. Harrison, chairman of the National Research Council (NRC), Charles Thom, principle microbiologist at the United States Department of Agriculture's (USDA) Bureau of Plant Industry, and Percy Wells, head of the USDA's Eastern Regional Research Laboratory (ERRL).

After hearing Florey's description of the British production problem, Thom and Wells immediately suggested that he visit the USDA's Northern Regional Research Laboratory (NRRL) at Peoria, where an elite team of fermentation specialists was already developing commercial-scale mould fermentation as a means of utilizing surplus farming produce. Shortly thereafter, Wells contacted NRRL director, Orville May, and arranged for a visit by the British scientists. On 14 July 1941 Florey and Heatley travelled by train to Peoria where they met with the staff to discuss penicillin production. Their visit resulted in an exchange of information that was unparalleled in the history of the penicillin programme. The British researchers could not have asked for a group better prepared to address the problem of producing large quantities of penicillin via fermentation.[10] Heatley remained in Peoria while Florey continued his efforts to attract the interest of pharmaceutical houses in the USA and Canada. He had little success until meeting with Arthur N. Richards, chairman of the CMR. Richards, a professor of pharmacology at the University of Pennsylvania, and long-time consultant to the Merck Pharmaceutical Corporation, was able to crack the corporate barrier and involve Merck, Pfizer, Squibb and Lederle in a special penicillin programme. Richards also used the CMR's military connection to promote clinical testing and production of penicillin as a tool in the treatment of war wounds.

THE COMMITTEE ON MEDICAL RESEARCH

The Committee on Medical Research was established by executive order on 28 June 1941. This same order created the committee's parent organization, the Office of Scientific Research and Development, headed by Vannevar Bush. The committee was assigned the task of mobilizing the nation's medical and scientific personnel to conduct research on medical problems related to national defence.[11] The CMR and its parent agency were created entirely for military purposes and were staffed by a combination of civilian scientists and military personnel. From the beginning the CMR worked closely with military medical personnel and responded to their requests for information. This liaison was facilitated further when CMR division chiefs and select committee members were given official positions within the army and navy.[12]

The CMR is best known for its wartime work on antimalarials, insecticides, blood and blood substitutes, aviation medicine and penicillin, to name just a few of their numerous projects. Their most immediate problem was the need to combat malaria both by mass-producing antimalarial drugs and developing methods for effective insect control. One of their greatest achievements was to encourage the widespread use of DDT both to control mosquitoes and to kill typhus-carrying body lice among civilian populations in the wake of the Second World War. From a medical perspective their large-scale clinical testing of penicillin was also pivotal and led immediately to successful mass production of the revolutionary new antibiotic. In this instance, A.N. Richards spearheaded the effort by prioritizing and solving the many medical problems assigned to his office by the military.

The committee first became involved with penicillin when Florey met with Richards on 7 August 1941, a little more than four weeks after the OSRD was formed. The two had met previously at the University of Pennsylvania where Florey worked briefly in 1925 while visiting with a Rockefeller fellowship. Because of his long-time association with Merck and chairmanship of the CMR, Richards was the ideal person to approach if penicillin were to be mass produced in the USA. He used his government position and connections with industry to convene a series of meetings between administrators, scientists and representatives from large pharmaceutical manufacturers in an effort to encourage production. At the same time he also supported extensive clinical testing of the new drug. Richards's unique background was not unlike those of the oft-criticized 'dollar-a-year men' who flocked to Washington where they aided the war effort by acting as liaisons between government and big business. Richards and other 'dollar-a-year scientists' such as Vannevar Bush, Karl T. Compton, and James B. Conant played key roles in the direction of Second World War science.[13]

CLINICAL TESTING

Initially, the CMR focused most of its attention on clinical tests of penicillin. These investigations were supervised by Chester S. Keefer, head of the NRC's Committee on Chemotherapeutics and a CMR consultant, who used OSRD funds to purchase $1,900,000 worth of penicillin from industry for wartime tests. Pharmaceutical companies responded slowly to Florey's efforts to encourage penicillin production and even after A.N. Richards interceded output was minuscule. The first small quantities of US-produced penicillin were available by the spring of 1942 but by the end of that year there was still only enough material to treat 100 patients. In order to optimize the clinical effectiveness of this small supply, penicillin producers and the OSRD agreed that the entire supply of the antibiotic should be turned over to the CMR. Before 1943, when mass production began, the supply was so small that only a select group of 'accredited investigators' chosen by Keefer were allowed to use the antibiotic.[14] The primary objective of Keefer's group was to gather information on dosage, methods of administration, duration of treatment and reactions.[15]

One of the most important early tests of penicillin took place after the devastating Cocoanut Grove fire. The fire occurred late in the evening of 29 November 1942 when a busboy used a match to illuminate a basement wall while checking a light bulb. The match set fire to an artificial palm tree and shortly after fire broke out in the stucco and brick building. The club was filled with an unusually large Saturday night crowd of an estimated 1,000 people, far more than its 600-person capacity. Among the revellers were cowboy movie star Buck Jones and his entourage, surrounded by patrons seeking autographs. In their efforts to escape the club, many of the revellers made a mad dash to the front exit. The result was catastrophic as 440 people died and 173 were injured, many of them with serious burns.[16] Cocoanut Grove was one of the worst civilian disasters in American history and is still the second worst building fire ever.[17] Buck Jones was among those who survived the fire but died two days later in the hospital. The injured were rushed to Boston area hospitals including Massachusetts General. Local authorities responded quickly to the disaster by releasing emergency supplies of blood plasma and medical support. Francis D. Moore, a surgical resident in charge of the emergency ward, recalled arriving to find the bodies of numerous young people lining the halls with their skin 'either deep blue (suffocation) or cherry pink (carbon monoxide) or they had froth emerging from lips and mouth (irritant gases)'.[18]

Treatment of the Cocoanut Grove victims took place at a unique time in the history of burn care.[19] Doctors were already focused on improving burn treatment methods, particularly after caring for the numerous burn victims injured during the attack on Pearl Harbor. Cocoanut Grove posed an even greater challenge, resulting in 'a number of important advances in burn treatment, including the first comprehensive descriptions of inhalation injury, improvements in topical treatment of burn wounds, resuscitation of shock, use of antibiotics, and understanding of metabolic response to injury'.[20] To the CMR, Cocoanut Grove presented an ideal opportunity to test penicillin's effect on staphyloccal infections occurring in the respiratory tracts of the fire victims. Upon learning of the tragedy, Chester Keefer gave the order to release penicillin to Champ Lyons for use on a select group of thirteen patients (there were a total of thirty-nine burn patients at the hospital). Lyons was a former surgical instructor at Harvard whose previous research had focused in particular upon haemolytic streptococcus infections. After consulting with Keefer, Lyons decided on a dosage plan of 5,000 units administered every four hours (this amount was later determined to be too small). While administering the antibiotic, Lyons collected valuable data on patient reaction to injection and temperature. In several instances patients experienced intramuscular pain. In all but one case a reduction in temperature occurred after the antibiotic was administered. Lyons also examined the bacteriological changes in patients' wounds before and after administration of the drug. In all cases, penicillin was administered in conjunction with sulfadiazine. Because of the emergency nature of the Cocoanut Grove fire and the use of a low dose of penicillin, Lyons was unable to accurately appraise the efficacy of penicillin therapy.[21] He did find, however, that there were no toxic reactions to the antibiotic. Lyons's results, along with those of several other doctors at Massachusetts General, were published together as a symposium in the *Annals of Surgery*.[22] Prior to printing, Lyons's paper was not the only one that alluded to the use of penicillin. His colleague, Oliver Cope, contributed a paper on treatment of surface burns to the journal, also under the auspices of the CMR. Evidently Cope's original draft of the paper did not meet Richards's approval as he requested the 'deletion or correction of reference to penicillin'. Cope's published paper did note, however, that 'of the deep burns, the wounds remained unusually free of active or invasive infection'.[23] He also stated that the 'subsequent lack of invasive infection was presumably due to the chemotherapy rather than to any unusual cleanliness of the burns on arrival for they were grossly dirty, and there were many chances for fecal and respiratory tract contamination before arrival at the hospital'.[24] Richards was probably concerned that too much publicity on the civilian use of penicillin might lead to an increase in demand for the antibiotic from the general public, and might divert supplies away from the military where it was much needed.

At the time of the Cocoanut Grove fire, there was no government stockpile of penicillin. Lyons's small supply came from the Merck corporation after the CMR placed an emergency order for as much penicillin as they could produce in time to help the fire victims. According to John Sheehan, the Merck chemist who synthesized penicillin in 1959, the company worked around the clock in relay in order to produce a 32-litre supply of the drug by the morning of 2 December 1942.[25]

Keefer added Lyons's Cocoanut Grove results to his growing clinical database on penicillin, and by March 1943 he completed analysis of data from 200 cases where penicillin was used. Shortly after he informed Richards that the time was ripe for clinical tests on wounded soldiers. At this point the military was well aware of the shortcomings of the sulphonamides, which were ineffective against staphylococcal infections and often had debilitating side effects including confusion, inhibited motor skills, and vomiting or nausea in 12 per cent of patients treated. Major Frank B. Queen, chief of laboratory services at Bushnell General Hospital in Brigham, Utah, provided the first opportunity for military testing when he contacted Keefer about his hospital's 'two hundred orthopedic cases many of whom had compound fractures with osteomyelitis and other complications'.[26] Sulfa drugs had already proved ineffective and Queen wanted to try penicillin. Keefer realized the importance of Queen's request and immediately pressed Richards to help establish an army programme at Bushnell. He also suggested that the CMR introduce penicillin 'on the basis of treating patients rather than experimenting with it' as he felt the army would be more receptive to this position.[27]

Richards was well aware of the need to interest the army in penicillin and immediately recommended Champ Lyons to lead the investigation. Shortly thereafter, on 1 April 1943, the Office of the Surgeon-General established a pilot unit for penicillin therapy at Bushnell General Hospital. The army's Surgical Consultants Division worked closely with the CMR to facilitate the study. Fortunately, by the spring of 1943 when Major Queen approached Keefer, enough penicillin was being produced to contemplate treatment of wounded soldiers.[28]

Champ Lyons's army study took place just as the first large quantities of penicillin became available. Lyons joined the army's Surgical Consultants and was given the rank of major. At Bushnell, he was able to administer the antibiotic both parenterally and locally, and to measure therapeutic and pharmacological effects. Lyons followed Keefer's suggestion that the new drug be tested on wounded soldiers only. He, too, was convinced that if the army saw spectacular results they would commit the necessary funding to promote large-scale funding for production. At Bushnell, Lyons and Queen established a special ward unit for penicillin therapy. Extensive efforts were made to prevent cross-infection and secondary contamination of the patients' wounds, including the use of separate rooms for each patient. Surgical dressings were applied under operating room conditions, patients and attendants wore masks, and dressers were scrubbed, gowned and gloved. Individual sterile dressing packets of instruments were also used.[29]

Lyons evaluated methods of penicillin administration, optimum dosages and resultant side effects. He also measured the drug's effectiveness in the treatment of acute pyrogenic infections and its role in the treatment of chronically septic compound fractures. Lyons's work at Bushnell constituted the earliest large-scale clinical test of penicillin and was described by Keefer, Richards and others as the most significant penicillin trial conducted during the early 1940s.[30] One of the most interesting aspects of the Bushnell study was Lyons's listing of patient reactions to penicillin. In his report, published in the *Journal of the American Medical Association*, Lyons commented that 'increasing experience leads to the conviction that certain untoward reactions are peculiar to particular batches of the drug and are attributable to toxic impurities rather than to the active penicillin fraction'. According to Lyons, these impurities constituted 80 to 90 per cent of the final product and varied from batch to batch in the hands of a single researcher. The Bushnell team concluded that patients receiving deeply coloured penicillin that foamed during preparation or contained a non-filterable residue were more likely to have a reaction.[31]

Lyons listed a range of adverse reactions associated with the impure batches of penicillin but found that most could be prevented by Seitz filtration of the solution before injection.[32] Although he listed the reactions in his paper and acknowledged that they were caused by impurities, Lyons never publicly pointed a finger at a particular batch of penicillin. This reticence did not carry over into his personal correspondence. In a 22 April letter to Richards, Lyons expressed more detailed concern for the incidence of phlebitis: 'It is our clinical impression here that the Squibb's penicillin is very irritating. In addition to the flushing and headache I described to you, every patient has had some phlebitis after the injection of Squibb's product. Every one of the nine patients receiving Squibb's penicillin has developed active phlebitis. The problem has been carefully observed and we are in agreement that these reactions have not followed the injection of Merck's penicillin.'[33] Richards replied that 'the imperfection of the Squibb material has given me much concern, not to say annoyance. It is damn near criminal of them to have shortcut a process without finding out what the shortcut would do'. Richards was particularly irritated when, because of Squibb's bad batch, the CMR was 'obliged to cable Africa to say that the twenty million units of their material is unsuitable for intravenous use; perhaps only suitable for topical use'. He commented to Lyons that the whole affair 'ought to be humiliating to them (Squibb)'.[34]

The greatest achievement of the Bushnell study was convincing the army that penicillin was vital to the war effort. Upon learning of Lyons's success, the Surgeon-General visited the hospital and was very impressed with the results of penicillin therapy. Shortly after, on 3 June 1943, a second clinical unit was assembled at Halloran General Hospital on Staten Island, New York. Once again, Champ Lyons was placed in charge of the Wound Unit Study where he treated 209 cases with penicillin. While at Halloran, Lyons contributed to a special meeting of the CMR's Panel on Chemotherapy where he discussed the potential benefits of penicillin. When questioned about the drug's effectiveness in fighting malaria, Lyons reported that there was no effect at all and that he had observed relapses of malaria among patients undergoing penicillin treatment for wound infections.[35] Lyons was also asked to comment on whether there was any contraindication for using sulfa drugs in conjunction with penicillin. He reported that there was not but added that this conclusion was based on limited observation: 'you can all appreciate that when you are trying to evaluate the benefit of one drug it is difficult to do so when you are using two different agents at the same time'.[36] He concluded that 'penicillin therapy is here to stay' and that the drug was 'an infinitely more effective antibacterial agent than the sulfonamides'.[37]

Lyons was also unable to judge penicillin's effectiveness against gas gangrene, the scourge of the First World War, mainly because there were not enough cases. He did mention the rumour of 'considerable gas gangrene on the Russian front' and was confident that 'we will find out what the effective treatment for gas gangrene is only when we get into the continent and begin to fight there'.[38] Once Lyons's clinical and experimental work was complete, Bushnell and Halloran were used as penicillin therapy schools for medical officers from other army hospitals, many of whom contributed data to the penicillin evaluation programme. Officers were assigned to the schools for one-month periods and eventually nine other army hospitals participated in the clinical testing programme.[39]

Trainees at the penicillin schools were 'charged with the full responsibility of determining the cases to be treated and the details and procedure in their treatment'. This included performing the necessary laboratory studies and forwarding case records to the army's Surgical Consultants division. The Division used these records to develop protocols for doctors at the front; 'In this way, an immense amount of quite accurate information was quickly obtained with the least waste of a scarce product.'[40] Lyons's successful clinical tests at Bushnell and Halloran convinced the army that penicillin worked, and led to a call for mass production. This was a pivotal step because without army involvement, it would not have been possible to expedite the industrial process in wartime USA.

PRODUCTION OF PENICILLIN

In addition to directing early testing, Richards focused considerable attention toward the arduous task of convincing US pharmaceutical firms that penicillin was a worthwhile investment from a production perspective. The major turning point in production came long before the army clinical tests, on 17 December 1941, at Richards's third penicillin meeting with major pharmaceutical houses.[41] The corporate chiefs assured Richards of their willingness to cooperate, but were very pessimistic about the possibility of mass-producing penicillin. George Merck reported that even with his company's best fermentation and recovery yields, it was not humanly possible to produce even the kilogram of penicillin that Florey wanted for clinical testing.

Immediately following Merck's speech, Robert Coghill, head of the NRRL's fermentation research group, gave his report on the production of penicillin, a project that had started with Florey and Heatley's opportune visit just five months earlier. The audience was stunned by the data showing yields of 24 units per ml in a simple medium containing corn steep liquor and lactose, using an improved NRRL *Penicillium* mould strain. Coghill later remarked that as a result of the NRRL report a new pharmaceutical industry was born. After listening to Coghill, Merck reversed his opinion on the spot, stating that if the results could be confirmed in Merck's laboratories, penicillin production was a definite possibility.[42]

Richards, himself a noted pharmacologist, was somewhat pessimistic about the possibility of scaling up fermentation. In fact, the CMR's most significant effort was to organize an unsuccessful attempt to produce synthetic penicillin. This project involved contracts with sixteen commercial firms and two government agencies.[43] The CMR spent $350,000 on synthesis research at universities, while the five pharmaceutical firms, no doubt hoping that synthesis would give them the 'leg up' on fermentation, expended $3 million of their own money. The 'Big Three' US pharmaceutical firms, Merck, Pfizer and Squibb, believed that synthesis would enable them to vastly exceed production via fermentation, thus cornering the market for penicillin.[44] During the 1930s Merck's researchers had experienced great success in synthesizing B vitamins, obviating the need for more expensive natural production processes. George Merck and other large pharmaceutical manufacturers were convinced that their chemists could duplicate this feat with penicillin. Merck was so confident that he allotted $781,000 to the project, promising OSRD a bottle of synthetic penicillin by New Year's Day,1945.[45] However, despite the large expenditure of funds and manpower, the government–industry research programme was unable to synthesize penicillin and today fermentation is still the preferred method of production.[46]

The CMR's commitment to synthesis is reflected in their insignificant financial contribution toward research into the scaling up of penicillin production using fermentation processes. In October 1941 the eminent mycologist Charles Thom reported on the success at the NRRL, urging the CMR to supply badly needed funds for additional equipment and personnel. As a result, Coghill received a grant of $8,250. An additional sum of $6,650 was granted in July 1943. By July 1944 NRRL had received a grand total of $30,700 from the CMR.[47] These funds were less than 1 per cent of the total committed to the unsuccessful effort to synthesize penicillin.

Even after the success of the NRRL, Richards also remained convinced that the key to mass production was held by large pharmaceutical companies and particularly by Merck. Richards served as a paid consultant to Merck throughout the 1930s and was not above recommending their research and development capabilities to influential government officials.[48] In a January 1943 letter to Ferdinand Eberstadt, vice-chairman of the War Production Board and author of the highly regarded Controlled Materials Plan, Richards requested that Merck be given high priority materials needed to expand penicillin production. Formed in January 1942, the WPB was the supreme US agency in charge of manufacturing and Richards knew that no industrial concern could proceed without the board's approval.[49] He described Merck as 'pioneers in this country in research which has supplied most of the existing information regarding feasible methods of growing the mold and extracting the substance'. According to Richards, Merck's organization was capable of providing the supply, or a significant part of it, which 'we foresee will soon be called for'.[50]

Champ Lyons's clinical report and the resulting surge in military interest changed the production picture entirely. On 5 June 1943, immediately after Lyons's data became available, Surgeon-General Norman T. Kirk contacted Richards for information on the status of penicillin production. Richards replied that the 'manufacture of penicillin is still to be regarded as in the experimental stage', but informed Kirk that the CMR had engaged Robert Coghill, 'an expert in this field', to visit the plants of all companies already producing or interested in producing penicillin.[51] Coghill's survey was completed three days before General Kirk's letter arrived and Richards was able to reassure him that, with a new priority ranking from the WPB, plant expansions would result in an increase from two to nine billion units of penicillin a week by 1 October. All of the projected material would be produced using a fermentation process developed by the NRRL.[52]

THE MILITARY AND MASS PRODUCTION

Unlike Richards, the army was not enamoured with the idea of synthesizing penicillin. In a very concise report on penicillin production, Major John A.

Purinton, chief of the army's Medicinals Section of the Army Service Forces, commented that although progress on the synthetic work was highly secret, 'synthetic processes will not be commercially available in quantity until some time after the peak military demand has been reached'.[53] In short, as far as the army was concerned, fermentation was the only choice for mass production. After reviewing Coghill's report on manufacturers' production potential, CMR and army officials approached the War Production Board's Chemical Division with the request that penicillin production be given top priority.[54]

In June 1943 the National Academy of Sciences helped to organize the shift to mass production by hosting a meeting of government representatives. These included Richards and Keefer of the CMR, Elihu Root of the National Academy of Sciences, Major Purinton of the army, and Robert Coghill. The WPB's Chemical Division was represented by Fred Stock, William J. McManus, Roy S. Koch and John N. McDonnell. Their discussion focused on priorities, allocation and 'whether to permit producers to operate on their own responsibility or to introduce Government interest directly into the matter'.[55] Stock made it clear that since research on penicillin had reached a stage where mass production could be achieved it was time for the WPB to assist in expediting the programme. A beginning production goal of 200 billion units per month was set. This figure soon proved to be overly ambitious, as total production for the first five months was a mere 400 million units (4,000 packages of 100,000 units).[56]

The WPB's inability to meet initial production goals led to criticism from the Army Service Forces, which felt that a personality clash between Stock and McManus was hindering production. The army was particularly concerned by their failure to employ a technically knowledgeable troubleshooter to coordinate the activities of companies manufacturing penicillin. Army representatives complained that we are 'begging them to get somebody and put them in charge', but 'for five weeks they have been dickering about who it might be'.[57] These observations were relayed to WPB chief Donald Nelson, who assigned blanket AA-1 ratings for all materials and equipment needed to expedite the penicillin programme.[58] He also appointed Albert Elder, a chemist, as programme coordinator.

As 'penicillin czar', Elder worked closely with the WPB's Chemical Division, which handled business and administrative aspects of the project. He was also assisted by Major Purinton who assigned a group of officers to the project. In March 1943 Elder began his tenure with a tour of all ongoing penicillin production facilities. Following the war, Elder recalled that the most significant deterrent to the mass production of penicillin was the tremendous emphasis placed on synthesis by Richards and the CMR. Elder was 'ridiculed by some of my closest scientific friends' for 'allowing myself to become associated with what obviously was to be a flop – namely the commercial production of penicillin by a fermentation process'. He pointed to the army's 'bird in the hand is worth two in the bush' attitude as a mainstay in ensuring continued production of penicillin via fermentation.[59]

Elder's concerns about the emphasis on synthesis were echoed in a 27 November 1943 progress report by James Biller, a WPB investigator, who conducted a survey of the thirteen major participants in the WPB programme. After visiting Squibb, Biller remarked that while a pilot plant was 80 per cent complete, and a new plant was well along toward completion by the projected date of 15 December, the 'Squibb people felt there might be a delay of 2 or 3 months beyond this date in order to prove their process'. Biller described this delay as unreasonable and suggested that the WPB request an explanation. He concluded that: 'Belief that synthesis of the drug may be imminent may be contributing to a lackadaisical attitude on the part of some producers who feel that it would be foolish to waste a lot of time and money on a relatively inefficient method of production when large scale production of a synthetic may be just around the corner.'[60]

Assisted by the Army Service Forces, Elder minimized delay by obtaining in advance the necessary scientific control instruments, critical steel equipment, motors, filters, air-conditioning equipment, heat exchangers, centrifuges, sterilizers, vacuum pumps, drying ovens and numerous other items needed for the production of penicillin. Captain A.B. Hatch was assigned to Elder's office with the task of following up on biological developments.[61] In October 1943 WPB Requirements Committee chairman J.A. Krug reaffirmed the programme's top preference rating (AA-1) for materials and equipment. The estimated total cost of the programme was $13,983,110 for a projected 176.9 billion units of penicillin per month.[62]

The military also assisted scientists working in Robert Coghill's fermentation group. In hopes of finding a more productive *Penicillium* strain, Kenneth Raper, the NRRL's chief mycologist, enlisted the aid of the Army Transport Command in gathering soil samples from all over the world. Of these, the most promising strains were isolated from soil collected in Chungking, Bombay and Cape Town. According to Coghill, 'the travesty of this worldwide hunt was that the best producer of all was cultured from a moldy cantaloupe picked up in a Peoria fruit market'.[63] The 'cantaloupe strain' or 'NRRL 1951', became the standard from which several more productive strains were subsequently derived.[64] The more productive strains were distributed to manufacturers by the WPB, increasing one hundredfold the amount of penicillin available for the treatment of wounded soldiers. At the front in Europe and the Pacific, both the US and British Armies continued to collect data on the use of penicillin.

PENICILLIN AT THE FRONT

The first large supply of penicillin was delivered to Britain in May 1943 at the request of the Office of the Surgeon-General. Colonel Elliot Carr Cutler, the US army's Chief Consultant in Surgery, took delivery of the shipment from the

Merck corporation and immediately contacted Howard Florey for help in training laboratory officers how to store penicillin and recover it from the urine of patients treated with it.[65] Cutler then met with Chief Surgeon Major General Paul R. Hawley who decided that the limited supply would be used for cases of gas gangrene, serious general infections (usually wounds with osteomyelitis and preferably infected with *Staphylococcus aureus*), eye infections and septic hands. The British initiated testing of penicillin at the battlefront in July 1942 when Lieutenant Colonel R.J.V. Pulvertaft used penicillin from the Oxford Group to treat war wounds in Cairo. Pulvertaft was so impressed that he began manufacturing penicillin on location in Cairo after his supply from Oxford ran out.[66] An estimated ten gallons of filtrate were produced each week at Pulvertaft's makeshift facility. Pulvertaft applied the crude product externally to infected wounds and reported that it 'appears to be just as efficient as the purified product'.[67]

Shortly afterwards, in June 1943, Howard Florey and Brigadier General Hugh Cairns, consulting neurosurgeon to the Army, travelled to North Africa where they participated in the testing programme. Their chief objective was to determine whether penicillin could be 'used effectively in the field at all; and, if so, how much is required, and at what place in the Army organization can it be used to the best advantage?'[68] Florey and Cairns brought with them a supply of penicillin from Oxford, ICI and the Therapeutic Research Corporation. One immediate conclusion made by the British Army investigators was that 'it was far too late to start penicillin treatment weeks or months after wounding, at a Rear Base hospital, and that its use should be tried much earlier, before the establishment of serious infection'.[69] As a result, all British Army investigations were moved to forward hospitals. In North Africa, the military's primary concern was keeping men in the field and to this end they wished to 'improve on the present methods for treating the larger flesh wounds so that infection could be prevented and the possibility of early suture became the rule'. In particular, it was hoped that immediate application of penicillin at forward hospitals would speed recovery by facilitating early suturing.[70]

After using penicillin on 300 patients Florey and Cairns concluded that 'there can be no question that parenteral administration should in nearly all cases be practiced'. However, because the 1943 penicillin supply was small, it was 'necessary to explore the possibility of using locally much smaller quantities than are necessary for intramuscular or intravenous use'.[71] Penicillin was available for treatment of the wounded during the amphibious assault on Salerno in September 1943. Ian Fraser, a doctor trained by Florey in a programme sponsored by the Royal Army Medical Corps and the Medical Research Council, recalled carrying two types of penicillin: 'One was a fine powder which we blew on to the open wound with an insufflator having diluted it with sulphonamide powder to give it bulk.' The second type, used for intramuscular injection, 'was a fine brown powder which, when diluted, produced a deep yellow fluid almost like mustard'; Fraser's experience with the latter confirmed Champ Lyons's earlier concerns as injection of the fluid 'caused tremendous pain, because 9/10ths consisted of impurities derived from the fluid in which the mould had grown'.[72]

British Army investigators also collected data on treatment of gonorrhoea with penicillin. Florey and Cairns recalled that Major Priest, the Adviser in Venereology for Tunisia, 'informed us that many cases of gonorrhoea were occurring in highly-trained fighting troops, such as parachutists, shortly before they were due to fight; and that an undue proportion of cases did not respond to sulphonamides'.[73] At Priest's request, nine sulphonamide-resistant cases were treated with penicillin while other treatment was withheld. The results were spectacular, as 'urethral discharges promptly disappeared in every case – like turning off a tap'.[74] Meanwhile, the US army also investigated the use of penicillin in battlefield situations.

In the Mediterranean, Champ Lyons again played a major role in collecting data on the use of penicillin in the treatment of wounds. After leaving Halloran General Hospital, Lyons was reassigned to the army's Surgical Consultants Division where he served as Surgical Infections and Wound Management Consultant in the Mediterranean theatre of operation until 1945. The Surgical Consultants Division was a new addition to the army's Medical Department, one which had a profound impact on the composition of the military's medical staff during the war. Each consultant was responsible for hand-picking key personnel in their area of jurisdiction. In Italy, Lyons refined methods for administering penicillin while treating patients. As one soldier recalled, Lyons was an active participant in the treatment of the wounded following the costly Allied amphibious assault at Anzio:

> You will not remember me, I was just another scared G.I. patient to you. But I will surely remember you, always. You and Captain John Modlin operated on me during the early part of April, 1944 at the 81st General Hospital in Naples, Italy. I had a compound comminuted fracture of the left femur, lower third, as a result of being hit by a shell fragment at Anzio on March 24, 1944. I shall never forget those penicillin shots one every four hours, morning, noon and midnight for what seemed an eternity. Although, it was probably not much longer than two weeks. I also recall that the needles they shot us with were generally dull and the skin made a 'popping' sound as they broke through.[75]

Lyons noted later that the winter campaign in Italy during the early months of 1944 afforded 'an unusual opportunity for the study of wounds of the extremity'.[76] At a bacteriological laboratory headed by Lieutenant Robert Rustigian, Lyons collected data on the types of bacteria infecting wounds in one out of every thirty-six patients received at base section hospitals. During his tour of duty in Italy, Lyons compiled a wealth of data on the role of chemotherapy in wound management. He also continued to educate other doctors in the use of penicillin, conducting numerous penicillin seminars at evacuation hospitals. Together with Colonel Hampton, Lyons 'worked in one hospital for six weeks, demonstrating surgery of the extremities, with special emphasis on adequate debridement, correct splinting, the liberal use of whole blood, and the correct use of penicillin'.[77] Lyons and Hampton set up a septic ward where they administered penicillin in dosages of 200,000 Florey units daily (25,000 units every three hours) by the intramuscular route.[78] This was a far cry from the dosage used following the Cocoanut Grove disaster where Lyons treated patients with 5,000 units administered every four hours.[79]

CONCLUSION

Army participation in clinical testing and mass production of penicillin during the Second World War exemplifies the positive aspect of technology transfer between civil and military spheres, from laboratory to mass production, and from clinical testing to widespread use. Because the armed forces had access to the largest supply of penicillin, Army clinicians were able to make significant progress in a very short period of time. Also, the exigencies of war meant that the Army had numerous human subjects whose rampant infectious diseases were an ideal testing ground for penicillin. At military hospitals Champ Lyons and his co-workers assembled the necessary clinical data and refined methods administering the penicillin that later facilitated transfer of the antibiotic from the hospital to the battlefront.

Despite evidence of clinical effectiveness in Great Britain and the US, pharmaceutical houses were not prepared to unilaterally take on the task of producing the drug. Here again, a combination of government and military incentives and financial assistance breached the boundary between science and industry. With Lyons's clinical data in hand, the military was convinced that penicillin could aid in the treatment of the wounded and as a result they helped implement an effective production process. In particular, military support for fermentation, the most expedient means for mass production, paved the way for a whole new antibiotics industry in the postwar era. By 1944 the combined efforts of government and industry resulted in a production increase from 4 units per ml in 1941 to over 900 units per ml.[80] As a result, total US production of penicillin for 1944 was 1,663 billion units. In 1945 production increased to 6,852 billion units (estimated) or 34,260,000 daily doses of Champ Lyons's 200,000 unit intramuscular protocol.[81] By the close of the Second World War, penicillin production exceeded military requirements and was released to the general public.

In the case of penicillin, the combination of medicine and military efficiency was a winning formula. With the support of the military, War Production Board, and other government agencies, the transition – from laboratory to pilot plant, and finally mass production – took place in an amazingly short period of time. Clinical testing accelerated the development of effective protocols and propelled penicillin from the hospital to the battlefront. The end result was an enormously successful postwar antibiotics industry that brought about a revolution in treatment of infectious disease.

ACKNOWLEDGEMENTS

My thanks to Champ Lyons, Jr for providing valuable insight into his late father's work and to Daniel J. Kevles for his support. Funds for research for this chapter were provided in the form of travel grants from the Beckman Institute for the History of Chemistry and the Wellcome Institute for the History of Medicine.

Notes

1 Telephone interview with Champ Lyons, Jr by P. Neushul, Santa Barbara, CA (28 October 1996).

2 Historians of technology use the term 'technology transfer' to describe the geographic transit of technology. A common example is the transfer of technology from Great Britain to the USA during the nineteenth century. See Carroll W. Pursell, *The Machine in America* (Baltimore, The Johns Hopkins University Press, 1995); Darwin H. Stapleton, *The Transfer of Early Industrial Technologies to America* (Philadelphia, American Philosophical Society, 1987). Social historians explore the relationships between science, technology and medicine in John V. Pickstone (ed.), *Medical Innovations in Historical Perspective* (New York, St Martin's Press, 1992).

3 John F. Fulton, 'Penicillin, Plasma Fractionation, and the Physician', *The Atlantic*, 176 (1945), 107–14. Further statistical data is found in John Parascandola, 'The Introduction of Antibiotics into Therapeutics' in Yozio Kawakita, Shizu Sakai and Jasuo Otsuka (eds), *History of Therapy, Proceedings of the 10th International Symposium on the Comparative History of Medicine – East and West* (Tokyo, Ishiyaku EuroAmerica, Inc., 1990), pp. 261–81. Some of the other applications for the new antibiotic were in the treatment of hemolytic streptococcal infections, lobar pneumonia, venereal diseases, infected wounds, meningitis, endocarditis, mastoiditis, empyema, osteomyelitis and anthrax.

4 For a general perspective on mycology and the *Penicillium* moulds see Constantine J. Alexopoulos, *Introductory Mycology* (New York, John Wiley & Sons, 1962). More focused reviews are found in Charles Thom, 'Molds, Mutants and Monographers', *Mycologia*, 44 (1952), 61–85; Thom, 'Mycology Presents Penicillin', *Mycologia*, 37 (1945), 460–75. In the dairy industry, *Penicillium roqueforti* and *Penicillium camemberti* are used to flavour Roquefort and Camembert cheeses. Danish blue and Italian Gorgonzola are also ripened using *Penicillium* moulds. While several species of *Penicillium* moulds produce penicillin, the two most prominent sources are *Penicillium notatum* and *Penicillium chrysogenum*.

5 Accounts of Fleming's work include Ronald Hare, *The Birth of Penicillin and the Disarming of Microbes* (London, Allen & Unwin, 1970); A. Maurois, *The Life of Sir Alexander Fleming* (New York, E.P. Dutton, 1959); Gwyn Macfarlane, *Alexander Fleming, The Man and the Myth* (Cambridge, MA Harvard University Press, 1984).

6 E. Chain, H.W. Florey, A.D. Gardner, N.G. Heatley, M.A. Jennings, J. Orr-Ewing and A.G. Saunders, 'Penicillin as a Chemotherapeutic Agent', *Lancet*, 2 (1941), 226–8.

7 A summary of Rockefeller funding of the Oxford Group is found at the Rockefeller Archive Center (hereafter RAC), North Tarrytown, NY, Record Group (RG) 1.1, box 37, folder 484.

8 Accounts of the Oxford Group's work are found in Gwyn Macfarlane, *Howard Florey, The Making of a Great Scientist* (Oxford University Press, 1979); Trevor I. Williams, *Howard Florey, Penicillin and After* (Oxford University Press, 1984); Leonard Bickel, *Rise Up To Life* (London, Angus & Robertson, 1972). For information on Ernst Chain see Ronald W. Clark, *The Life of Ernst Chain, Penicillin and Beyond* (London, Weidenfeld & Nicolson, 1985).

9 For a description of British penicillin production see Jonathan Liebenau, 'The British Success With Penicillin', *Social Studies of Science*, 17 (1987), 69–86. Despite the opportunity for a head start, British manufacturers were never able to reach the wartime production scale achieved by US manufacturers.

10 Florey to W. Weaver (14 July 1941), RAC, RG 1.1, box 37, folder 481.

11 E.C. Andrus et al. (eds), *Advances in Military Medicine* (Boston, Little, Brown & Co., 1948), p. xii. For information on Bush see G. Pascal Zachary, *Endless Frontier: Vannevar Bush, Engineer of the American Century* (New York, The Free Press, 1997). Zachary's book barely mentions Bush's interest in the penicillin programme and does not explore his postwar career as Chief Executive Officer of Merck Chemical Corporation. This is somewhat astonishing considering Bush's insistence that penicillin was one of OSRD's greatest achievements; Zachary, p. 221.

12 The army member of the CMR was Brig Gen James Stevens Simmons who served as chief of the Division of Preventive Medicine in the Office of the Surgeon-General. The navy was represented by Rear Adm Harold W. Smith, chief of the Research Division of the Bureau of Medicine and Surgery. Detlev W. Bronk, chief of the CMR's Division of Aviation Medicine, also served as Coordinator of Research in the Office of the Air Surgeon.

13 The role played by these key individuals is discussed in James Phinney Baxter, *Scientists Against Time* (Boston, Little, Brown & Co. 1946).

14 Keefer is sometimes referred to as the 'penicillin czar' because of his absolute control over the small quantities produced during 1942–3. A more likely candidate was Albert Elder, the chemist who was assigned the task of coordinating mass production of the antibiotic.

15 Chester S. Keefer, 'Penicillin, A Wartime Achievement' in E.C. Andrus et al. (eds), *Advances in Military Medicine*, pp. 717–19. For a historical assessment of clinical testing of penicillin see Harry Marks, *The Progress of Experiment: Science and Therapeutic Reform in the United States, 1900–1990* (Cambridge University Press, 1997). Marks focuses in particular on clinical tests of penicillin for treatment of syphilis. Further information on clinical testing of penicillin is found in Wallace E. Herrell, *Penicillin and Other Antibiotic Agents* (Philadelphia, W.B. Saunders Co., 1945).

16 *The New York Times* (29 November 1942), 1.

17 The worst US building fire occurred at Chicago's Iroquois Theater in 1903, killing 575 people. A.B.C. Whipple 'Holiday Inferno', *Reader's Digest*, 141 (1992), 122. For a detailed assessment of the fire see Casey Grant, 'The Last Dance at the Cocoanut Grove', *NFPA Journal* (May/June 1991), 71–84. The final casualty was reported in the *The New York Times* (6 September 1944), p. 17.

18 Francis D. Moore, *A Miracle and A Privilege: Recounting a Half Century of Surgical Advance* (Washington, DC, Joseph Henry Press, 1995), p. 62.

19 Dave Anderson, 'The Biggest Upset, the Party, the Fire', *The New York Times* (22 November 1992), p. 29.

20 Jeffrey R. Saffle, 'The 1942 Fire at Boston's Cocoanut Grove Nightclub', *American Journal of Surgery*, 166 (1993), p. 581.

21 Champ Lyons, 'Problems of Infection and Chemotherapy', *Annals of Surgery*, 117 (1943), 99–100. Lyons's paper was under contract, recommended by the Committee on Medical Research, between the OSRD and the Massachusetts General Hospital.

22 Annals of Surgery, 117 (1943), republished as Joseph C. Aub, Henry K. Beecher, Bradford Cannon, Stanley Cobb, Oliver Cope, N.W. Faxon, Champ Lyons, Tracy Mallory, Richard Schatzki, *Management of the Cocoanut Grove Burns at the Massachusetts General Hospital* (Philadelphia, J.B. Lippincott Co., 1943). The volume includes a selection of colour photographs.

23 Oliver Cope, 'Treatment of Surface Burns', *Annals of Surgery*, 117 (1943), p. 92.

24 Ibid.

25 John C. Sheehan, *The Enchanted Ring: The Untold Story of Penicillin* (Cambridge, MA, MIT Press, 1982).

26 David P. Adams, *The Greatest Good for the Greatest Number: Penicillin Rationing on the American Home Front* (New York, P. Lang, 1991), p. 35.

27 Ibid.

28 John Boyd Coates (ed.), *Surgery in World War II, Activities of Surgical Consultants*, vol. 1 (Washington, DC, Office of the Surgeon-General, Department of the Army, 1962), pp. 20–1.

29 Gladys L. Hobby, *Penicillin Meeting the Challenge* (New Haven, Yale University Press, 1985), p. 149.

30 Baxter, *Scientists Against Time*, p. 353; Chester Keefer et al., panel discussion: 'Chemotherapy – II, Application and Results', *Clinics*, 2 (1944), 1094; Fred W. Rankin et al., panel discussion: 'Chemotherapy – II, War Wounds and Burns', *Clinics*, 2 (1944), 1195.

31 Champ Lyons, 'Penicillin Therapy of Surgical Infections in the U.S. Army', *Journal of the American Medical Association*, 123 (1943), p. 1008.

32 Reactions associated with impure batches of penicillin included chills with or without fever after intravenous injection, Eosinophilia of 20 to 30 per cent, burning pain at the site of intramuscular injection, headache, faintness and flushing of the face, unpleasant taste after parenteral injection, tingling in the testes, muscle cramps and femoral phlebothrombosis.

33 Champ Lyons to A.N. Richards (22 April 1943), A.N. Richards Papers, box 9, the University of Pennsylvania Archives, Philadelphia, PA.

34 Richards to Lyons (29 April 1943), Richards Papers, box 9.

35 Champ Lyons, in Keefer et al., 'Chemotherapy – II, Applications and Results', p. 1099.

36 Ibid., p. 1100.

37 Champ Lyons, in Rankin et al., 'Chemotherapy – II, War Wounds and Burns', p. 1209.

38 Lyons, in Keefer et al., 'Chemotherapy – II, Applications and Results', p. 1100.

39 Coates (ed.), *Surgery in World War II*, p. 20.

40 Ibid.

41 W.H. Helfand et al., 'Wartime Industrial Development of Penicillin in the United States' in John Parascandola (ed.), *The History of Antibiotics, A Symposium* (Madison, Wis., American Institute for the History of Pharmacy, 1980), attach great significance to the first penicillin meeting that took place on 8 October 1941. Richards, Vannevar Bush and Charles Thom were present along with the research directors from several large pharmaceutical manufacturers. In fact, little was accomplished at this meeting other than to acquaint corporate leaders with the CMR's desire to expedite production. A second meeting on 17 November was also inconclusive.

42 Robert D. Coghill, 'The development of penicillin strains' in Albert Elder (ed.), *The History of Penicillin Production* (New York, American Institute of Chemical Engineers, 1970), p. 17.

43 Excellent historical reviews of OSRD's synthetic penicillin are found in John P. Swann, 'The Search for Synthetic Penicillin During World War II', *British Journal for the History of Science*, 16 (1983), 154–90, and Sheehan, *The Enchanted Ring*. Also of interest is Hans T. Clarke, John R. Johnson and Sir Robert Robinson (eds), *The Chemistry of Penicillin* (Princeton University Press, 1949). This classic work contains descriptions of work on all government penicillin research projects during the Second World War.

44 Sheehan, *The Enchanted Ring*, p. 82.

45 Tom Mahoney, *The Merchants of Life: An Account of the American Pharmaceutical Industry* (New York, Harper & Brothers, 1959), p. 197.

46 John C. Sheehan and K.R. Henery-Logan finally succeeded in synthesizing penicillin in 1959. See J.C. Sheehan and K.R. Henery-Logan, 'The Total Synthesis of Penicillin V', *Journal of the American Chemical Society*, 81 (1959), 3089–94. For a general discussion of fermentation and penicillin see Robert Bud, *The Uses of Life: A History of Biotechnology* (Cambridge University Press, 1993), pp. 104–6.

47 Peter Neushul, 'Science, Government, and the Mass Production of Penicillin', *Journal of the History of Medicine and Allied Sciences*, 48 (1993), p. 382.

48 For a description of Richards's relationship with Merck, see John P. Swann, *Academic Scientists and the Pharmaceutical Industry* (Baltimore, The Johns Hopkins University Press, 1988), pp. 65–87.

49 For further detail on the WPB see Peter Neushul, 'Science, Technology and the Arsenal of Democracy: Production Research and Development during World War II' (unpub. Ph.D. thesis, University of California, Santa Barbara, 1993).

50 Richards to Ferdinand Eberstadt (2 January 1943), Papers of the World War II War Production Board, National Archives, Washington, DC, Record Group (NA, WPB, RG) 179, document no. 533.80.

51 A.N. Richards to Gen Norman T. Kirk, Richards Papers, box 9.

52 Neushul, 'Science, Government and Mass Production', pp. 377–81.

53 J.A. Purinton, 'Summary Review, Penicillin Production Program', Richards Papers, box 9, Army Reports folder.

54 Neushul, 'Science, Government and Mass Production', p. 384.

55 John N. McDonnell to Fred J. Stock (4 June 1943), NA, WPB, RG 179, document no. 533.8134.

56 Neushul, 'Science, Government and Mass Production', p. 384.

57 Transcript of phone conversation between Col F.R. Denton and W.B. Murphy, deputy vice-chairman for production in the WPB's Office of Operations (10 September 1943), NA, WPB, RG 1687, document no. 533.8107.

58 Donald M. Nelson to Donald D. Davis (17 September 1943), NA, WPB, RG 179, document no. 533.81428.

59 Elder, *The History of Penicillin Production*, p. 4.

60 Memorandum from James C. Biller to Robinson Newcomb (27 November 1943), NA, WPB, RG 179, document no. 533.81405.

61 Albert L. Elder, 'Penicillin', *The Scientific Monthly*, 58 (1944), 405–9.

62 J.A. Krug to Hiland G. Batcheller (4 October 1943), NA, WPB, RG 179, document no. 533.81.

63 R.D. Coghill, 'The Development of Penicillin Strains', pp. 16–17.

64 Kenneth B. Raper, 'The Penicillin Saga Remembered', *American Society for Microbiology News*, 44 (1978), 645–53.

65 Coates (ed.), *Surgery in World War II*, p. 68.

66 Scott Thomson, et al., 'Penicillin in War Wounds, A Report from the Mediterranean', *Lancet* (11 December 1943), 742–5. Pulvertaft also developed a special aspirating device for use in treating wounds with penicillin. See R.J.T. Pulvertaft and M.D. Camb, 'Local Therapy of War Wounds with Penicillin', *Lancet* (18 September 1943), 341–6.

67 H.V. Wyatt, 'Robert Pulvertaft's Use of Crude Penicillin in Cairo', *Medical History*, 34 (1990), 320–326. Pulvertaft's clinical research did not go unrecognized and in December 1943, during Churchill's sudden attack of pneumonia, the Cairo physician was flown to Bizerta to advise the Prime Minister's physicians on an appropriate treatment. Churchill was given sulpha to combat the disease.

68 H.W. Florey and Hugh Cairns, *Investigation of War Wounds. Penicillin: A Preliminary Report to The War Office and The Medical Research Council on Investigations concerning The Use of Penicillin in War Wounds* (British War Office, AMD 7, October 1943), p. 1. A copy of this confidential report is at the Wellcome Library, London.

69 Ibid., p. 4.

70 Ibid., p. 5.

71 Ibid., p. 7.

72 Sir Ian Fraser, 'Random recollections, Part 2: Penicillin and the Normandy landings', *Annals of the Royal College of Surgeons of England*, 77 (suppl., 1995), 198–201.

73 Florey and Cairns, *Investigation of War Wounds*, p. 27.

74 Thomson et al., 'Penicillin in War Wounds', p. 745.

75 Robert H. Caldwell, Jr to Champ Lyons (31 August 1960). A copy of Caldwell's letter was provided by Champ Lyons, Jr.

76 Champ Lyons, 'An Investigation of the Role of Chemotherapy in Wound Management in the Mediterranean Theater', *Annals of Surgery*, 123 (1946), p. 902.

77 Coates (ed.), *Surgery in World War II*, p. 359.

78 Ibid., p. 422.

79 After the war, Lyons returned to Alabama where, as the first full-time clinical teacher, he led the effort to introduce clinical departments to the state's medical college. See Tinsley R. Harrison, 'The Effect of Champ Lyons on Medical Education in Alabama', *Journal of the Medical Association of the State of Alabama*, 35 (1966), 602–9.

80 Kenneth B. Raper, 'The Penicillin Saga Remembered', p. 651.

81 Production figures are found in Robert D. Coghill and R. S. Koch, 'Penicillin a Wartime Accomplishment', *Chemical and Engineering News*, 23 (1945), 2310.

12

DISCIPLINING THE EMOTIONS: FEAR, PSYCHIATRY AND THE SECOND WORLD WAR

Joanna Bourke

The mission of the medical department of the Army is the conservation of manpower and the preservation of the strength of the military forces. The performance of this mission includes evacuation and hospitalization of casualties in order that they may be speedily restored to health and fighting efficiency. Where restoration to duty is impossible, a secondary mission . . . is the methodical disposition of the sick and wounded so as to insure retention of effectives and to relieve the fighting forces of non-effectives.[1]

With these words, the US army regulations encapsulated the role of medicine in modern warfare. The key word was manpower. Ideal modes of operation demanded efficiency, speed and method; the primary mood strove to reduce human agency to that of impersonal, mechanical 'effectives' or 'non-effectives'. In the context of the Second World War, medicine embraced the tenets of regulation, surveillance and management. Furthermore, it did this on an unprecedented scale. Modern instruments of destruction inspired a most unholy terror which affected everyone; men, women and children cringed under the frightening bombardments of war. Even more than the conflict of 1914–18, the Second World War was a uniquely modern form of warfare in which civilians were the target of mass technologies of mutilation and murder. The global mobilization of society for the purposes of war required not only the total application of manpower and material resources, it also demanded absolute management of the emotions. It was the mission of medical men to transform unruly emotions into restrained ones, and the most disruptive of all emotions was fear.

During the war, military medicine was stretched to encompass every aspect of life – from training men to march efficiently, to designing outdoor toilet paper holders for the soldiers' comfort, to advising on sanitary care of civilians in bombed cities.[2] Military psychiatry was a sub-speciality of military medicine. For these doctors, the most urgent focus was the management of fear reactions. Although they believed that fear was one of the primary emotions in animal and human life throughout time, psychiatrists in the first decades of the twentieth century also thought that 'civilized man' was particularly susceptible to feeling

severely frightened. Modern individuals suffered 'more obtrusive and less
transitory' emotional states than did 'primitive races and animal species',
according to John A. Ryle, Professor of Social Medicine at Oxford University.
The discouragement of outward displays of emotion, sophisticated nervous
systems, retentive memories and powers of foresight rendered 'civilized man'
especially sensitive to dangerous stimuli.[3] This inherent cultural weakness was
exacerbated by the peculiar nature of conflict during the Second World War. To
a much greater extent than in the First World War, the war of 1939–45 saw the
distinction between the 'home' and 'military' fronts dissolve. In the same way
that military psychiatrists at the front were employed to restrain expressions of
fear and enforce the regularization of other emotions in troops,[4] medical
personnel at home had to ensure that civilian emotions remained 'under control'.
Medical men saw the war as a vast laboratory for experimentation and the
testing of their theories, and techniques of fear management learnt within the
military context were applied virtually unaltered to entire populations. The 'total
environment of control' which was accepted as inevitable within the armed forces
was overlaid onto civilian society. In the stern words of a doctor in the *British
Medical Journal* in 1939, the 'civilian population must be treated as if they were
combatant troops; they must be under authority'.[5]

In addition, it was recognized very quickly that this was a war in which fear
reactions were going to predominate. Unlike the First World War when
hysterical reactions vastly outnumbered fear reactions, from 1940 there were
epidemics of acute anxiety. While some doctors speculated about the emotional
deterioration of modern youth (words like 'soft' and 'pampered' being recited
repeatedly), it was more generally believed that there was something unique
about this particular conflict. In the words of two prominent psychiatrists in the
last year of the war: 'the calamitous and horrifying situations produced by
modern war machines penetrate deeper and more acutely sensitive levels.
Destruction is on a larger scale. Scarcely anyone is immune. Speed makes
suddenness and unpredictability the rule. . . . The organism must be
continuously mobilized and on the alert, which means more continuous
stimulation and strain and consequent fatigue than in World War I.'[6] In other
words, mechanized terror, extreme mobility, vastly more efficient killing
machines, omnipresent danger and unpredictability sparked intense panic.
Furthermore, if these fear reactions were not controlled, they could sabotage all
hope of victory. The state could not afford to ignore 'the knowledge which
psychoanalysts and psychiatrists have about anxiety, panic, aggression,
submission, death, fears, etc.', warned one psychiatrist in 1943. Failure to use
their knowledge would be 'as fatal for America and world civilization as was
the refusal of the French army to build sufficient planes and antitank defenses'.[7]
As the self-appointed 'scientific' specialists of the emotions, psychiatric experts
were essential to the war effort.

Of course, medical men did not believe that fear was always counter-productive. It could stimulate attention, sharpen judgement and energize people.[8] In the words of the most popular psychology textbook of the first half of the twentieth century, *Psychology for the Fighting Man* (1943), fear could lead to appropriate physiological responses: 'The heart pounds faster, pumping blood more rapidly to the arms and legs and brain, where its oxygen is needed. The lungs do their part by quickening breathing. Blood pressure goes up. Adrenaline, which is nature's own "shot in the arm", is poured liberally into the blood stream. Sugar is released into the blood to act as fuel to the human fighting machine.'[9]

Fear was only dysfunctional in two contexts: firstly, when it inhibited aggression and led to 'freezing' and, secondly, when it disrupted the regularized, disciplined 'social unit' and overrode emotions such as loyalty to comrades.[10] Awareness of the seriousness of the first of these problems reached almost hysterical levels during the Second World War as it became increasingly evident that large numbers of combatants were too frightened to fire their weapons. In contrast to warfare in the past (where there was an emphasis on the passionate bayonet fight or the frenzied cavalry charge), modern military technology required a steady hand and measuring eye. Yet frightened men lacked the requisite self-control. For instance, Lieutenant Colonel Robert G. Cole (the man in charge of the 502nd Parachute Infantry which was considered to be one of the best units in the US army) was horrified to find that when his men were being attacked along the Carenton Causeway on 10 June 1944 it was impossible to force them to fire. 'Not one man in twenty-five voluntarily used his weapon', he lamented, despite the fact that they could not dig in or take cover so their only protection was to ensure that the enemy kept 'his head down'. They 'had been taught this principle in training. They all knew it very well', Cole continued, '[b]ut they could not force themselves to act upon it. When I ordered the men who were right around me to fire, they did so. But the moment I passed on, they quit. I walked up and down the line yelling "God damn it! Start shooting!" But it did very little good. They fired only while I watched them or while some other soldier stood over them.'[11]

The extent of the problem, however, was exposed by Colonel S.L.A. Marshall. He interviewed men in 400 infantry companies in the Central Pacific and European theatres, only to reveal that not more than 15 per cent of men had actually fired at enemy positions or personnel with rifles, carbines, grenades, bazookas, Browning Automatic Rifles or machine-guns during the course of an entire engagement. During the actions he had investigated it would have been possible for at least 80 per cent of the men to have fired and nearly all men were (at some stage) within firing distance of the enemy. Furthermore, the operations he examined were not 'casual' ones, but actions crucial for the unit. To be counted as a 'firer', a man would only have had to fire his weapon or lobbed a grenade 'roughly in the direction of the enemy' once or twice. Even allowing for the dead and wounded, and assuming that in their numbers there would be the same proportion of active firers as among the living, the proportion of 'active combat personnel' did not rise above 25 per cent. The terrain, tactical situation, experience of the troops, nature of the enemy, and accuracy of the enemy fire seemed to have no effect on the proportion of firers to non-firers and there was little to differentiate well-trained and campaign-seasoned troops from the rest.[12] Soldiers were not (technically speaking) 'cowards' – after all, they were there to *be* killed – but fear rendered them incapable of the 'active attitude' essential for 'combat-effectiveness'.[13]

The second reason fear generated such concern was that it was the primary cause of psychological breakdown and thus 'manpower wastage'. Levels of collapse varied dramatically by theatre of war and unit (for instance, during the 1942–3 campaign against the Japanese in the Arakon, everyone in the 14th Indian Division was said to be a psychiatric casualty; in contrast, psychiatric breakdown among the Australian troops during this war was thought to be as low as 5 per cent).[14] Overall, however, between 20 and 50 per cent of all discharges during the 1939–45 war were labelled 'psychiatric casualties'. Because of the extent of the problem and because these men could be found everywhere in the service (according to one estimate, over 60 per cent of men in medical wards and over 45 per cent of men in surgical wards were suffering from mental disorders),[15] fear concerned every medical officer, and not just those who specialized in psychiatry.[16] Indeed, it was argued that the 'wound of the spirit or psyche' did the greatest damage to military morale. It was even more dangerous than mortal physical wounds which at least might arouse the survivors to renewed acts of aggression against the enemy. In contrast, people who witnessed their comrades or neighbours collapse emotionally were often rendered 'ineffective' themselves.[17] Fear was a 'virus'.[18]

The problem of what to do with people who suffered severe and uncontrolled fear reactions preoccupied military psychiatry. For each sufferer the pain was unique: every headache was harboured within a separate, hidden sector of a particular unconscious; each flashback was peopled with different, recognizable landscapes and demons; each sleepless man tossed to a very personal rhythm. In the face of the unprecedented terrors of modern war, however, there was neither the time nor the inclination for attention to be paid to such unique, personal pain. The group rather than the individual remained paramount.[19] Military psychiatrists had only one aim and that was to determine whether 'additional combat usefulness' remained in an individual. The psychiatrist was not to concern himself with '"cure", nor with solicitude for the psychic pain [the sufferer] would have to endure to serve a few more combat days, nor even with speculations on the eventual consequence to his personality', lectured one prominent psychiatrist. In war, medical personnel had to 'temper their humanitarian approach to the individual patient with a concern for the . . . morale and efficiency of the group'.[20]

Machine metaphors also distanced psychiatrists from individual sufferers. *Psychology for the Fighting Man* popularized this motif and led its compiler to brag that readers would be left with no doubt that humans were 'a mechanism, that there are laws that govern his actions, that he ought to take that point of view toward human problems in the Army, that psychology is a great thing'.[21] Or, as another psychiatrist insisted in the *American Psychologist* in 1946: 'Wars are not fought by machines nor by men alone, but by men-machine units. The machine must be designed for the man, and the man must be selected and trained for the machine.' Just as the engineer recognized the importance of testing each discrete part of the machine, so too 'efficient human performance depends on a multitude of capacities and abilities, which must be analyzed and correlated with the demands of the total job if an efficient man-machine unit is to result'.[22] Each individual had to learn how to 'merge and sublimate all his individual energies to the common purpose of building up a military team or machine'.[23] This was the case not only in the armed forces but on the home front as well. The 'fetish of independence' had to be removed, and the individual submerged into the group.[24] Thus, an article in the *Lancet* in 1938 entitled 'Air Raids, Discipline and Panic', agreed that while civilians had to retain a 'faith in personal freedom', discipline remained important. The author assured readers that the 'advantages of discipline are undeniable; for fighting purposes it is indispensable, and the discipline that depends upon submergence of the individual in the mass produces a formidable machine before which an undisciplined crowd would be helpless, even with equality of armament'.[25]

Part of the process of coping with fearful people involved the construction of complex classification schemes. While previous wars had seen the elaborate classification of somatic and psychiatric disorders, during the Second World War attention increasingly focused upon the emotions. For instance, unhappy with the sixty-six categories of psychoses as defined by the *Standard Classification Nomenclature of Disease* in its 1942 edition, before the end of the conflict the US War Department had issued a bulletin which vastly inflated the number of categories for neurotic syndromes and included entirely new sections concerned with personality types and immaturity reactions.[26] Medical men engaged in wholesale programmes of categorizing and administering, slotting frightened men and women into a rapidly expanding list of complex and specialized diagnoses.

Less precise distinctions were also made. Psychiatrists believed that the inability to sublimate or repress the terror of war was substantially more likely to occur under certain conditions and among certain groups. The traditional military environment was thought to provide a bulwark against fear. The fact that the soldier had limited, and well-defined, avenues for escape was considered efficacious.[27] Conventional ways of training combatants to regulate their own emotions remained important: discipline, punishment, depersonalization and disorientation followed by rites of reorganization according to military codes were frequently commended. As part of this, explicit training of the emotions was stressed. For instance, military training had to include education not only in the attack but in retreat as well. In the words of *Psychology for the Fighting Man*: 'One of the main causes of panic is lack of training. Training must cover practice in defense and retreat as well as in attack, if panic is to be avoided – if the retreat is not to turn into rout. Troops trained only in methods of attack, may, when forced into quick retreat and separated from their leaders turn into a typical mob. The example of other men then calls the tune, instead of orders or the habits practiced in training and maneuvers.'[28] This principle was applied to civilians too. Psychiatrists encouraged military techniques of 'realism training' (in which soldiers in training camps were subjected to frightening stimuli in order to prevent them from becoming 'jumpy' in combat) to be applied to civil defence workers. One experiment was carried out in the cellars of Caldecote Hall in which doctors observed people exposed to 'blitz-concerts' of very loud noise played over a gramophone and found that while blood pressures rose appreciably at first, people became accustomed to the noise and by the third concert scarcely reacted at all. This form of 'conditioning' was regarded as potentially useful in preparing civilians to meet the terrors of aerial bombardment with a cool head.[29]

In addition, psychiatrists argued that certain group and environmental characteristics rendered people less vulnerable to fear. Indisputably, the most important of these were loyalty to one's comrades and confidence in one's leaders.[30] Although the first of these steadying forces has been emphasized by historians, during the Second World War psychiatrists placed much greater stress on leadership. The officer in war 'occupies a place that to his men is close to godhead', agreed most military psychiatrists, and the influence of this leader was central in restraining harmful emotions in military and in civilian contexts.[31] Other minor considerations included warnings against sleep deprivation or exhaustion and disillusionment with the reasons for fighting. In certain theatres sleep was a serious concern, as in Italy during 1945 when one-third of riflemen averaged four hours' (or less) sleep a night.[32] It was discovered that riflemen serving in this theatre could last twice the amount of time without serious psychiatric breakdown if they were given regular periods of rest away from the front line.[33] Disillusionment also predisposed men to emotional collapse. During the Second World War, this was an especially serious problem in the air forces where the fearful 'reality' of battle (in contrast to romantic myths of aerial combat) provided too stressful for many young pilots.[34]

In all cases, there were certain types of men and women who (it was argued) were more liable to be overwhelmed by fear, in particular foreigners, cowards and 'womanish' men. Foreigners (especially Jews) were accused of emotional weakness. During the air raids on London, Jews were singled out for expressing excessive terror – they were said to lack the 'British' tradition of conquering adversities, of bulldog endurance.[35] More typically, medical officers believed that anxiety reactions were a form of malingering or cowardice.[36] It was widely argued that diagnoses like 'combat exhaustion' gave 'fear a respectable name' and encouraged the 'weaklings' to malinger 'in cold blood'.[37] The exaggeration of neurotic traits, or the invention of them, could exempt an individual from dangerous duties if not from the armed forces or civil defence forces altogether.[38] In the words of one psychological consultant to the Royal Navy in 1947: 'The neuropsychiatrist is constantly confronted with the dilemma whether to keep men at duty who are liable to prove unsatisfactory, or by invaliding such individuals to make escape too easy, thus creating a bad precedent.'[39] Attempts to distinguish the malingerer from the 'genuinely' frightened person were inconclusive and generally rested upon pragmatic issues of manpower requirements and group morale.[40]

Finally, psychiatrists never tired of implying that men who collapsed under the strain of war were 'feminine' or 'latent homosexuals'. 'Socially and emotionally immature soldiers' who 'shrunk from combat with almost feminine despair and indignation' were disparaged by the highly respected Madison-based psychiatrist, Philip S. Wagner, in 1946. He contended that their passive 'insulationism' was as selfish as Nazi egocentricity. The words Wagner used to describe these men were harsh: they were narcissistic, excessively dependent on mother figures, concerned only with 'self-pleasure', and were 'poseurs'. Worried that such 'socially and emotionally stunted' individuals were being rewarded by being excused from combat, he recommended that they be immediately forced back to the battlefields and threatened with disciplinary action should their symptoms reappear.[41]

Within this context where people were failing to perform their duty because of excessive, uncontrolled fear, the psychiatric profession dedicated itself to delineating a philosophy of the emotions which would render fear reactions ethically illegitimate and would enable people to build up their 'will power' so that they would not succumb to fright. These psychiatrists did not eschew moral pronouncements; they encapsulated them. Religious representatives traditionally fulfilled this function for the military, but increasingly many of their responsibilities were transferred to medical men who consciously adopted padre-like roles and languages.[42] Military training itself became 'treatment for an unadjusted conscience' according to a textbook entitled *Psychology for the Armed Forces* and published by the National Research Council in 1945.[43] The military establishment recognized the value of these scientists of the emotions if primarily 'civilian combatants' were to be able to resist the enemy and if pensions were to be refused to people suffering severe anxiety reactions as a result of the war (on the grounds that pensions rewarded them for their emotional inadequacies).

During the war, psychiatry conformed effortlessly to the military demands of rationalization, standardization and hierarchical discipline. From the start, psychiatry recognized that the fundamental unit within which the solution to fear was to be found was inevitably artificial; that is, they agreed on the urgency of creating mass 'communities', whether this be within the armed forces or within air-raid shelters. Because they understood that the solitary individual was more liable to succumb to his or her fears than the individual within a group, they insisted on the construction of mass air-raid shelters (an example of psychological considerations overturning safety arguments). However, they also admitted that expectations of solidarity could not be assumed but had to be forged – and medical psychology was the discipline able to delineate processes of group formation. Enforcing conformity was also part of their job. Anxiety could not 'be verbalized or socially accepted' in times of immense stress.[44] The 'severe attitude' towards fear entailed 'high demands upon the self to suppress (and possibly to repress) anxiety symptoms'.[45] Individual marks of identity had to be erased. Even in military hospitals, men suffering from a variety of anxiety states had to observe military discipline, including the wearing of uniforms and the observation of courtesies such as standing to attention when speaking to officers. 'Self-discipline takes the place of the restraining sheet in the military hospital', bragged one group of Army psychiatrists, but it was a 'self-discipline' imposed by the all-embracing and inescapable institution to which they were referring.[46] The development of rational conduct was achieved through discipline; thus, they argued that the only difference between a brave person and a coward was that 'the fear of the one is controlled whilst the fear of the other is uncontrolled'.[47] The external sign of emotional conformity *was* the emotion.

Of course, the project of modernity in wartime was neither uniform nor unidirectional. Although they focused upon the scientific management of the emotions, irrational and religious elements could never be wholly discarded – indeed, psychiatric models attempted to encompass such elements within a 'scientific' rhetoric. Even dedicated psychoanalysts, such as Leonard R. Sillman of Columbia University, acknowledged the potential usefulness of 'God' in warding off unbearable fear,[48] and the Committee for National Morale in the United States encouraged officers to 'play up' to exaggerated religious feelings during bombardment, if only on the grounds that 'purposeful activity' reduced the risk of panic.[49]

Furthermore, despite their obsession with categorizing and in spite of their sensitivity to nomenclature, fear reactions were never able to be 'scientifically' contained. Attempts at psychometric measurement for purposes of selecting effective combat personnel had proved a failure. Emotional breakdown was as high as it had been during the First World War when psychiatric screening procedures had been absent. It was obvious to many that 'mousey little men' could behave 'like lions' under the stresses of war, while 'swaggering braggarts' turned out to be 'miserable cowards'.[50] In addition, it became evident that the categories being employed (and invented) were inherently muddled. The extent of psychiatric confusion was most dramatically revealed in 1947 when one researcher asked fourteen military psychiatrists to re-examine 200 randomly-selected psychiatric cases from a military hospital. This study found that 4 out of every 10 patients were placed in entirely different generic classes to their original diagnosis. For 14 per cent of the patients, the psychiatrists agreed on the generic class but not the specific disorder. In only 44 per cent of cases was there any agreement about the specific disorder. The chief disagreement (common to one-third of the diagnoses) was over whether the patient was suffering from a neurosis or a psychosis and, in two instances, one psychiatrist diagnosed a psychosis while another found no mental illness at all.[51] No revision of classification schemes and no insistence upon rational signs of terror could deny the uniqueness of the terrified self.

Finally, psychiatric attempts to control fear reactions were not a component of a progressive, liberal agenda. Admittedly, there were some military psychiatrists who attempted to resist the harsh logic of standardization, rationalization and management. M. Ralph Kaufman, for example, was the divisional surgeon on Guadalcanal during the Second World War. His commanding officer was notoriously brutal towards panic-stricken officers. Kaufman responded by diagnosing all distressed officers as suffering from organic disorders.[52] Other radical medical officers launched furious attacks upon their colleagues. In 1946, Major William Needles of the US army accused a 'goodly proportion' of military psychiatrists of being authoritarian personalities (or, worse, sadists) who regarded malingering as ubiquitous, took pride in the number of patients they returned to duty (despite having no idea about how these men coped in service), misused drug therapy, and physically, emotionally and psychologically punished men for exhibiting neuropsychiatric symptoms. With finely-toned sarcasm, he described the 'memorable experience' of watching a 'dynamic, chest-thumping psychiatrist, who had never been exposed to anything more devastating than a toy pistol' harangue combat soldiers about the need to 'stand up like a man'. Needles acknowledged that military psychiatrists had two allegiances, but believed that most did not give the individual even the slightest consideration.[53]

However, these psychiatrists were not typical. More usually, regimentation and discipline were wholeheartedly embraced. Little sympathy was expressed for fearful persons, who were described as 'dull and backward', lacking the ability to understand 'complex ideas' (such as 'patriotism, appreciation of the alternative to winning the war, tradition').[54] Men who experienced emotional conflicts were 'psychologically inadequate individuals' or were 'ineffectives' who required 'salvaging'.[55] Forcing a combat-exhausted man back into the front line was in his own interests since, if he was evacuated, 'he would be tempted to maintain his sickness as part of a masochistic penance for having failed to return to his unit and his duty'.[56] Psychiatrists recommended against giving pensions for men suffering psychoneuroses on the grounds that it was a form of 'secondary gain', rewarding men for emotional inadequacies and tempting the neurotic to become chronically ill. It was, they reasoned, a 'moral duty, not only to the public but to the neurotic person' to refuse compensation.[57] Others were harsher still. In *The Military Surgeon*, Colonel Amos R. Koontz insisted that men who had broken down in service should be sterilized – only such a measure would prevent men from showing fear. 'Is it not time that our country stopped being soft', he argued, 'and abandoned its program of mollycoddling no-goods?'[58] Men had to be prepared to give not only their limbs or life for their country, but their 'guts' and 'nerves' as well.[59] Human sympathy took second place to the rational discipline of the emotion of fear.

Psychiatry was fundamentally engaged in the task of disciplining the emotions. In wartime, concerns about the possible effects of fear and anxiety within the armed forces and on the home front rendered the professional services of psychiatry essential to the war effort. Although recourse to the language of internal control was not absent, the emphasis was on external, secular restraint predicated upon external sources of authority (military command). This had not been absent in earlier wars but measurement and conformity increased with the Second World War as psychological measurements supplemented (and even supplanted) the physical measurements employed during the First World War. Furthermore, while in earlier conflicts the emotions were understood primarily in terms of literature and history, by the Second World War the arts had been ousted, to be replaced by the 'sciences', particularly psychology and psychiatry. Military medicine was essential in forging the Weberian 'iron cage' of rules, regulations and disciplines that characterized the modernist project, and with the Second World War, it came to encage the emotions as much as the bodies of its subjects. The explosion of the atom bomb on 6 August 1945 may have signalled the end of the modernist dream of progress but it reinforced the knowledge that if human life was to continue, it would have to learn to discipline the emotions to an even higher level.[60]

Notes

1 Lt Col William C. Porter, Capt John G. Novak, and 1st Lt Paul V. Lemkau, 'Therapeutic Considerations for Army Psychiatrists', *The Military Surgeon*, 92 (1943), 372, quoting from US army regulations 40–5, section 1, paragraph 2.

2 Col Dunlap P. Penhallow, 'An Out-Door Toilet Paper Holder', *The Military Surgeon*, 88 (1941), 668–9; Capt Lucius W. Johnson, 'Medical and Sanitary Care of the Civilian Population Necessitated by Attacks from Hostile Aircraft', *The Military Surgeon*, 88 (1941), 1–24; Lt Col A. Steindler, 'Marching Efficiently', *The Military Surgeon*, 86 (1940), 256–63.

3 Dr John A. Ryle, 'The Twenty-First Maudsley Lecture: Nosophobia', *Journal of Mental Science*, 394 (1948), p. 3.

4 Maj. H.H. Garner, 'Psychiatric Casualties in Combat', *War Medicine*, 8 (1945), 348.

5 Dr Maurice B. Wright, 'Psychological Emergencies in War Time', *British Medical Journal* (9 September 1939), p. 576. Also see Major Greenwood, 'Letter to the Editor. Helping the Homeless', *British Medical Journal* (28 September 1940), 430.

6 Edward A. Strecker and Kenneth E. Appel, *Psychiatry in Modern Warfare* (New York, The Macmillan Company, 1945), p. 27. Also see Edward A. Strecker, 'War Neuroses', *The Military Surgeon*, 94 (1944), 197.

7 Leonard R. Sillman, 'Morale', *War Medicine*, 3 (May 1943), 502.

8 Air Ministry, *Psychological Disorders in Flying Personnel of the Royal Air Force Investigated During the War of 1939–1945* (London, HMSO, 1947), p. 65; Maj William G. Barrett, 'Psychologic Armoring for the Air Force', *War Medicine*, 5 (1944), 143; Strecker, 'War Neuroses', p. 198; C.P. Symonds, 'The Human Response to Flying Stress', *British Medical Journal* (4 December 1943), 705.

9 E.G. Boring and M. van de Water (compilers), *Psychology for the Fighting Man. What You Should Know About Yourself and Others* (Washington, The Infantry Journal, 1943), pp. 298–9. Also see 'Psychiatric Casualties. Hints to Medical Officers in the Middle East Forces' (September 1942) in Lt Col William Hamilton, 'Papers', in Contemporary Medical Archives Centre RAMC 1652/3.

10 C.P. Symonds, 'The Human Response to Flying Stress', *British Medical Journal*, (4 December 1943), 705.

11 Col S.L.A. Marshall, *Men Against Fire. The Problem of Battle Command in Future War* (New York, William Morrow & Co., 1947), p. 72. See also Hugh Dundas, *Flying Start. A Fighter Pilot's War Years* (London, Stanley Paul, 1988), p. 2; Lt Col George Juskalian, 'Why Didn't They Shoot More?', *Army Combat Forces Journal*, 5 (1954), 35; '152nd Infantry Brigade. Discussion on Lessons Learned During the Year of Fighting from El Alamein to Messina' (1943), in Public Record Office (PRO), WO231/16.

12 Marshall, *Men Against Fire*, pp. 50, 54–9, 65.

13 Irvin L. Child, 'Morale: A Bibliographical Review', *Psychological Bulletin*, 38 (1941), 413.

14 'Psychiatry – Arakan Campaign' (n.d.), p. 3, PRO, WO222/1571; Anne-Marie Conde, '"The Ordeal of Adjustment": Australian Psychiatric Casualties of the Second World War', *War and Society*, 15 (1997), 61–74.

15 Stecker and Appel, *Psychiatry in Modern Warfare*, p. 50.

16 For instance, see the discussions by Capt E.L. Caveny, 'Aviation Psychiatry', *The Military Surgeon*, 98 (1946), 289 and Col William C. Menninger, 'Relationships of Neuropsychiatry to General Medicine and Surgery in the Army', *The Military Surgeon*, 96 (1945), 134.

17 Strecker, 'War Neuroses', p. 196.

18 Boring and de Water, *Psychology for the Fighting Man*, pp. 300–4; Albert J. Glass, 'Preventive Psychiatry in the Combat Zone', *United States Armed Forces Medical Journal*, 4 (1953), 685.

19 Lt Gen Sir Neil Cantlie, 'Papers', p. 1, his reply to a War Office questionnaire (1946), Contemporary Medical Archives Center RAMC 465/10; George S. Goldman, 'The Psychiatrist's Job in War and Peace', *Psychiatry*, 9 (1946), 265; John Rawlings Rees, *The Shaping of Psychiatry by War* (London, Chapman and Hall, 1945), p. 19.

20 Eli Ginzberg, *Breakdown and Recovery* (New York, Columbia University Press, 1959), p. 86. Also see Harry Trosman and I. Hyman Weiland, 'Application of Psychodynamic Principles to Psychotherapy in Military Service', *United States Armed Forces Medical Journal*, 8 (1957), 1359.

21 Boring in a letter to Marjorie van de Water (19 May 1943), cited by James Herbert Capshew, 'Psychology on the March: American Psychologists and World War II' (Ph.D. thesis, University of Pennsylvania, 1986), pp. 200–1.

22 Walter S. Hunter (chief of the US Applied Psychology Panel), 'Psychology in the War', *American Psychologist*, 1 (1946), 479.

23 Maj S.A. Sandler, 'The Army and the Maladjusted Soldier', *The Military Surgeon*, 96 (1945), 91.

24 Alexander Reid Martin, 'The Prevention of Panic', *Mental Hygiene*, 26 (1942), 548–9.

25 'Air Raids, Discipline and Panic', *Lancet* (7 May 1938), 1061.

26 For a description, see William C. Menninger, *Psychiatry in a Troubled World. Yesterday's War and Today's Challenge* (New York, The Macmillan Co., 1948), p. 258.

27 Garner, 'Psychiatric Casualties in Combat', p. 343.

28 Boring and de Water, *Psychology for the Fighting Man*, p. 393.

29 'Conditioning to Bangs', *Lancet* (14 March 1942), 330–1.

30 Circular to all medical officers, 'Morale, Discipline and Mental Fitness' (n.d.), p. 4, PRO, WO222/218; Boring and de Water, *Psychology for the Fighting Man*, p. 396; Albert J. Glass, 'Combat Exhaustion', *United States Armed Forces Medical Journal*, 11 (1951), 1476; Eli Ginzberg, John L. Herma and Sol. W. Ginsburg, *Psychiatry and Military Manpower Policy. A Reappraisal of the Experience in World War II* (New York, King's Crown Press, 1953), pp. 17–18, 31; 'The Third Meeting of Command Specialists in Psychological Breakdown' (21 September 1940), p. 3, PRO, WO222/1584; Maj Edwin A. Weinstein and Lt Col Calvin S. Drayer, 'A Dynamic Approach to the Problem of Combat-Induced Anxiety', *The Bulletin of the US Army Medical Department*, 9, suppl. (November 1949), 12.

31 Capt C.T. Lanham, 'Panic' in Col Joseph I. Greene (ed.), *The Infantry Journal Reader* (New York, Doubleday, Doran and Co., 1943), p. 288. Also see Air Ministry, *Psychological Disorders in Flying Personnel of the Royal Air Force*, pp. 76–7; Norman Copeland, *Psychology and the Soldier* (Harrisberg, PA, Military Service Publishing Co., 1944), p. 73; Ginzberg, Herma and Ginsburg, *Psychiatry and Military Manpower Policy*, pp. 31–3; Martin, 'The Prevention of Panic', pp. 551–2; Joost A.M. Meerloo, *Patterns of Panic* (Westport, Conn., The Greenwood Press, 1950), p. 65; John Rickman, 'A Discursive Review', *The British Journal of Medical Psychology*, 17 (1938), 362; John A. Ryle, *Fears May be Liars* (London, Allen & Unwin Ltd., 1941), pp. 26, 77.

32 Samuel A. Stouffer et al., *The American Soldier: Combat and Its Aftermath* (Princeton University Press, 1949), p. 79, based on a survey of 1,766 soldiers in rifle and heavy weapons companies. See also Eli Ginzberg, *Patterns of Performance* (New York, Columbia University Press, 1959), p. 38.

33 'Preventative Psychiatry', *The Bulletin of the US Army Medical Department*, 6 (1946), 493.

34 Maj Charles W. Miller, 'Delayed Combat Reactions in Air Force Personnel', *War Medicine*, 8 (1945), 256.

35 Lord Horder, 'The Modern Troglodyte', *Lancet* (19 April 1941), 501; P.E. Vernon, 'Psychological Effects of Air Raids', *Journal of Abnormal and Social Psychology*, 36 (1941), 474.

36 Amalgamated Union of Building Trade Workers, *The Case of Sapper Hasties* (London, 1943), p. 3, in Modern Records Centre MSS 292/443/4; 'Minister's Meeting with Representatives of War Pensions Committees. Extract from the Summary of Proceedings of the Meeting Held at Bristol on 25th April 1930', PRO, PIN15/2946.

37 Lord Moran, *The Anatomy of Courage* (London, Constable, 1945), p. 186.

38 See 'Report of a Conference on Psychiatry in Forward Areas', Calcutta (8–10 August 1944), p. 2, address by Maj Gen Cantlie, in PRO, WO32/11550.

39 Surgeon Capt D. Curran, 'Functional Nervous States in Relation to Service in the Royal Navy', in Maj Gen Sir Henry Letheby Tidy (ed.), *Inter-Allied Conferences on War Medicine 1942–1945* (London, Staples Press Ltd, 1947), p. 220. See also 'Survey of Conditions by DDMS 5 Corps' (9 March–31 May 1943), p. 8, Contemporary Medical Archives Centre RAMC 465/6.

40 For a further discussion, see Joanna Bourke, *Dismembering the Male: Men's Bodies, Britain, and the Great War* (London and Chicago, Reaktion Press and Chicago University Press, 1996), ch. 2.

41 Philip S. Wagner, 'Psychiatric Activities During the Normandy Offensive, June 20–August 20, 1944', *Psychiatry*, 9 (1946), 348, 356. See also Lt Col Albert Groves Hulett, 'Malingering – A Study', *The Military Surgeon*, 89 (1941), 138; S.R. Warson, 'The Management of Acute Excitements', *The Military Surgeon*, 91 (1942), 59; Sir Andrew MacPhail, *Official History of the Canadian Forces in the Great War 1914–19. The Medical Services* (Ottowa, F.A. Acland, 1925), p. 278.

42 For example, see Col Francis W. Pruitt, 'Doctor–Patient Relationships in the Army', *United States Armed Forces Medical Journal*, 5 (1954), 204.

43 E.G. Boring (ed.), *Psychology for the Armed Forces* (Washington, The Infantry Journal, 1945). See also Pruitt, 'Doctor–Patient Relationships in the Army', 204.

44 Roy R. Grinker and John P. Spiegel, *Men Under Stress* (London, J. and A. Churchill, 1945), p. 104.

45 Stouffer, *The American Soldier*, p. 206.

46 Lt Col William C. Porter, Capt John G. Novak, and 1st Lt Paul V. Lemkau, 'Therapeutic Considerations for Army Psychiatrists', *The Military Surgeon*, 92 (1943), 375.

47 Copeland, *Psychology and the Soldier*, p. 75.

48 Leonard R. Sillman, 'Morale', *War Medicine*, 3 (1943), 499–500.

49 Ladislas Farago, *German Psychological Warfare* (New York, G.P. Putnam's Sons, 1942), p. 117.

50 Col Amos R. Koontz, 'Psychiatry in the Next War: Shall We Again Waste Manpower?', *The Military Surgeon*, 103 (1948), 200. For an almost identical comment, see Blair W. Sparks and Oliver K. Niess, 'Psychiatric Screening of Combat Pilots', *United States Armed Forces Medical Journal*, 7 (1956), 811–12.

51 Isidore S. Edelman, *Diseases of the Nervous System*, 8 (June 1947), 171–4.

52 M. Ralph Kaufman and Lindsay E. Beaton, 'South Pacific Area', in Lt Gen Hal B. Jennings (ed.), *Neuropsychiatry in World War II*, volume 2, *Overseas Theatres* (Washington, Office of the Surgeon-General, 1973), p. 461.

53 Maj William Needles, 'The Regression of Psychiatry in the Army', *Psychiatry*, 9 (1946), 167–85.

54 'Report of a Conference on Psychiatry in Forward Areas' (8–10 August 1944), p. 13, PRO, WO32/11550.

55 Maj J.O. Langley, 'Tactical Implications of the Human Factors in Warfare', *Australian Army Journal*, 107 (April 1958), 14; Maj H.A. Palmer, 'The Problem of the P & N Casualty – A Study of 12,000 Cases' (1944), p. 3, in Contemporary Medical Archives Center RAMC 466/49.

56 Wagner, 'Psychiatric Activities During the Normandy Offensive', p. 358.

57 Ernest Lewy, 'Compensation for War Neuroses', *War Medicine*, 1 (1941), 892.

58 Col Amos R. Koontz, 'Psychiatry in the Next War: Shall We Again Waste Manpower?', *The Military Surgeon*, 103 (1948), 200.

59 Palmer, 'The Problem of the P & N Casualty', p. 11.

60 For a detailed description of what will be needed, see Bertrand Russell, *The Impact of Science on Society* (London, Allen & Unwin Ltd, 1952), p. 96. For further discussion of fear and the military, see Joanna Bourke, *An Intimate History of Killing. Face-to-Face Killing in Twentieth-Century Warfare* (London, Granta, 1999).

BIBLIOGRAPHY

(*The place of publication is London unless otherwise indicated*)

Abel-Smith, Brian. *A History of the Nursing Profession*, Heinemann, 1960

Adas, Michael. *Machines as the Measure of Men: Science, Technology, and Ideologies of Western Dominance*, Ithaca, Cornell University Press, 1984

Ahrenfeldt, R.H. *Psychiatry in the British Army in the Second World War*, Routledge & Kegan Paul, 1958

Alter, Peter. *The Reluctant Patron: Science and the State in Britain, 1850–1920*, trs. A. Davies, Oxford, Berg, 1987

Aly, Gotz, Chroust, Peter and Pross, Christian. *Cleansing the Fatherland: Nazi Medicine and Racial Hygiene*, trs. Belinda Cooper, with a Foreword by Michael H. Kater, Baltimore, Johns Hopkins, 1994

Anderson, Olive. 'The Growth of Christian Militarism in Mid-Victorian Britain', *English Historical Review* 86 (1971), 46–72

Armfield, B.B. *Medical Department, US Army: Organization and Administration in World War II*, Washington, DC, Office of the Surgeon-General's Department of the Army, 1963

Armstrong, David. *The Political Anatomy of the Body: Medical Knowledge in Britain in the Twentieth Century*, Cambridge University Press, 1993

Austoker, J. and Bryder, L. (eds). *Historical Perspectives on the Role of the MRC: Essays in the History of the Medical Research Council of the United Kingdom and its Predecessor, the Medical Research Committee, 1913–1953*, Oxford University Press, 1989

Babington, Anthony. *For the Sake of Example: Capital Courts Martial, 1914–1920*, Leo Cooper in association with Secker & Warburg, 1983

———. *Military Intervention in Britain: from the Gordon Riots to the Gibraltar Incident*, Routledge, 1990

———. *No Memorial: My Experiences in Hospital After Being Severely Wounded at the End of the 1939–45 War*, Heinemann, 1954

Baly, Monica. *Florence Nightingale and the Nursing Legacy*, New York, Croom Helm, 1986

Bamji, Andrew. 'Facial Surgery: the Patient's Experience', in Hugh Cecil and Peter Liddle (eds), *Facing Armageddon: The First World War Experienced*, Barnsley, Leo Cooper, 1996, pp. 490–501

Barger, A.C., Benison, S., and Wolfe, E.L. 'Walter B. Cannon and the Mystery of Shock: A Study of Anglo-American Co-operation in World War I', *Medical History* 35 (1991), 217–49

Bartlett, F. *Psychology and the Soldier*, Cambridge University Press, 1927

Bartov, Omer. *Murder in Our Midst: The Holocaust, Industrial Killing, and Representation*, New York, Oxford University Press, 1996

Bauman, Zygmunt. *Modernity and the Holocaust*, Cambridge, Polity Press, 1989

Beardsley, E.H. 'Allied Against Sin: American and British Responses to Venereal Disease in World War I', *Medical History* 20 (1976), 189–202

Beckett, I.F.W. and Simpson, K. (eds). *A Nation in Arms: A Social Study of the British Army in the First World War*, Manchester University Press, 1985

Berridge, Virginia, Webster, Charles and Walt, Gill. 'Mobilisation for Total Welfare, 1948 to 1974', in Charles Webster (ed.), *Caring for Health*, Milton Keynes, Open University Press, 1993, 107–25

Best, Geoffrey. *Humanity in Warfare: The Modern History of the International Law of Armed Conflicts*, Weidenfeld & Nicholson, 1980

Bijker, W.E., Hughes, T.P. and Pinch, T.J. (eds). *The Social Construction of Technological Systems: New Directions in the Sociology and History of Technology*, Cambridge, MA, MIT Press, 1987

Binneveld, Hans. *From Shellshock to Combat Stress: A Comparative History of Military Psychology*, Amsterdam University Press, 1997

Bleker, Johanna and Schiniedebach, Heinz-Peter (eds). *Medizin und krieg: vom dilemma der heilberufe 1865 bis zum 1985*, Frankfurt, Fischer Taschenbuch, 1987

Bogacz, Ted. 'War Neuroses and Social Cultural Change in England, 1914–22: The Work of the War Office Committee into "Shell Shock"', *Journal of Contemporary History* 24 (1989), 227–56

Bosanquet, Nick. 'Health Systems in Khaki: The British and American Medical Experience', in H. Cecil and P. Liddle (eds), *Facing Armageddon: The First World War Experienced*, Barnsley, Leo Cooper, 1996, pp. 451–65

Bourke, Joanna. *Dismembering the Male: Men's Bodies and the Great War*, Reaktion Books, 1996

——. 'The Experience of Medicine in Wartime', in Roger Cooter and John Pickstone (eds), *The History of Medicine in the Twentieth Century*, Reading, Harwood International, 1999

——. *An Intimate History of Killing: Face-to-Face Killing in Twentieth-Century Warfare*, Granta, 1999

Brand, Jeanne L. *Doctors and the State: The British Medical Profession and Government Action in Public Health, 1870–1912*, Baltimore, Johns Hopkins, 1965

Brandt, Allan M. *No Magic Bullet: A Social History of Venereal Disease in the United States Since 1880*, New York, Oxford University Press, 1985

Bristow, Edward J. *Prostitution and Prejudice: The Jewish Fight Against White Slavery, 1870–1939*, New York, Oxford University Press, 1982

——. *Vice and Vigilance: Purity Movements in Britain Since 1700*, Dublin, Gill & Macmillan, 1977

Bristow, Nancy K. *Making Men Moral: Social Engineering During the Great War*, New York University Press, 1996

Bryder, Linda. 'The First World War: Healthy or Hungry?', *History Workshop Journal* 24 (1987), 141–57

Buckley, Suzanne. 'The Failure to Resolve the Problem of Venereal Disease Among the Troops in Britain During World War I', in B. Bond and I. Roy (eds), *War and Society: A Yearbook of Military History*, vol. 2, New York, Holmes & Meier, 1977, pp. 65–85

Burk, Kathleen (ed.). *War and the State: The Transformation of British Government, 1914–1919*, Allen & Unwin, 1982

Burnham, John C. 'The New Psychology: from Narcissism to Social Control', in J. Braeman, R.H. Brencher and D. Brody (eds), *Change and Continuity in Twentieth Century America: The 1920s*, New York, 1968, pp. 351–98

Cantlie, Sir Neil. *A History of the Army Medical Department*, 2 vols, Edinburgh, Churchill Livingstone, 1974

Casarini, A. *La Medicina Militaire nella Storia*, Rome, Ministero della Geurra, 1929

Cohen, Deborah. 'The War Come Home: Disabled Veterans in Great Britain and Germany' (unpub. Ph.D. thesis, University of California, Berkeley, 1996)

Cooter, Roger. 'Discourses on War', *Studies in the History and Philosophy of Science* 26 (1995), 637–47

——. 'Medicine and the Goodness of War', *Canadian Bulletin of Medical History* 12 (1990), 147–59

——. 'The Moment of the Accident: Culture, Militarism and Modernity In Late-Victorian Britain', in Roger Cooter and Bill Luckin (eds), *Accidents in History: Injuries, Fatalities and Social Relations*, Amsterdam, Rodopi, 1996, pp. 107–57

——. *Surgery and Society in Peace and War: Orthopaedics and the Organization of Modern Medicine, 1880–1948*, Macmillan, 1993

——. 'War and Modern Medicine', in W.F. Bynum and R. Porter (eds), *Companion Encyclopedia of the History of Medicine*, Routledge, 1994, pp. 1536–73

Cooter, Roger, Harrison, Mark and Sturdy, Steve (eds). *Medicine and the Management Of Modern Warfare*, Amsterdam, Rodopi, forthcoming

Cope, Zachary (ed.). *History of the Second World War UK Medical Services: Surgery*, HMSO, 1953

——. 'The Medical Balance Sheet of War', in his *Some Famous General Practitioners and Other Medical Historical Essays*, Pitman Medical, 1961

Copp, Terry and McAndrew, Bill. *Battle Exhaustion: Soldiers and Psychiatrists in the Canadian Army, 1939–1945*, Montreal, McGill/Queen's University Press, 1990

Cowdrey, Albert E. *Fighting for Life: American Military Medicine in World War II*, New York, Free Press, 1994

——. '"Germ Warfare" and Public Health in the Korean Conflict', *Journal of the History of Medicine* 39 (1984), 153–72

——. *War and Healing: Stanhope Bayne-Jones and the Maturing of American Medicine*, Baton Rouge, Louisiana State University Press, 1992

Crew, F.A.E. *The Army Medical Services. Administration; Campaigns*, 6 vols, HMSO, 1953–67

Crofton, Eileen. *The Women of Royaumont: A Scottish Women's Hospital on the Western Front*, East Linton, Tuckwell Press, 1997

Crook, A. *Barbed-wire Doctor: One Doctor's War: Memoirs of Brigadier Crook*, Edinburgh, Pentland Press, 1996

Crook, Paul. *Darwinism, War and History*, Cambridge University Press, 1994

Crosland, Maurice. 'Science and the Franco-Prussian War', *Social Studies of Science* 6 (1976), 185–214

Crosthwait, E. 'The Girl Behind the Man Behind the Gun: The Position of the WAAC in World War One' (unpublished MA thesis, Essex University, 1990)

Cunningham, Horace H. *Doctors in Gray: the Confederate Medical Service*, Baton Rouge, Louisiana State University Press, 1958; 2nd edn, 1960

Cunningham, Hugh. 'The Language of Patriotism', in Raphael Samuel (ed.), *Patriotism: The Making and Unmasking of British National Identity*, vol. 1 of *History and Politics*, Routledge, 1989, pp. 57–89

———. *The Volunteer Force: A Social and Political History, 1859–1908*, Hamden, Connecticut, Archon Books, 1975

Curtin, Philip. *Death By Migration: Europe's Encounter with the Tropical World in the Nineteenth Century*, Cambridge University Press, 1988

Dandeker, Christopher. *Capitalism, Bureaucracy and Surveillance*, Oxford, Polity Press, 1988

Davin, Anna. 'Imperialism and Motherhood', *History Workshop 5* (1978), 9–65

Dewey, P.E. 'Nutrition and Living Standards in Wartime Britain', in Richard Wall and Jay Winter (eds), *The Upheaval of War: Family, Work and Welfare in Europe, 1914–1918*, Cambridge University Press, 1988, pp. 197–220

Diehl, James M. *The Thanks of the Fatherland: German Veterans After the Second World War*, Chapel Hill, University of North Carolina Press, 1993

Digby, Anne. *Making a Medical Living: Doctors and Patients in the English Market for Medicine, 1720–1911*, Cambridge University Press, 1994

Donner, Henriette. 'Under the Cross: Why V.A.D.s Performed the Filthiest Task in the Dirtiest War: Red Cross Women Volunteers, 1914–1918', *Journal of Social History* 30 (1997), 687–704

Doorn, Jacques Van. *The Soldier and Social Change: Comparative Studies in the History and Sociology of the Military*, Beverly Hills, Sage, 1975

Drew, Robert. *Commissioned Officers in the Medical Services of the British Army 1660–1960*, vol. 2 of *Roll of Officers in the Royal Army Medical Corps 1898–1960*, Wellcome Historical Medical Library, 1968

Dwork, Deborah. *War is Good for Babies and Other Young Children: A History of the Infant and Child Welfare Movement in England, 1898–1918*, Tavistock, 1987

Dyhouse, Carol. *Women in Medicine During World War II: Twelve Eyewitness Accounts*, Liverpool Medical History Society, 1997

Eckart, W.U. and Gradmann, C. (eds). *Die Medizin und der Erste Weltkrieg*, Pfaffenweiler, Centaurus, 1996

Edgerton, David. 'British Scientific Intellectuals and the Relations of Science, Technology and War', in P. Forman and J.M. Sanchez-Rons (eds), *National Military Establishments and the Advancement of Science and Technology*, Amsterdam, Kluwer, 1996, pp. 1–35

——. *England and the Aeroplane: An Essay on a Militant and Technological Nation*, Macmillan, 1991

——. 'Liberal Militarism and the British State', *New Left Review* 185 (1991), 138–96

Eksteins, Modris. *The Rites of Spring: The Great War and the Birth of the Modern Age*, New York, Anchor, 1989

Ellis, John. *Eye-Deep in Hell: Trench Warfare in World War I*, Baltimore, Johns Hopkins, 1976

——. *The Sharp End of War: The Fighting Man in World War II*, Newton Abbot, David & Charles, 1980, chapter 5, 'Casualties'

——. *The Social History of the Machine Gun*, The Cresset Library, 1975

Engelman, R.C. and Joy, R.T.J. *Two Hundred Years of Military Medicine*, Fort Detrick, US Army Medical Department, 1975

Englander, David. 'Soldiers and Social Reform in the First and Second World Wars', *Historical Research* 57 (1994), 318–26

English, Peter C. *Shock, Physiological Surgery, and George Washington Crile: Medical Innovation in the Progressive Era*, Westport, Conn., Greenwood, 1980

Fessler, Diane B. *No Time for Fear: Voices of American Military Nurses in World War II*, Michigan State University Press, 1996

Feudtner, J.C. 'The Description of Shell Shock as a Functional Nervous Disorder' (unpub. MA thesis, University of Lancaster, 1986)

——. '"Minds The Dead Have Ravished": Shell Shock, History, and the Ecology of Disease-Systems', *History of Science* 31 (1993), 377–420

Finlayson, G. *Citizen, State and Social Welfare in Britain, 1830–1990*, Oxford University Press, 1994

Fischer, H. *Der deutsche Sanitätsdienst, 1921–1945: Organisation, Dokumente, und persoenliche Erfahrungen*, Osnabruck, Biblio Verlag, 1984

Fussell, Paul. *The Great War and Modern Memory*, Oxford University Press, 1975

Fyrth, Jim. *The Signal was Spain: The Aid Spain Movement in Britain, 1936–39*, Lawrence & Wishart, 1986

Gabriel, Richard A. and Metz, Karen S. *A History of Military Medicine*, 2 vols, New York, Westport, Conn., 1992

Garrison, Fielding. *Notes on the History of Military Medicine*, Washington, DC, Association of Military Surgeons, 1922

Gibson, T.M. and Harrison, M.H. *Into Thin Air: A History of Aviation Medicine*, Robert Hale, 1984

Giddens, Anthony. *The Consequences of Modernity*, Stanford University Press, 1990

——. *The Nation State and Violence*, vol. 2 of *A Contemporary Critique of Historical Materialism*, Cambridge, Polity Press, 1985

Gillespie, R.D. *The Psychological Effects of War on Citizen and Soldier*, Norton, 1942

Gillis, John R. (ed.). *The Militarization of the Western World*, New Brunswick, NJ, Rutgers University Press, 1989

Glass, A.E. *Neuropsychology in World War II*, Washington, DC, Office of the Surgeon-General, 1973

Godden, L.J. (ed.). *History of the Royal Army Dental Corps*, Aldershot, Royal Army Dental Corps, 1971

Gradmann, Christoph. '"Vornehmlich beängstigend" – Medizin, Gesundheit und chemische Kriegsürung im deutschen Heer 1914–1918', in W.U. Eckart and C. Gradmann (eds), *Die Medizin und der Erste Weltkrieg*, Pfaffenweiler, Centaurus, 1996.

Green, F.H.K. and Covell, Sir G. (eds). *Medical Research: Medical History of the Second World War*, HMSO, 1953

Guth, E. (ed.). *Vorträge zur Militärgeschichte, ii: Sanitätswesen im Zweiten Weltkrieg*, Bonn, 1990

Haber, L.F. *The Poisonous Cloud: Chemical Warfare in the First World War*, Oxford, Clarendon Press, 1986

Haber, Samuel. *Efficiency and Uplift: Scientific Management in the Progressive Era, 1890–1920*, Chicago University Press, 1964

Hacker, Barton C. 'Military Institutions, Weapons, and Social Change: Towards a New History of Military Technology', *Technology and Culture* 35 (1994), 768–834

Hagerman, Edward. *The American Civil War and the Origins of Modern Warfare: Ideas, Organization, and Field Command*, Bloomington and Indianapolis, University of Indiana Press, 1992

Hales, M. 'Management Science and the "Second Industrial Revolution"' in L. Levidov (ed.), *Radical Science Essays*, Free Association Books, 1986, pp. 62–87

Haley, Bruce. *The Healthy Body and Victorian Culture*, Cambridge, MA, Harvard University Press, 1978

Hall, Lesley A. *Hidden Anxieties: Male Sexuality, 1900–1950*, Cambridge, Polity, 1991

Haller, John S. Jr. 'Civil War Anthropometry: The Making of a Racial Ideology', in his *Outcasts from Evolution: Scientific Attitudes of Racial Inferiority, 1859–1900*, Urbana/Chicago, University of Illinois Press, 1971, pp. 19–39

——. *Farmcarts to Fords: A History of the Military Ambulance 1790–1925*, Carbondale and Edwardsville, Southern Illinois University Press, 1992

Harris, Bernard. 'The Demographic Impact of the First World War: An Anthropometric Perspective', *Social History of Medicine* 6 (1993), 343–66

——. *The Health of the School Child: A History of the School Medical Service in England and Wales*, Buckingham, Open University, 1995

Harris, Jose. 'Enterprise and Welfare States: A Comparative Perspective', *Transactions of the Royal Historical Society*, 5th ser, 40 (1991), 175–95

——. 'War and Social History: Britain and the Home Front During the Second World War', *Contemporary European History* 1 (1992), 17–35

Harris, Ruth. 'The "Child of the Barbarian": Rape, Race and Nationalism in France During the First World War', *Past and Present* 141 (1993), 171–206

Harris, Sheldon H. *Factories of Death: Japanese Biological Warfare 1932–45 and the American Cover Up*, Routledge, 1994

Harrison, Mark. 'The British Army and the Problem of Venereal Disease in France and Egypt during the First World War', *Medical History* 39 (1995), 133–58

——. 'The Fight Against Disease in the Mesopotamia Campaign' in P. Liddle and H. Cecil (eds), *Facing Armageddon: The First World War Experienced*, Barnsley, Leo Cooper, 1996, pp. 475–89

——. 'The Medicalization of War – The Militarization of Medicine', *Social History of Medicine* 9 (1996), 267–76

——. *Medicine and British Warfare: British Military Medicine, 1898–1918*, forthcoming

——. 'Medicine and the Culture of Command: The Case of Malaria Control in the British Army During the Two World Wars', *Medical History* 40 (1996), 437–52

——. 'Medicine and the Management of Modern Warfare', *History of Science* 34 (1996), 379–410

Hartcup, Guy. *The War of Invention: Scientific Developments, 1914–18*, Brassey, 1988

Hay, Ian. *One Hundred Years of Army Nursing: The Story of the British Army Nursing Services from the time of Florence Nightingale to the Present Day*, Cassell, 1953

Healy, David. *Images of Trauma: From Hysteria to Post-Traumatic Stress Disorder*, Faber & Faber, 1993

Herbert, James. 'Psychology on the March: American Psychologists and World War II' (unpub. Ph.D. thesis, University of Pennsylvania, 1986)

Herrick, Claire E.J. 'Of War and Wounds: The Propaganda, Politics and Experience of Medicine in World War I' (unpub. Ph.D. thesis, University of Manchester, 1996)

——. 'The Broken Soldier, the Bonesetter and the Medical Profession: Manipulating Identities During the First World War', in Bertrand Taithe and T. Thornton (eds), *War: Identities in Conflict, 1300–2000*, Stroud, Sutton, 1998, pp. 173–92

Herschbach, Lisa. 'Prosthetic Reconstructions: Making the Industry, Remaking the Body, Modelling the Nation', *History Workshop Journal* 44 (1997), 20–57

Horne, John N. *Labour at War: France and Britain, 1914–1918*, Oxford, Clarendon Press, 1991

Howell, Joel D. *Technology in the Hospital: Transforming Patient Care in the Early Twentieth Century*, Baltimore, Johns Hopkins, 1995

Hutchinson, John. 'World War I and the Control of Public Health', in his *The Cleansing Hurricane: Politics and Public Health in Revolutionary Russia, 1890–1918*, Baltimore, Johns Hopkins, 1990

——. *Champions of Charity: War and the Rise of the Red Cross*, Boulder, Westview Press, 1995

Hyam, Ronald. *Empire and Sexuality: The British Experience*, Manchester University Press, 1991

Hynes, Samuel. *A War Imagined: The First World War and English Culture*, Bodley Head, 1990

Hyson, John M. *The U.S. Military Academy Dental Service: A History, 1825–1920*, West Point, New York, US Military Academy, US Army, 1987

Jones, Colin. 'The Welfare of the French Foot-Soldier from Richleau to Napoleon', in his *The Charitable Imperative: Hospitals and Nursing in Ancien Regime and Revolutionary France*, Routledge, 1989, pp. 209–40

Kater, Michael H. *Doctors Under Hitler*, Chapel Hill, University of North Carolina Press, 1989

Keegan, John. *The Face of Battle: A Study of Agincourt, Waterloo and the Somme*, 2nd edn, Barrie & Jenkins, 1988

——. *A History of Warfare*, New York, Alfred A. Knopf, 1994

Kehoe, Jean. 'Medicine, Sexuality, and Imperialism. British Medical Discourses Surrounding Venereal Disease in New Zealand and Japan: A Socio-historical and Comparative Study' (unpub. Ph.D. thesis, University of Wellington, NZ, 1992)

Kelly, Patrick J. *Creating a National Home: Building the Veterans' Welfare State, 1860–1900*, Cambridge, MA, Harvard University Press, 1997

Kendrick, D.B. *Medical Department, US Army Blood Program in World War II*, Washington, DC, Office of the Surgeon-General's Department of the Army, 1964

Kimball, C.C. 'The Ex Service Movement in England and Wales, 1916–1930' (unpub. Ph.D. thesis, Stanford University, 1990)

Koven, Seth. 'Remembering and Dismemberment: Crippled Children, Wounded Soldiers, and the Great War in Great Britain', *American Historical Review* 44 (1994), 1167–202

Langley, Harold D. *A History of Medicine in the Early U.S. Navy*, Baltimore, Johns Hopkins, 1995

Lankford, N.D. 'The Victorian Medical Profession and Military Practice: Army Doctors and National Origins', *Bulletin of the History of Medicine* 54 (1984), 325–46

Lawrence, Christopher. 'Democratic, Divine and Heroic: The History and Historiography of Surgery', in his (ed.), *Medical Theory, Surgical Practice*, Routledge, 1992, pp. 1–47

——. 'Disciplining Diseases: Scurvy, the Navy and Imperial Expansion, 1750–1825', in David Miller and Peter Reill (eds), *Visions of Empire*, Cambridge University Press, 1996, pp. 80–106

——. 'Incommunicable Knowledge: Science, Technology and the Clinical Art in Britain, 1859–1914', *Journal of Contemporary History* 20 (1985), 503–20

——. *Medicine and the Making of Modern Britain*, Routledge, 1994

——. 'Moderns and Ancients: The "New Cardiology" in Britain, 1880–1930', *Medical History*, suppl. no. 5 (1985), 1–33

Lederer, Susan. 'Military Personnel as Research Subjects', *Encyclopedia of Bioethics*, revised edn, New York, Macmillan, 1995, pp. 1174–6

Leed, Eric. *No Man's Land: Combat and Identity in World War I*, Cambridge University Press, 1979

Leese, Peter. 'A Social And Cultural History of Shellshock, With Particular Reference to the Experience of British Soldiers During and After the Great War' (unpub. Ph.D. thesis, Open University, 1989)

Lemahieu, D.L. *A Culture for Democracy: Mass Communication and the Cultivated Mind in Britain Between the Wars*, Oxford, Clarendon Press, 1988

Leneman, Leah. *In the Service of Life: The Story of Elsie Inglis and the Scottish Women's Hospitals*, Edinburgh, Mercat Press, 1994

Lerner, Paul. 'Rationalizing the Therapeutic Arsenal: German Neuropsychiatry in World War I', in Manfred Berg and Geoffrey Cocks (eds), *Medicine and Modernity: Public Health and Medical Care in Nineteenth- and Twentieth-century Germany*, Cambridge University Press, 1997, pp. 121–48

Levine, Philippa. 'Venereal Disease, Prostitution, and the Politics of Empire: The Case of British India', *Journal of the History of Sexuality* 4 (1994), 579–602

——. 'Rereading the 1890s: Venereal Disease as "Constitutional Crisis" in Britain and British India', *Journal of Asian Studies* 55 (1996), 585–612

Lewer, Nick. *Physicians and the Peace Movement*, Cass, 1992

Lifton, Robert J. *The Nazi Doctors: Medical Killing and the Psychology of Genocide*, Papermac, 1986

Lindee, M. Susan. *Suffering Made Real: American Science and the Survivors at Hiroshima*, Chicago University Press, 1994

Lynch, P.J. 'The Exploitation of Courage: Psychiatric Care in the British Army, 1914–1918' (unpub. M.Phil. thesis, University College, London, 1977)

Lyon, David. 'The Military, War and Modern Surveillance', in his *The Electronic Eye: The Rise of Surveillance Society*, Cambridge, Polity Press, 1994, 27–9

Lyons, J.B., *The Citizen Surgeon: A Biography of Sir Victor Horsley, F.R.S., F.R.C.S., 1857–1916*, Downay, 1966

MacDonald, Lyn. *The Roses of No Man's Land*, M. Joseph, 1993

McLaughlin, R. *The Royal Army Medical Corps*, Leo Cooper, 1972

MacLeod, R. (ed.). *Government and Expertise: Specialists, Administrators and Professionals, 1860–1919*, Cambridge University Press, 1988

MacNalty, Sir A.S. (ed.). *History of the Second World War, UK Medical Services*, 21 vols, HMSO, 1952–72

McNeill, William. *The Pursuit of Power: Technology, Armed Force and Society Since AD 1000*, Chicago University Press, 1982

MacPherson, Sir William et al. (eds). *History of the Great War Based on Official Documents. Medical Services*, 22 vols, HMSO, 1922

Maier, Charles S. 'Between Taylorism and Technocracy: European Ideologies and the Vision of Industrial Productivity in the 1920s', *Journal of Contemporary History* 5 (1970), 27–61

Mangan, J.A. and Walvin, J. (eds). *Manliness and Morality: Middle-Class Masculinity in Britain and America, 1880–1940*, Manchester University Press, 1987

Marwick, Arthur (ed.). *Total War and Social Change*, Macmillan, 1988

Marwick, Arthur, Emsley, Clive and Simpson, Wendy (eds). *War, Peace and Social Change in Twentieth-century Europe*, Milton Keynes, Open University Press, 1989

Marx, Leo and Roe Smith, Merrit (eds). *Does Technology Drive History? The Dilemma of Technological Determinism*, Cambridge, MA, MIT Press, 1995

Merksey, Harold. 'Shell Shock', in G.E. Berrios and H. Freeman (eds), *150 Years of British Psychiatry, 1841–1991*, Gaskell, 1991, pp. 245–67

Micale, Mark S. 'Hysteria and its Historiography: A Review of Past and Present Writings', *History of Science* 27 (1989), 223–61 and 319–51

Micale, Mark S. and Rainey, Lawrence (eds). *The Mind of Modernism: Medicine, Psychology, and the Arts, 1880–1940*, New Haven, Yale University Press, forthcoming

Micale, Mark S. and Lerner, Paul (eds). *Traumatic Pasts: Studies in History, Psychiatry and Trauma in the Modern Age*, Cambridge University Press, forthcoming

Morris, Peter (ed.). *First Aid to the Battlefield: Life and Letters of Sir Vincent Kennett-Barrington (1844–1903)*, Stroud, Sutton, 1992

Mosse, George L. *Nationalism and Sexuality: Middle Class Morality and Sexual Norms in Modern Europe*, Madison, University of Wisconsin Press, 1988

Murard, Lion and Zylberman, Patrick. 'L'autre guerre (1914–1918) la santé publique en France sous l'oeil de l'Amerique', *Revue historique* 206 (1986), 367–99

Murray, Williamson and Millett, Allan (eds). *Military Innovation in the Interwar Period*, Cambridge University Press, 1996

Naythons, Matthew et al. *The Face of Mercy: A Photographic History of Medicine at War*, New York, Random House, 1993

Neushul, Peter. 'Science, Government and the Mass Production of Penicillin', *Journal of the History of Medicine and Allied Sciences* 38 (1993), 371–95

Noble, David E. 'Mental Material: The Militarization of Learning and Intelligence in US Education', in Les Levidow and Kevin Robins (eds), *Cyborg Worlds: The Military Information Society*, Free Association Books, 1989

Noon, Geoffrey. 'The Treatment of Casualties in the Great War', in Paddy Griffith (ed.), *British Fighting Methods in the Great War*, Cass, 1996, pp. 87–112

O'Keefe, Brendan and Smith, F.B. *Medicine at War: Medical Aspects of Australia's Involvement in South East Asian Conflicts, 1950–1972*, St Leonards, New South Wales, Allen & Unwin, 1994

Oosterhuis, Harry. 'Medicine, Male Bonding and Homosexuality in Nazi Germany', *Journal of Contemporary History* 32 (1997), 187–208

Osborne, Michael. 'French Military Epidemiology and the Limits of the Laboratory: The Case of Louis-Félix-Achille Kelsch', in Andrew Cunningham and P. Williams (eds), *The Laboratory Revolution in Medicine*, Cambridge University Press, 1992, pp. 189–208

Panchasi, Roxanne. 'Reconstructions: Prosthetics and the Rehabilitation of the Male Body in World War I France', *Differences: A Journal of Feminist Cultural Studies*, 7 (1995), 109–40

Perkin, Harold. *The Rise of Professional Society. England Since 1880*, Routledge, 1989

Peterson, Jeanne M. *The Medical Profession in Mid-Victorian London*, Berkeley, University of California Press, 1978

Pick, Daniel. *Faces of Degeneration: A European Disorder, c. 1848–c. 1918*, Cambridge University Press, 1989

———. *War Machine: The Rationalisation of Slaughter in the Modern Age*, New Haven, Yale University Press, 1993

Pickstone, J.V. (ed.). *Medical Innovations in Historical Perspective*, Macmillan, 1992

Porter, Dorothy (ed.). *The History of Public Health and the Modern State*, Amsterdam, Rodopi, 1994

Price, R. *An Imperial War and the British Working Class*, Routledge, 1972

Proctor, Robert N. *Racial Hygiene: Medicine Under the Nazis*, Cambridge, MA, Harvard University Press, 1988

Prost, Antoine. *In the Wake of War: 'Les Anciens Combatants' and French Society, 1914–1939*, trs. H. McPhail, Oxford, Berg, 1992

Quétel, Claude. *History of Syphilis*, trs. J. Braddock and B. Pike, Cambridge, Polity Press, 1990

Quiroga, Virginia A.M. *Occupational Therapy: The First Thirty Years, 1900 to 1930*, Bethesda, American Occupational Therapy Association, 1995

Rabinbach, Anson. *The Human Motor: Energy, Fatigue and the Origins of Modernity*, New York, Basic Books, 1990

Ramsey, L.J. 'Bullet Wounds and X-rays in Britain's Little Wars', *Journal of the Society for Army Historical Research* 60 (1982), 91–102

Reverby, Susan. 'Stealing the Golden Eggs: Ernest Amory Codman and the Science and Management of Medicine', *Bulletin of the History of Medicine* 55 (1981), 156–71

Richter, Donald. *Chemical Soldiers: British Gas Warfare in World War One*, Lawrence, Kansas, University of Kansas Press, 1992

Rieux, J. and Hassenforder, J. *Centenaire de l'Ecole d'Application du Service de Santé et du Val-de-Grace*, Paris, Charles Lavarzelle, 1951

Ring, Friedrich. *Zur Geschichte der Militarmedizin in Deutschland*, Berlin, Deutscher Verlag, 1962

Rose, Nikolas. *The Psychological Complex: Psychology, Politics and Society in England, 1869–1939*, Routledge & Kegan Paul, 1985

———. *Governing the Soul: The Shaping of the Private Self*, Routledge, 1990

Rosen, George. *The Specialization of Medicine with Particular Reference to Ophthalmology*, New York, Froben Press, 1944

——. 'The Efficiency Criterion in Medical Care, 1900–1920: An Early Approach to an Evaluation of Health Service', *Bulletin of the History of Medicine* 50 (1976), 28–44

Rosenberg, Charles. 'Inward Vision and Outward Glance: The Shaping of the American Hospital, 1880–1914', *Bulletin of the History of Medicine* 53 (1976), 346–91

Roudebush, Marc. 'A Battle of Nerves: Hysteria and Its Treatment in France During World War I' (unpub. Ph.D. thesis, University of California, Berkeley, 1995)

Sarnecky, Mary T. 'Women, Medicine, and War', in Paula N. Poulos (ed.), *A Woman's War Too: U.S. Women in the Military in World War II*, Washington, DC, National Archives and Record Administration, 1996, pp. 71–81

Sauerteig, Lutz. 'Militär, Medizin und Moral: Sexualität im Ersten Weltkrieg', in W.U. Eckart and C. Gradmann (eds), *Medizin und der Erste Weltkrieg*, Pfaffenweiler, Centauras, 1966, pp. 197–226

Searle, Geoffrey R. *The Quest for National Efficiency: A Study of British Politics and Political Thought, 1899–1914*, Oxford, Blackwell, 1971

Semmel, Bernard. *Imperialism and Social Reform: English Social-Imperial Thought, 1895–1914*, Allen & Unwin, 1960

Shephard, Ben. '"The Early Treatment of Mental Disorders": R.G. Rows and Maghull, 1914–1918', in G. Berrios and H. Freeman (eds), *150 Years of British Psychiatry*, vol. 2, *The Aftermath*, Gaskell, 1996, pp. 434–64

Shepherd, John. *The Crimean Doctors: A History of the British Medical Services in the Crimean War*, 2 vols, Liverpool University Press, 1991

Showalter, Elaine. *The Female Malady: Women, Madness and English Culture, 1830–1980*, Virago, 1985

Simpson, Keith. 'Dr James Durin and Shell-shock', in H. Cecil and P. Liddle (eds), *Facing Armageddon: The First World War Experienced*, Barnsley, Leo Cooper, 1996, pp. 502–20

Skelley, Alan R. *The Victorian Army at Home: The Recruitment and Terms and Conditions of the British Regular*, Croom Helm, 1977

Skocpol, Theda. *Protecting Soldiers and Mothers: The Political Origins of Social Policy in the United States*, Cambridge, MA, Harvard University Press, 1992

Smith, F.B. 'Ethics and Disease in the Late-Nineteenth Century: The Contagious Diseases Acts', *Historical Studies* 15 (1971), 118–35

——. *Florence Nightingale. Reputation and Power*, New York, St Martin's Press, 1982

Smith, Harold L. (ed.). *War and Social Change: British Society in the Second World War*, Manchester University Press, 1986

Solomon, Susan G. and Hutchinson, John F. (eds). *Health and Society in Revolutionary Russia*, Bloomington and Indianapolis, Indiana University Press, 1990

Spiers, Edward M. *Haldane: An Army Reformer*, Edinburgh University Press, 1980

Spongberg, Mary. 'The Sick Rose: Constructing the Body of the Prostitute in Nineteenth Century British Medical Discourse' (unpub. Ph.D. thesis, University of Sydney, 1993)

Stone, Martin. 'Shellshock and the Psychologists', in W.F. Bynum, R. Porter and M. Shepherd (eds), *The Anatomy of Madness: Essays in the History of Psychiatry*, volume 2, *Institutions and Society*, Routledge, 1985, pp. 242–71

——. 'The Military and Industrial Roots of Clinical Psychology in Britain, 1900–45' (unpub. Ph.D. thesis, University of London, 1985)

Stott, Rosalie. 'Medicine in the Services', in Gerald Jordan (ed.), *British Military History: A Supplement to Robin Higham's Guide to the Sources*, New York, Garland, 1988, pp. 525–51

Sturdy, Steve. 'From the Trenches to the Hospitals at Home: Physiologists, Clinicians and Oxygen Therapy, 1914–30', in J.V. Pickstone (ed.), *Medical Innovations in Historical Perspective*, Macmillan, 1992, pp. 104–23

——. 'The Political Economy of Scientific Medicine: Science, Education and the Transformation of Medical Practice in Sheffield, 1890–1922', *Medical History* 36 (1992), 125–59

Sturdy, Steve and Cooter, Roger. 'Science, Scientific Management, and the Transformation of Medicine in Britain, *c.* 1870–1950', *History of Science* 36 (1998), in press

Summers, Anne. 'Militarism in Britain Before the Great War', *History Workshop Journal* 2 (1976), 104–23

——. *Angels and Citizens: British Women as Military Nurses, 1854–1914*, Routledge, 1988

Swaan, Abram de. *In Care of the State: Health Care, Education and Welfare in Europe and the USA in the Modern Era*, Cambridge, Polity Press, 1988

Taliaferro, William H. (ed.). *Medicine and the War*, New York, Books for Libraries Press, 1972

Taylor, Erie. *Front-line Nurse: British Nurses in World War II*, Robert Hale, 1997

Titmuss, Richard. *Problems of Social Policy*, HMSO, 1950

Tomblin, Barbara B. *G.I. Nightingales: The Army Nurse Corps in World War II*, Lexington, University Press of Kentucky, 1996

Tomkins, S.M. 'Palminate or Permanganate: The Venereal Prophylaxis Debate in Britain, 1916–1926', *Medical History* 37 (1993), 82–98

Towers, Bridget A. 'Health Education Policy 1916–1926: Venereal Disease and the Prophylaxis Dilemma', *Medical History* 24 (1980), 70–87

Traver, Tim. *The Killing Ground: The British Army, the Western Front and the Emergence of Modern Warfare*, Macmillan, 1987

Trumpener, Ulrich. 'The Road to Ypres: The Beginnings of Gas Warfare in World War I', *Journal of Modern History* 47 (1975), 460–80

Trustram, Myna. *Women of the Regiment: Marriage and the Victorian Army*, Cambridge University Press, 1984

Tyquin, Michael. *Gallipoli: The Medical War. The Australian Army Medical Services in the Dardanelles Campaign of 1915*, Kensington, New South Wales University Press, 1993

Vagts, Alfred. *A History of Militarism*, Hollis & Carter, 1959

Van Bergen, Leo. 'For Our Honour and Our Rights: the Dutch East Indies and the First Atjeh Expeditions', in H. Binneveld and R. Dekker (eds), *Curing and Insuring: Essays on Illness in Past Times: The Netherlands, Belgium, England and Italy, 16th–20th Centuries*, Verloren, Hilversum, 1993, pp. 135–49

——. *De Zwaargewonden Eerst? Het Nederlandsche Roode Kruis en het Vraagstuk van Oorlog en Verde, 1867–1945*, Rotterdam, Erasmus, 1994

Weber, Max. 'The Technological Advantages of Bureaucratic Organisation', in *From Max Weber: Essays in Sociology*, ed. and trs. H. Gerth and C.W. Mills, Routledge and Kegan Paul, 1970

Webster, Charles. *The Health Services Since the War*. Volume 1, *Problems of Health Care: The National Health Service Before 1957*, HMSO, 1988

Weeks, Jeffrey. *Sex, Politics and Society: The Regulation of Sexuality Since 1800*, Longman, 1989

Weindling, Paul. *Delousing Eastern Europe: German Bacteriology between Disinfection and Genocide, 1890s–1940s*, Oxford University Press, 1999

——. *Health, Race and German Politics between National Unification and Nazism, 1870–1945*, Cambridge University Press, 1989

Whalen, R.W. *Bitter Wounds: German Victims of the Great War, 1914–1939*, Ithaca, Cornell University Press, 1984

Whitehead. Ian. 'Not a Doctor's Work? The Role of British Regimental Medical Officers in the Field', in H. Cecil and P. Liddle (eds), *Facing Armageddon: The First World War Experienced*, Barnsley, Leo Cooper, 1996, pp. 466–74

Winter, Jay. *The Great War and the British People*, Macmillan, 1986

——. *Sites of Memory, Sites of Mourning: The Great War in European Cultural History*, Cambridge University Press, 1995

——. (ed.), *War and Economic Development: Essays in Memory of David Joslin*, Cambridge University Press, 1975

Winter, Jay and Robert, J-L. *Capital Cities at War: Paris, London, Berlin, 1914–1919*, Cambridge University Press, 1997

Woloch, Isser. *The French Veteran from the Revolution to the Restoration*, Chapel Hill, University of North Carolina Press, 1979

Young, Allan. *The Harmony of Illusions: Inventing Post-Traumatic Stress Disorder*, Princeton University Press, 1995

INDEX

African-American women physicians 107, 112
air raids 229, 230, 232
Allbutt, Clifford 87, 91, 93
ambulances (i.e., field hospitals) 27, 29, 30, 31, 32, 33–4
American Army Educational Commission, Social Hygiene Division 172
American Civil War 3, 4, 22, 28, 29, 85, 110
American Medical Association 117–19
American Women's Hospitals 106, 108
Anglo-Boer War 11, 48–59, 150, 153
anxiety 226, 231, 232
Arfer, Marya 139
Army Medical Service (Great Britain) 66, 68, 73, 75–6, 77
Army Nurse Corps (US) 110
Aron, Raymond 23
Association of Hospital Matrons 195
asylums, death rates in 155
Athlone Committee 189
atom bomb 234

bacteriology 49, 58–9, 128, 130
Baker, Newton D. 108, 109, 116
Balcom, Emily 116
barbarization/brutalization 24, 28–9, 35
Barcroft, Joseph 69, 71, 73
basic research 93
Bates, Mary Elizabeth 114–16, 117, 119
Bayliss, W.M. 71
Beck, Ulrich 5
Best, Geoffrey 24, 25
Bevin, Ernest 135, 141
Bickford-Smith, Vivian 52
Blanc, Honoré 3
Blaschko, Alfred 171
Bloch, Iwan 172
Blumenfeld, Erwin 168, 177
Bourke, Joanna 167, 180–1
Brigham, Carl 158

British Association for the Advancement of Science 151
British Medical Association 137
brothels 167–8, 175, 176–7
Brown, Mary L. 112
Bruce, David 55, 58
bureaucracy 1, 2
Bush, Vannevar 206, 207
Bushnell General Hospital, Utah 209–10, 211
business 76

Cairns, Hugh 216, 217
Cannon, W.B. 73
Cardiac Club 97–101
Cardwell, Mae 116
Census of Women Physicians 108–9, 112, 119
Central Advisory Board for Nursing 190
Central Association for the Care of Mental Defectives 155
chemical weapons 65–74, 76
Child, W.B. 138
citizenship 13
   women physicians' claim to 106, 107, 113–18, 119, 122 n. 30
Civil Nursing Reserve 190, 191
civilians, as victims 27
Clausewitz, Carl von 4, 22–3
clinical research 98
clinical testing 203, 205, 207–11, 216–17, 218
   treatment vs. experimentation 209
Cocoanut Grove fire 203, 207–9, 218
Coghill, Robert 212, 213, 214, 215
Colchester Heart Hospital 91, 93
Cole, Robert G. 227
Collie, John 126, 131, 133, 134, 139, 140
Colorado Medical Women's War Service League, Committee on Recognition of Medical Women (Bates Committee) 114–16
'combat-effectiveness' 228
'combat exhaustion' 231

Committee for National Morale 232
concentration camps (South Africa) 57
condoms 177
conscription 23, 34, 91, 151, 159
Contagious Diseases Acts 175
Cope, Oliver 208–9
courts martial 130, 131, 136, 139
cowardice 94, 228, 230, 231, 232, 233
Crimean War 189, 194
Culpin, Millais 135

Defence of the Realm Act 176
demobilization 156–7
discipline 3, 9, 13, 15–16, 58, 153, 154, 160,
    227, 229, 230, 232, 233, 234
Douglas, C.G. 68, 71–2
droit des gens 26, 33
Dunant, Henry 29, 38

Eberstadt, Ferdinand 213
efficiency 3, 16, 58, 76, 150, 155, 161, 225,
    229
    cardiac 88
Eksteins, Modris 4, 167
Elder, Albert 214–15
electrocardiogram 90–1, 92–3, 97, 99, 100
Elias, Norbert 30
emotions 225–34
eugenics 133, 153

fatigue 78, 82 n. 24, 226
fear 154, 225–34
Feeble-minded, Royal Commission on the Care
    and Control of 150
First World War 4–5, 11–15, 22–3, 65ff., 226,
    233, 234
Fisher, Jessie W. 112–13
Florey, Howard W. 205–6, 216, 217
Foucault, Michel 8
Franco-Prussian War 3, 10–11, 22–39
French Revolutionary Wars 2–3, 23
Freud, Sigmund 130, 138
Fussel, Paul 4, 172

Galen 127
Gambetta, Léon 22, 23

Geddes, Auckland 133
General Medical Board, Council of National
    Defense (US) 107
    Committee of Women Physicians of 108,
    111
General Nursing Council 194
general practitioners 98–9, 139–40, 141, 142
Geneva Convention 25–6, 27, 34, 42 n. 52
German Society for Combatting Venereal
    Disease (*Deutsche Gesellschaft zur Bekämpfung der
    Geschlechtskrankheiten*) 171, 176
German Wars (1864–6) 22, 29
Gilmore, Emma Wheat 111
Gorgas, William Crawford 109, 116, 117
Graham, T.L. 49
Graves, Robert 167, 168
Gregory, A.J. 49, 50, 51, 52, 55, 59
guerre à outrance 22, 24, 26

Haffkine's prophylactic 50–1, 54, 58–9
Hague War Crimes Tribunal 24
Haines, Frances Edith 111
Haldane, J.S. 65–6, 71–2
Haldane, R.B. (Viscount) 66, 75
Halloran General Hospital, Staten Island 211
Hamilton, Alice 119
Hardy, W.B. 68, 69, 71
health insurance 125, 130, *see also* National
    Health Insurance
Hill, Leonard 71
Hippocratic medicine 129
Hocker, Elizabeth Van Cortlandt 111–12
Holocaust 5
Home Office (England and Wales) 175
homosexuality 172–3, 231
Horder, Thomas 198
Howard, Michael 24
humanitarianism 10, 24–39
    and free enterprise 29, 32, 34
    and nationalism 35–7
    and religion 33
Hutchinson, John 24, 36
Hynes, Samuel 4

illegitimate births, attitudes towards 169
industrialization 3, 4

innovation and war 12, 15
administrative 75, 76, 78
technical 75, 76, 78
inoculation for plague 50–1, 55, 58–9
isolation for control of plague 51–2, 53, 56, 58

Jews 231
Jones, Dame Katherine 194–6, 197, 199–200

Kaufman, M. Ralph 233
Keefer, Chester S. 207, 208, 209, 210, 214
Keogh, Alfred 66, 67–8, 72–3, 75–6
Kitchener, H.H. 55, 57, 65, 66, 174
Koontz, Amos R. 234

laboratories 74
laboratory medicine 49, 58–9
labour batallions 151, 158, 160
Laqueur, Thomas 25
leadership 230
levée en masse 26, 40 n. 23
Lewis, Thomas 89, 90, 91, 92, 93, 95, 96, 97, 98
Lewis, Wyndham 4
Lloyd George, David 68, 76, 77
Lovejoy, Esther Pohl 111
Lumsden, Thomas 137
Lyons, Champ 203, 208–10, 211, 213, 217–18

MacDonald, Peter 140
McDougall, William 137
McGee, Anita Newcombe 109–10, 116
Mackenzie, James 87, 88–9, 90, 91, 93, 98, 99
MacLachlan, Mary 116
machine-gun 3
machine metaphors 229
Maitland Plague Hospital 51–2, 53, 55
malingering 13, 93, 94, 125–42, 154, 231, 233
management 77, 129, 225, 226, 232, 233
Manion, Katherine 116
manpower 3, 12, 13–14, 15, 38, 53, 56, 72, 73, 91, 149–61, 170, 180, 225, 228
Mapother, Edward 153
Marshall, S.L.A. 227
Marx, Karl 4
masculinity 150

Massachusetts General Hospital 203, 207–8
Mass 'communities' 232
mass killing, technologies of 225
mass mobilization 2, 3, 23, 34, 106, 107, 225, see also levée en masse
mass production 3, 4, 203–4, 206, 211, 213–15, 218, 219
masturbation 172
Meakins, J.C. 72
medical detective work 128–9, 131, 139
medical ethics 130, 140
Medical Research Committee/Council (UK) 66, 71, 72–3, 78–9, 90, 91, 92, 96, 98, 216
Medical Women's National Association 106, 107–8, 109, 114
medicalization 125–6, 135–6, 139, 142
of sexuality 171–2, 181
medicine and the state 126, 128–9, 136–7, 139–41
medicine, forensic aspects of 130, 134, 135
mental deficiency/defectives 13–14, 149–61
Mental Deficiency Act 1913 (Great Britain) 150
mental disablement rate in the forces 152, 158–9, 160
mental hygiene 160
Merck Pharmaceutical Corporation 206, 209, 210, 212, 213, 216
Metropolitan Asylums Board 155
militarism 189, 200
militarization 2–3, 4, 10, 11, 23–39, 56–8, 76, 194–201, 226
of medicine 7
Milkman, Ruth 118
Milner, Alfred 55
Ministry for the Interior (Bavaria) 175
Ministry of Food (Great Britain) 77
Ministry of Health (England and Wales) 189, 190, 191, 194, 200
Ministry of Munitions (Great Britain) 68, 69, 70, 71, 72, 73, 76, 77, 78, 79
Ministry of National Service (Great Britain) 151, 152, 153
Ministry of Pensions 94–7, 99
modernism 4–5, 8, 22
modernity 1–6, 8–9, 125–36, 140, 149, 226, 232

modernization in the military 58–9
moral education 173–4, 178, 181
morale 58, 132, 167, 228, 229, 230
morality 167, 169–70, 172, 180–1, 231
Morton, Rosalie Slaughter 108, 119
mother and child welfare 169
Mott, Frederick 138
Mount Vernon Hospital, Hampstead (Hampstead
    Heart Hospital) 91, 92, 93
mustard gas 73, 81 n. 12
Myers, C.S. 152

Napoleonic Wars 127
narratives of illness 128
'nation in arms' 75, *see also* mass mobilization
National Academy of Sciences (US) 214
National Council for Combatting Venereal
    Disease 174
National Health Insurance (Great Britain) 98,
    131, 132, 134, 136, 140–1
National Health Service (Great Britain) 200
National Research Council (US) 158, 205,
    231
    Committee on Chemotherapeutics 207
Nationalverein 26
Navy, Royal 67
Ndabeni segregation camp 48
Neisser, Albert 171, 176
Netley, Royal Victoria Hospital and Royal
    Army Medical College 86, 152
neutrality, concept of 26
'new cardiology' 88–9, 90, 93
night lodgers (*Schlafgänger*) 170
Nightingale, Florence 189, 194, 197
Norris, Donald 134
notification of infectious diseases 52–3
Nuremberg Trials 24
nurses 15–16, 27, 35, 114, 189–201
    Voluntary Aid Detachments 190, 192, 193
Nurses Act 1943 192
nursing, as women's work 194, 198–9
    Auxiliary Territorial Service 192, 193, 195
    Salmon Reforms 201

Office of Scientific Research and Development
    (US) 204, 206

Committee on Medical Research 204,
    206–7, 208, 209, 210, 211, 212–13, 214
Order of St John 190, 192
Osler, William 91
Owen–Dyer Bill 107
oxygen, therapeutic use of 71–2, 73

Paris 22
    Commune 34, 36–7
    Neurological Society 132
Paton, Stewart 158
patriotism 24
Pearl Harbor 208
Pedersen, Susan 169
penicillin 16, 203–19
    effect on mortality due to infections 204
    fermentation vs. synthesis 212–15
    Oxford Group 205, 216
pensions 12, 72, 92, 94–7, 99, 134, 136, 231–2, 234
people's war 23–5
Pfizer 206, 212
pharmaceutical industry 16, 203–4, 205, 206,
    207, 212–13, 214, 218
philanthropy 30, 33
Physical Deterioration, Interdepartmental
    Committee on 150
physiology 11–12, 15, 65–79, 93, 94
Pick, Daniel 3, 4, 23
Pickstone, J.V. 128
Pinero, Dolores M. 112
plague 11, 48–59
    as a 'filth disease' 54
    in Adelaide 54
    in Calcutta 50
    in Cape Town 48–59
    in Hong Kong and India 57–8
Poor Law (Great Britain) 136, 140
population policy 169–70
Porton Down 69, 73, 74
press, representations of war in 26–9
prisoners of war, sexual relations with 170
pronatalism 169
prophylactics 174, 177–80, 181
prostitution 172, 174–7, 178, 181, *see also*
    brothels
    definitions of 174–5

regulation of 175–7
psychiatric casualties, rates of 228, 233
psychiatric classification schemes 229, 233
psychiatry 132, 135, 138, 225–34
psychoanalysis 128, 226, 232
psychologization 126, 132–6, 137–9, 140–1
psychology 15, 16–17, 94, 151, 158–60, 161, 227, 229, 232, 234
Psychology for the Armed Forces (1945) 231
Psychology for the Fighting Man (1943) 227, 229, 230
psychometric testing 14, 151–2, 157–60, 232, 234
public health medicine 49, 52–3, 56–7, 128
Purinton, John A. 213–14
Purnell, Caroline 110–11

Quain's *Dictionary of Medicine* 131
Queen Alexandra's Imperial Military Nursing Service 195, 197, 199
Queen, Frank B. 209, 210

Rabinbach, Anson 8
race, and psychological testing 158, 159–60
  as public health concern 48, 53
railways 8
rationalization 2, 3, 6, 9, 15, 70, 96, 232, 233
rats as vector for plague 50, 53, 54, 56
reconstruction 198
recruitment 150–1, 152, 158–9
Red Cross 10, 24–39, 42 n. 52
  and regulation of brothels 177
  British 190, 192, 193, 194
  French 24, 25, 27, 29–39
  French, *Comité de la presse* 30–2
  French, *Société de secours* 29–38
  women physicians serving with 112–13, 117, 118
religion, as protection against fear 231, 232
Rice, Harriet 112
Richards, Arthur N. 206, 207, 209, 210, 212, 213, 214
Rockefeller Foundation 205, 206
Rockefeller General Education Board 160
Root, Elihu 214
Rosen, George 97

Roussy, G. 153
Royal Air Force 196
Royal Army Medical Corps (Great Britain) 49, 55, 58, 71, 216
Royal College of Nursing 198
Royal Commission on Venereal Disease 173
Royal Navy 196
Royal Society of Medicine 90
Royal Society, Physiology (War) Committee 67, 68, 69–70, 72–3, 78, 79
Rushcliffe Committee 194
Ryle, John A. 226

Saunders, Christopher 52
Schivelbusch, Wolfgang 8
Scottish Women's Hospitals 108
Second World War 4, 15–17, 135, 136, 189ff.
segregation of black Africans 48, 52, 54, 56, 57, 59
sexual behaviour 14–15, 167–81
  abstinence 171–2, 173–4, 178
  regulation 150
sexual relations, non-marital 175
Shafroth, John Franklin 115, 116
shell-shock 8, 94, 129–30, 134, 136, 141, 149, 152, 153–4, 157, 161
shock 77, 82 n. 27
Showalter, Elaine 5
Shuttleworth, George 153
Sillman, Leonard R. 232
Simpson, William 50, 51, 52
Smith, W. Ramsay 54–5, 58
social status and mental deficiency 154, 159–60
'socialized medicine' 136, *see also* medicine and the state
'soldier's heart' 12, 85–101
  anatomical/mechanical vs. functional conceptions of 85–7, 88–90, 92, 93, 95
  prevalence of 85, 88
soldiers' wives, separation allowances for 169
  sexual behaviour of 169–70
Souvenir de Solferino 29
Spanish-American War 116
Spanish Civil War 190
specialization 96–101, 107, 125, 137–8, 139
  technology as a factor in 97, 100

Spier-Irving, Isaak 167, 169–70, 172
Squibb 206, 210–11, 212, 215
standardization 1, 232, 233
Stanford Read, C. 152, 153
Starling, E.H. 67, 68, 71
Stewart, Gershom 149–50, 161
Stone, Mitchell 58
sulphonamides 208, 209, 211, 217
Summers, Anne 194, 195
Surgeon-General (US) 125, 211
Surgeon-General, Office of (US) 94, 209
surveillance 8, 14, 51–2, 129, 170, 225

Taylor, F.W. 126
teamwork 229
Terman, Lewis 158
Territorial Army (Great Britain) 75
    Nursing Service 199
Thom, Charles 205, 213
Titmuss, Richard 7
'total war' 2, 12, 13, 22–39, 76
Towles, Caroline 111
training, military 230
transfer of science and technology 203–4,
    218–19
Tredgold, Alfred 156
tuberculosis 89, 155
'Typhoid Mary' 128

United States Army, Surgical Consultants
    Division 209, 211, 217
United States Army Service Forces 214, 215
United States Department of Agriculture 205
United States Department of Agriculture,
    Northern Regional Research Laboratory,
    Peoria 205, 212, 213, 215
University College Hospital, London 89, 90,
    91, 96, 98

Valéry, Paul 4
van Gasken, Frances 119
van Heyningen, Elizabeth 57
venereal disease 14–15, 127, 157, 167, 170–80,
    217

rates among soldiers 171, 176, 178
voluntarism, and nursing 193
voluntary movements 31–4, 35
volunteers 23

Wagner, Philip S. 231
Wakefield, Alice 119
War Committee for Warm Underwear
    (Kriegsausschuß für warme Unterkleidung) 177
war as good for medicine 6–8
    as experiment 74–7, 226
    as social aberration 7
war machine 23, 24
War Ministry (Prussia) 169, 172, 174
War Office (Great Britain) 50, 65, 66, 67, 69,
    70, 73, 74, 90, 91, 95, 176, 179, 191
War Production Board (US) 204, 213, 214, 215,
    219
weapons, illegal 27
weapons, modern, as cause of anxiety 27–9, 65,
    226
Weber, Max 1–2, 3, 5, 17, 234
welfare, in industry 77
welfare state 4
Whelpton, Martha 110
Wilson, W.D. 50, 53–5, 56, 58
woman suffrage 106, 107, 113, 114, 117,
    119–20, 122 n. 31
women, as objects of humanitarian concern 27
    double standard of sexual behaviour for 180
    feeble-minded 165
women physicians 13, 106–20
    as contract surgeons 109–12
    status of in the military 113
    struggle for commissions 113–18
    war service registration of 108–9, 119, see
    also Census of Women Physicians
Women Police Service/Volunteers 169
Women's Auxiliary Air Force 199
women's movement 170, 175, 176
Women's Royal Army Corps 199
workmen's compensation 125, 133–4, 135, 140

Yerkes, Robert 158